CW00553816

Alfred Hubert Roy Fedden (Rolls-Royce plc)

ROLLS-ROYCE HERITAGE TRUST

FEDDEN

– the life of Sir Roy Fedden

Bill Gunston OBE, FRAeS

HISTORICAL SERIES No 26

Published in 1998 by the
Rolls-Royce Heritage Trust
P O Box 31 Derby England DE24 8BJ

ISBN: 1 872922 13 9

The Historical Series is published as a joint initiative by the Rolls-Royce Heritage Trust and The Sir Henry Royce Memorial Foundation.

Previous volumes published in the Series are listed at the rear, together with volumes available in the Rolls-Royce Heritage Trust Technical Series.

Cover Picture: Fedden's first successful engine – the 9-cylinder air-cooled radial Jupiter. The aeroplanes in the background are Bristol Bulldogs, fitted with the Jupiter, one of the RAF's most successful inter-war fighter aircraft. The stylised 'Bristol' symbol was the trademark of the Bristol Aeroplane Company and was used for both aeroplane and aero engine products.

Books are available from:
The Rolls-Royce Heritage Trust, Rolls-Royce plc, Moor Lane, PO Box 31, Derby DE24 8BJ

Origination and Reproduction by Neartone Ltd, Arnold, Nottingham
Printed by Premier Print, Glaisdale Parkway, Bilborough, Nottingham

CONTENTS

INTRODUCTION

On behalf of the Rolls-Royce Heritage Trust, I would like to thank Bill Gunston for agreeing to the publication of this book, *Fedden,* by the Trust. *Fedden* is an updated and revised version of his original book, *By Jupiter,* published by the Royal Aeronautical Society in 1976 – but unobtainable for a long time.

The changes to the text of *Fedden* reflect new information that has been found by Bill and others since the original work, adding to the accuracy of the original narrative, painstakingly researched by Bill at that time.

Fedden has many new photographs, the majority of which I have obtained from the archives of Rolls-Royce plc at Bristol. However, I would like to thank the people and organisations that have supplied other artwork – acknowledged adjacent to the particular illustration.

Thanks are also due to Sue Trawin for reproducing the text of *By Jupiter* and to my wife, Marilyn, for producing the additions and amendments which resulted in *By Jupiter* turning into *Fedden.*

Peter Pavey
Secretary – Rolls-Royce Heritage Trust, Bristol Branch

August 1998

FOREWORD

Roy Fedden was a great man. We who knew him will never forget him. He was a patriot. He was kind and he was good. His views were convictions, firmly held and invariant. He was tireless in pursuing the ends he believed in. His integrity was absolute. He ended his earthly life peacefully on the 21st November 1973, in the care of his devoted wife, in his house on the edge of the Usk, and I think we can be sure that, as for Mr Valiant-for-Truth, all the trumpets sounded for him on the other side.

[The foregoing words concluded the address which Lord Kings Norton delivered at the memorial service for Sir Roy Fedden at the church of St Clement Danes, London, on 6th February 1974.]

PREFACE

This book tells the story of one of the few men who can properly be called a Titan. Indeed, some of his associates at times forgot that his whole purpose in life was good, and thought of him as a monster. So powerful was his personality, and so intense his way of working, that even a few minutes in his presence could leave people sucked dry and exhausted, like a limp rag. Yet many people who suffered him daily were glad to go on until they dropped. They knew that Alfred Hubert Roy Fedden was a man of destiny.

I did not experience this myself. When Fedden was at the peak of his career in the 1930s I was only a boy. But, like many boys at that time, I knew that Fedden's aero engines powered Britain's national airline, more than half the Royal Air Force, and about half the other airlines and air forces of the world. When I write "Fedden's aero engines" I do not mean he made them himself; in fact thousands of them were made under licence in distant lands, and like virtually all modern engineering products they were the result of the efforts of a team. But Fedden was the leader. He was the leader more powerfully and more purposefully than in any other engineering enterprise I can call to mind. Had he gone in for politics – a field he found supremely uninteresting – he would swiftly have become a giant figure on the world stage. Even in his chosen and relatively despised profession he was a household word as early as 1907 because he produced a car intended not for the wealthy but for ordinary owner-drivers, which nobody in Britain had previously thought of. More than 60 years later he was still hard at work.

In his extremely long active life he accomplished more, pleased more, angered more, planned more, earned more and worked more than any five ordinary men. Engineers as a species are often thought to be rather grey and boring people, but nobody could dream of levelling this charge at Fedden! It was for this reason, even more than the merit of his accomplishments, that made me accept like a shot when he asked me to write his life-story in 1971. I had met him in 1950, when I was a young journalist not long out of the RAF where I had sometimes flown with his engines. But I could not claim the privilege of his friendship, and it was Harald Penrose who suggested to him that I might be able to help him record his great and varied life. I was under no illusions regarding the magnitude of the task. One of the least of my problems was that, even at 86, Fedden was still a formidable personality. As I had half-expected, it was not I that was writing the story but Fedden himself. At one point we amicably severed our relationship entirely.

In 1973 he asked me to continue, this time with a freer hand. Due to his failing health we were unable to finish the manuscript before his death. Since his passing I have been able to talk with many more people and obtain a more balanced picture of this remarkable man – who still, in many ways, remains an enigma (for example, those nearest to him are undecided whether he was humourless, or rich in humour that never showed). Had he lived he would not have accepted major parts of this narrative, not because they are critical of him but because he had a highly developed sense of modesty and, among other things, tended to avoid the first person singular. He would fight – as he would have put it, "tooth and nail" – for whatever he believed in; but he was the last man on Earth to blow his own trumpet.

His story is by no means an ordinary, routine account of eventual success. Indeed, the record is characterised by violent fluctuations between peaks of prodigious success and troughs of bitter disappointment. It is the striking contrast of almost everything about RF's life which makes it so interesting.

He was one of the greatest intuitive engineers in history, and between the World Wars was the highest-paid engineer in Britain, and probably in Europe; yet he never formally qualified as an engineer. He was possessed of great charm and personal magnetism, and went out of his way to avoid causing the slightest offence; yet he made many bitter enemies. He sought to get the very best out of those who worked for him; yet he drove them close to the limits of their endurance, and some beyond it. He was gifted with remarkable strategic vision, which he was constantly using; yet he often failed to see that he was on a tactical collision-course. He was unbelievably meticulous about the wording of reports and memoranda; yet he used cliché after cliché, and his spoken style was extravagant.

Perhaps the most remarkable, and yet typical, event in his life is that in the middle of the Second World War, when he had just been knighted and was working night and day in the most vital of jobs, the Board of the Bristol Aeroplane Company pinned up notices announcing that he had left their employment, and refused to allow him to come back and remove his personal possessions from his desk.

Such was his relentless search for perfection in all things that he made himself a tyrant. He was totally unable to accept the slightest compromise on issues which he considered important, and at times he stretched the allegiance of even his closest friends. Yet, despite his many setbacks – so often unwittingly of his own making – RF never, never gave up. Right to the end of his days he was able to put aside despondency or disillusionment and attack some new problem with his incredible drive and enthusiasm.

Could he have achieved what he did without those qualities which so many of his contemporaries found infuriating? It is doubtful, and, in company with other great pioneering men, he had to carry the cross of his personality and at times paid dearly the price of his intolerance of those who crossed his path. Yet he was at heart the warmest and most good-natured of men.

He was in every way larger than life. Even in the pursuit of his pastimes of sailing, fishing, powerboat racing, and the management of his small estate in Wales, his accomplishments bore the stamp of his courage, his competitiveness and his uncanny tirelessness. When he no longer pitted himself against others in the struggle for technological advance, he led his personal staff in taming the river Usk which in full spate can rise 17 ft and had threatened to demolish his beloved Buckland Old Mill.

It is fitting that he should have departed this life in his room just a few feet above the Usk's swirling rapids, which symbolised so perfectly his restless and indomitable power.

To those who have assisted me I am profoundly grateful for doing their best to guide me on what was at best a long course (two said it was impossible). In particular I thank: Val Cleaver, of Rolls-Royce, who went to limitless lengths to help in every way; Cyril Cleverdon, Librarian of what (to RF's regret) has become the Cranfield Institute of Technology; Sir George Dowty, whose unswerving loyalty to Fedden was matched by the latter's devotion; Rex and Marjorie Goldby, both of whom worked many years for the man in his prime and were always honoured to serve him; Percie F Green, probably the last man at the great Bristol factory who regularly corresponded with Fedden; Lord Kings Norton, perhaps our greatest living engineer; Cyril Luby, former Fedden apprentice and later Managing Director at Bristol; Stanley Mansell and Freddie Mayer, leading members of "the team" throughout the great days at Bristol; Alex Moulton, of bicycle fame, whose objective viewpoint rests on hard years as RF's personal assistant; Bert Newport of Dowty Rotol, who joined Fedden in the early days of the Jupiter; Frank Nixon, one of our leading consulting engineers, who put me right on a great number of important topics; Frank Owner, who joined the team in 1922 yet is still outwardly a young man; Harald Penrose, gifted author and former Westland chief test pilot, who oiled the machinery that got the manuscript started; Eric Turner, who told me in his office at Bristol how, 45 years earlier, he had played the accordion on one of RF's staff riverboat outings; Sir Reginald Verdon Smith, who with great care furnished me with a more balanced view of the old Bristol Aeroplane Company; Cyril Uwins, who as Bristol chief test pilot took the Jupiter into the air in 1919 and flew Fedden's engines for 50 years; and Peter G Ware, of the Dunlop Company, who took me under his wing and with the greatest sympathy and patience tried to unravel the enigma of his old boss, of whose estate he is an executor.

There is one more person to whom I am indebted who cannot be tucked away in the alphabetical list. NLF – Norah, Lady Fedden – was the ideal partner for Roy. From childhood they were devoted to each other, and though their course ran anything but straight they eventually were able to enjoy many years of complete happiness together. She was fortunate to retain the services of Olive Stahl, Sir Roy's former secretary, who did everything she could to make my task easier, and whose help (assisted in 1973 by Elizabeth Smith) I gratefully acknowledge.

Lady Fedden has allowed me to present Roy Fedden's life in a completely unexpurgated way, which he would never even have considered. Her only criterion is that the record should be a true one. She believed RF will read it; and I know he thought that himself. Though we did not discuss religious matters, he embraced Christian Scientist beliefs and certainly regarded bodies as much less important than minds. He did not believe his passing from this world to be any kind of ending; and who is to deny that this almost superhuman man will continue to maintain contact with, and influence, those who survive him?

Haslemere, 1978 Bill Gunston

PREFACE TO NEW EDITION

The original edition of this book was well received, and almost immediately went out of print. Not one of my 340 books (to date) has generated a bigger response from readers. Most wanted to reminisce, and in doing so furnished me with valuable additional material which often clashed sharply with previous impressions. For example, Fedden's niece said "Austere and humourless? Not a bit of it! He was full of boyish humour." To which one might add "With you, perhaps".

As an increasing number of the correspondents asked where they could get hold of a copy, I am delighted that the Rolls-Royce Heritage Trust have decided to reprint *By Jupiter* in a corrected and slightly expanded form. All too often, when a company is taken over, the new masters have little time for the previous history. I know of numerous occasions in the British aircraft industry where irreplaceable archives have been wantonly destroyed. More power to Rolls-Royce, therefore, for caring about what went on at Bristol so many years before they purchased the company in 1966. I am sure the Heritage Trust will not regret taking the risk.

I would like to record my thanks to Peter Pavey of the Rolls-Royce Heritage Trust – Bristol Branch. Without his devoted help, this new edition, which is entitled simply *"Fedden"* would never have happened.

Haslemere, 1998 Bill Gunston, OBE

FEDDEN – THE LIFE OF SIR ROY FEDDEN

CHAPTER ONE

Boyhood

Many distinguished engineers and industrialists have risen to fame from a humble start, usually by working hard for high academic qualifications. It is characteristic of Roy Fedden that he did just the opposite. He renounced the social privileges of his family background, and shocked the genteel people around him by taking an apprenticeship on the factory floor. Such a thing was unheard-of! At the turn of the Century, this almost excommunicated him from his family and friends; but he set the pattern for the rest of his long and crowded life by doing things his way and not the way mapped out for him by others.

He was born into an eminent Bristol family. His father, Henry Fedden, descended from Eymer Fedden who settled in the city around 1620 as a sugar refiner. A brother of Eymer was a sugar planter and merchant in Barbados. The Fedden brigs shuttled across the wide Atlantic between the headquarters of the two brothers, and the business prospered. I V Hall, the historian of the Bristol sugar trade, wrote: "The Feddens … reached a position … in the local sugar industry never attained by any other family … Personal integrity, ambitious aims, and an acute awareness of the industrial and commercial trends of the times were the foundation of the Fedden success."

In the *Bristol Directory* of 1793 appear the entries, "William Fedden, sugar refiner" and "John Hall, glazier, Broadmead." The latter's son, the Rev Samuel Romilly Hall, President of the Methodist Conference of 1868, was the father of a strikingly handsome girl, Mary Elizabeth. In 1863, when she was 19 and one of the belles of Bristol society, she married Henry Fedden, who was 20 and the youngest of seven sons of the second William. Thus were combined the qualities of two exceptional families to continue a line of gifted people with strong personalities.

Apart from running the sugar business Henry Fedden lived an extremely full life. As a leader of Bristol's business and social communities, he had an outstanding sense of social responsibility, and devoted much of his time to the problems of welfare. It was an age when the scope for such work was unlimited. Though England prospered, the rewards of prosperity were distributed unevenly. Poverty to the point of starvation was as much part of the natural order of things as was the rigid and seemingly immutable structure of class distinction. Bristol was a thriving seaport, but large areas of the city were populated by people who, hard-working or lazy, gentle or vicious, were uniformly destitute. Worse, they seemed shut off from hope of improvement. Henry was a County Magistrate. His court, at Lawford's Gate, was in a slum so dangerous that it was unwise for "respectable citizens" to walk there alone. Each time his carriage drew up at the court, starving urchins would fight savagely for the privilege of opening the door, in the hope of catching a penny. Many agreed with Henry Fedden that this was not the way God intended people to live. None did more to try to change things.

His biggest enterprise was to help the poor boys of Bristol to pull themselves up and lead useful lives. By 1869 this work had become centred on *HMS Formidable,* one of the last and greatest ships of the line, launched in 1825. Henry Fedden was lent the vessel by the Admiralty, and had her towed to a mooring at Portishead. Here she was converted into a home and training ship for penniless or orphaned boys. The régime was tough, but it moulded the boys into fine men with seafaring skills and a new outlook and purpose in life.

A "start in life" really meant everything in those harsh days, and the *Formidable* hoisted thousands of lads over the otherwise impassable barrier which separated the "have-nots" from the "haves". Henry eventually corresponded with several hundred young men who had found careers, often serving the Queen in distant outposts of her great Empire, who had been lifted out of the gutters of Bristol through their training in *Formidable.*

Henry Fedden initiated the West Country branch of the Society for the Prevention of Cruelty to Children. He was President of the Bristol Lifeboat Institution. With the eccentric tobacco tycoon, his friend Sir Ernest Wills, he was a trustee of the Hall at Stoke Bishop, and a warden of Stoke Bishop church. Close by was the fine house, "St Mary's", which he built, partly with his own hands, and moved into in 1882.

At this time the family consisted of two boys, Vincent, born in 1872, and Romilly, born in 1877. The third son arrived on 6th June 1885, and was christened Alfred Hubert Roy.

One of Roy's earliest memories was of watching the Duke of Clarence unveil Bristol's statue of Queen Victoria on 25th July 1888. He also recalled his parents' dissatisfaction with the size of the garden at "St Mary's" (though it was by no means small by today's standards). In 1889 they found a house with more extensive grounds. Henbury was still a separate village to the north west of Bristol, and there, with a glorious garden commanding a fine view across the Severn to the Welsh hills, was "Fernhill". It was an old Quaker meeting-house with a succession of rooms which seemed endless. Under the supervision of butler Tinknell there were 15 scuttles of coal to be filled each day and more than 25 paraffin lamps to be attended to. Mrs Fedden found ample scope for her horticultural interests, specialising in prize Arum lilies grown under glass.

Young Roy's life was happy, devout and – except when his nurse Emily Caselton had to protect him from his big brothers – peaceful. He loved helping Salter, the gardener/coachman, and the under-gardeners, the village boys George and Billy. From them he learned how the other half lived, and his horizons expanded further when he was allowed to ride into Bristol with Salter on the box of the Victoria. He was measured by the tailor who made all the boys' suits, and the barber cut their hair for threepence, including a vigorous final brushing with a rotary brush driven by an overhead belt.

On Sundays the family attended services at Henbury's Norman church, with Henry Fedden wearing his frock coat and top hat. It was his habit to walk to all three services, and he taught a Sunday-school class in the afternoon. One Sunday he was shocked at Emily Caselton daring to wear bright flowers in her hat!

In 1893 Roy went as a day boy to St Goar's, a private school at Redland. His father drove him in the dog-cart each morning. In the afternoon Roy either returned the same way – the shop still exists where he used to buy a glass of milk while waiting for his father – or took a horse bus from Blackboy Hill and walked the last mile. Despite the long journey each day he found time for fishing, collecting butterflies, gardening and especially, carpentry. He spent hours in the workshop at "Fernhill", and eventually managed to persuade his skilled brothers to help him. He acquired the basic feel for fashioning materials into tools and toys, and began to acquire the pleasure to be derived from good design and construction.

The household was devout but open-minded, happy and always doing something new. One of the new things was to go away on an annual holiday, then by no means common. At the age of five Roy found himself required to alight from a coach at the foot of steep Porlock Hill in Devon and, with the other passengers, walk or help push. He slipped down from his mother's lap and clutched at the door post just as brother Romilly slammed the door; his right hand was squashed almost to pulp. By coincidence, 15 years later he was in Porlock with the St Agnes Clifton College Mission – a college charity set up to assist boys from poor families – and the very doctor who had attended him was amazed at the complete recovery of his hand. Just before the First World War, he was to return that way again. As Technical Director of Straker Squire cars, he tested a standard production model, fully laden, by making 25 climbs of the same gruelling hill in a day.

Henry once took Roy on a three-week tour with pony and trap through the highways and byways of Somerset. Later in life Roy was to appreciate how this trip, with days spent chatting to country folk and tradesmen in the small towns, helped to give him an understanding of the way those people thought and felt about the everyday things which were going on. At that time men in positions of authority made little or no effort to communicate with those working under them – especially with the young – and thus had virtually no understanding of their problems or point of view. When he was 87 Roy Fedden wrote "My sympathies with the underdog and young people struggling to get established often caused eyebrows to be raised. But this outlook earned me respect, affection and loyalty that money could never buy."

The Feddens were expert fly-fishermen, and this later became Roy's most enduring pastime. In the closing years of the 19th century he enjoyed several fishing holidays at Bettws-y-Coed in North Wales, and on one of these a fellow guest at the hotel was a wealthy American who owned a Duryea motor car. People came from miles around to see it, and Roy was lucky enough to be taken for a ride. Motors were forbidden to exceed 4 mph and had to be preceded by a pedestrian (though he no longer had to wave a red flag). The car industry in Britain was virtually non-existent, and most of the tiny handful of "eccentrics" who owned motors employed foreign chauffeurs.

Roy little thought what a big part such things would play in his life, nor how much he would see of the old mill on the bank of the Usk at Bwlch in Breconshire which he gazed at on another fishing holiday with his father around 1890. He used to imagine what the people were like who lived there, and dreamed that when he grew up he would save up enough money to buy it and fish the river all day. The dream came true.

In 1895 he went to the Prep and Junior School at Clifton College. Clifton

Clifton College at the time of RF's arrival (Clifton College)

had become a notable public school, with a noble chapel and fine academic buildings of mellow Cotswold stone set amidst superb grounds and playing fields. From the first Roy revelled in the environment, with firm discipline and high standards of personal conduct. His character had already begun to mature around a code of behaviour which today might be considered unreasonably rigid, and puritanical almost to the point of asceticism.

Probably the most fundamental principle taught in British public schools, and emphasised at Clifton, was that of "playing the game". Winning was nothing like as important as setting a perfect standard of team spirit and impeccable behaviour under the most extreme competitive stress. The aim was to fit boys for the stresses of life ahead, but Clifton also managed to turn out an extraordinary number of the greatest players in the history of many games, and especially of cricket. RF, as he had become known, played in a match which will be remembered as long as cricket is played.

MATCH BETWEEN ... and ... Innings ... Playground

	BATSMEN.	RUNS.	HOW OUT.	BOWLER'S NAME.	TOTAL.
1	Collins	[illegible]	not out		628
2	Champion	22122221122223	caught Monteath	Rendall	27
3	Gilbert	11223	bowled	Crew	9
4	Sheldon?	11213	caught Davis	Sainsbury	8
5	Sharff	1122	bowled	Crew	6
6	Galway	111224	bowled	Crew	11
7	Whitty	22232222222222233221	c & b	Monteath	42
8	Browne	x	bowled	Monteath	0
9	Sealey	23122213231312[illegible]	bowled	Monteath	32
10	Raine	4211131	bowled	Sainsbury	14
11	Redfern	11222[illegible]121	caught Eberle	Crew	13
	Byes	[illegible]			34
	Leg Byes	1			1
	Wide Balls	1111111111			10
	No Balls	1			1

RUNS AT THE FALL OF EACH WICKET.

1 for 127	2 for 169	3 for 226	4 for 268	5 for 311	6 for 436	7 for 451	8 for	9 for 698	10 for	11 for	TOTAL 836

ANALYSIS OF BOWLING.

	BOWLERS.	RUNS FOR EACH OVER (1–15)	WIDE BALLS	NO BALLS	RUNS	WICKETS	OVER	MAIDEN OVERS	BALLS BOWLED	AVERAGE RUNS PER WICKET
1	Sindrea	[illegible]	111		218	0	50	5	250	
2	Sainsbury	[illegible]	[illegible]	[illegible]	165	4	42	5	213	
3	Crew	[illegible]	[illegible]	[illegible]	[illegible]	[illegible]	[illegible]	[illegible]	[illegible]	[illegible]
4	Rendall	[illegible]	1		118	1	10	3		
5	Davies	[illegible]	1	1	74	0	14	0	70	
6	Monteath	[illegible]	[illegible]	[illegible]	113	3	17	2		
7	Sainsbury	[illegible]	[illegible]		[illegible]	4	32	7	160	
8	Sindrea	[illegible]	[illegible]	[illegible]	[illegible]	[illegible]	[illegible]	[illegible]	[illegible]	[illegible]

The scorecard showing Collins' 628 – RF did not bowl (Clifton College)

One summer day in 1899 he put on his cricketing cap for his Junior House (North Town, a black cap with narrow blue and white ribbons) and his friend A E J Collins put on his (Clark's House, black with yellow vertical stripes). There were three house pitches on the Junior School Close, but this match was played on another pitch next to Guthrie Road, with Emmanuel Church at one end and the Fives Courts at the other. Clark's batted, and it was soon evident that Collins was making an exceptional score. It got into the papers, so that a big crowd gathered for the later days of the match. On the fifth afternoon Clark's last wicket fell with the score at 836. Collins' score appeared in the book as "628 not out, plus or minus 20". It remains the all-time record innings in the history of cricket.

Roy fielded at cover-point throughout, and so impressed the two watching games masters that he found himself in the Junior First XI, hitting 40 not out against Cheltenham in his first match. In September 1899 he went as a boarder to the Senior School, in Brown's House, named after its first housemaster, the immortal Tom Brown of Rugby. When Roy joined, the housemaster was W W Asquith, brother of the Prime Minister. RF was a member of the Military Side because his parents had decided he should be educated for a Service career. The Military Side trailed behind the Classical Side which governed the school, but as Roy's main interest was sport he made a fetish of games and did the minimum of academic work. This presented no problems, and he was regarded as a popular and amicable rebel. He could both accept and give orders, having been a fag, head fag and finally a prefect while still in the fifth form. The fagging system was well administered at Clifton, testing the ability of boys at first to accept the authority of their immediate seniors, and eventually encouraging them to wield power justly and decisively. In his years at Clifton, Roy never saw an abuse of this privilege, nor any kind of bullying – he was clearly highly sensitive, and such a thing would have stuck in his mind indelibly.

The regime was arduous. Everyone had to be immaculately groomed for prayers with the house tutor at 7.00, followed by an hour's prep before breakfast. School chapel was at 9.00, after which the day's programme of lessons began in the main school until 6.00pm. Games were compulsory on two afternoons a week. In spare moments Roy went to the college baths, and in 1898 he took a remarkably clear photograph of a boy diving. The pool was indoors and such a photograph was then a rare achievement. Most cameras in those days were unwieldy boxes mounted on a tripod, with a shutter triggered by squeezing a rubber bulb to expose a plate-glass negative. Roy's camera, bought in 1896 from Dunscombe's in Bristol for the considerable sum of £5, was one of the revolutionary new roll-film bellows models. He took it to the Royal Review of the assembled fleets of many nations at Spithead in the summer of 1897 to mark Her Majesty's Diamond Jubilee.

The *Formidable's* tender was the *Polly,* a square-rigged brigantine, in which 40 boys trained at a time. Henry Fedden decided to sail her round to Portsmouth for the Review, 440 miles each way, with Roy among the complement.

In 1903, having been rejected by an Admiralty doctor because the alignment of his teeth was not absolutely perfect, Roy tried for the Royal Marines. He sat the examination for Sandhurst, but increasingly suffered doubts. Though he was tall, good-looking and strong, he was driven to the conclusion that a Service life was not for him. He wanted to do something "more useful" and important to humanity, but did not know what. While he was in this frame of mind, his father bought a motor car. Henry Fedden was already noted for his advanced ideas; he had for many years been a director of the original West Country Telephone Company, and even had one of the instruments at "Fernhill". He now felt that a car would be useful for commuting into Bristol, and after much family discussion Vincent was sent to London to make the purchase. He chose an 8½ horse-power two-cylinder Decauville imported by H M Hobson Ltd (later to be a major supplier to RF's engines). Vincent was in good company with his choice. A similar car was bought at the same time from the same agent by a young man named Henry Royce, who decided he could improve upon it. He developed three- and six-cylinder engines, and then set up a business with the Hon C S Rolls.

Roy had pleaded to be allowed to go with Vincent. Eventually a compromise was reached. He travelled by train to Reading, met Vincent and Hobson's mechanic, and the three of them drove merrily back to Bristol. There the new motor was registered AE4, the fourth in the Bristol region and about the 50th in Britain. The public tended to regard motor cars as evil monsters, and though many people were intrigued, the popular response was to jeer. What made things far worse was that the Decauville was a disaster. When it met the steep hills of Bristol it failed completely. Even on the level it could give trouble, as there were two gear levers, one for the bottom three gears and the other for top. At a good speed it was possible to change into top and discover – the hard way – that the other lever had not been in neutral. When the Decauville did go it ran sweetly, but it was unreliable and broke down in all parts of Bristol. Almost every trip ended with AE4 the centre of a sarcastic crowd. Hobson refused to have anything more to do with it, and eventually Henry Fedden managed to persuade the Bristol Motor Co to allow him a small sum in part exchange for one of their own cars. The Bristol gave the family many years of trouble-free motoring, though on one occasion there was trouble that was no fault of the car. Vincent and Roy drove to a dance, and on the way home found a man lying across the road. He seemed unconscious, and they lifted him up and carried him to the Bristol Infirmary. There he was merely pronounced dead drunk. Greatly relieved, the two

Feddens walked out and into the midst of an angry mob which had collected round their car. One burly man felled Roy to the ground, shouting in unspeakable terms that he would teach him not to run over innocent pedestrians. The brothers did not laugh about this until later.

In February 1904 Canon Glazebrook, the austere Headmaster at Clifton, wrote to Henry Fedden informing him what a good candidate his son would make for Sandhurst. His uniform had been bought, and he was due there within a month. But Roy had at last discovered the more useful calling that had been eluding him. He had enjoyed helping to repair the Decauville, and imagined himself to be a fully qualified engineer. The more he thought about it, the more such a career appealed to him. He broke the news to his father. Henry was a most approachable and understanding man, but this was a profound shock. Henry knew his youngest son too well to think that he had turned "yellow" and lacked the guts to make a career in uniform. But engineering! It was socially quite unacceptable, being regarded as little better than casual labouring. Was he not letting the side down very badly?

British engineers had pioneered the technology on which the Industrial Revolution had been based, and the booming economy of the nation was founded mainly upon engineering. But the subject itself was almost taboo in the best circles, and viewed with distaste. Fifty and more years earlier the Stephensons, Nasmyth, Whitworth, Brunel and the like had been known to all, and accepted as famous gentlemen; but gradually the notion of an engineer had slid down the social scale, largely through a misapprehension of what an engineer was. For any boy in a "good family" to show more than a dilettante interest in engineering was horrifying. When they learned the sad news, many of Roy's school chums begged him to think again. Friends of the family gathered and discussed what could be done to make such a nice boy return to his senses. One of them was a Mrs Crew, who had three strikingly beautiful daughters. One of her daughters, Norah, had from childhood been the special friend of Roy. Four years his junior, she had a personality as strong as his own. She was delighted when the 14-year-old boy informed her he would marry her when he was grown up. Her mother was pleased because the tall Fedden boy had impeccable manners and also happened to be an uncommonly good dancer. Now she could hardly believe her ears. In Roy's own words, pronounced over 70 years later, "She was convinced I was going to be some kind of plumber, dirty and brutish. She no longer wanted me in her house, and suggested that, if I did come, presumably I would go round to the *back* door."

Such was the popular opinion of engineers at the turn of the Century. But within the Fedden family there was no argument. They had brought up three fine sons to think for themselves. Henry Fedden's conclusion was simply, "If you are so keen on engineering, then that is what you must do".

CHAPTER TWO

The world of motors

Had Roy been French or German the Polytechnique or Technische Hochschule would have had sufficient social stature to overcome the dirty-overalls image, and conjure up instead a picture of brain-work and slide-rules. In Britain there were no such establishments, yet Bristol was well equipped for the training of engineers. Henry paid the huge sum of £250 for his son to take a premium apprenticeship with the Bristol Motor Co. At night the boy studied under Professor Morgan at the Merchant Venturers' Technical College.

The Merchant Venturers' Technical College (the car appears to be a 1927 bullnose Morris) (Merchant Venturers' Society)

Many engineering apprenticeships at the turn of the Century were unsatisfactory. The lad would spend most of his time doing menial tasks and essentially acting as an almost unpaid labourer. If he made himself a nuisance and badgered his superiors he might learn a few skills, but it was an uphill struggle. Bristol Motors were not so disinterested. At their works in Redcross Street they designed cars and made them by hand, right down to the smallest detail apart from cylinder castings. Roy realised that he was practically unique in Britain. The only other young-gentlemen apprentices were directors' sons who would be given polite attention in a superficial way, but never treated seriously or allowed to soil their hands. Roy made it clear he wanted to learn. He donned overalls and joined a small group working under a foreman master-mechanic. The latter was a martinet, whose sharp eye missed nothing. Today it is taken for granted that everyone starts packing up long before the end of the shift or working day, but Roy's first foreman insisted that nobody knocked off when the whistle blew until he had finished the job he was working on (in 1904 this was common practice). Then Roy had to lay out the foreman's lunch, and "wet" his tea, before he could touch his own.

Cylinder castings were brought from the Douglas motor-cycle works at nearby Kingswood, but Roy had a hand in every other metal part of the company's cars. He learned the rudiments of the design process, tested engines and materials, and learned how to operate a lathe, drill press and shaper, and how to hand-forge, heat-treat, quench and grind. He learned all the basic mechanical-engineering skills, and, as the months went by, the appeal of engineering did not pall but sharpened. The glow of a salt bath, the smell of cutting oil and the social environment of the factory became a pleasant way of life with a real meaning and purpose. Almost imperceptibly Roy acquired an understanding of good and bad design and manufacture, and to gain great pleasure from parts that were perfect in all respects. He also gained understanding of men.

Practical experience at Redcross Street was vital, but it was often conspicuously absent from the curriculum of young men seeking to become academically qualified engineers at that time. Between the wars it was taken for granted among British employers that a man with an engineering degree was almost regarded at a discount! Yet no amount of shop experience can make up for absence of theoretical knowledge, and this Roy gained under one of the finest engineering teachers there has ever been. Professor William Morgan occupied the chair of automobile engineering at Merchant Venturers' Technical College, near the theatre in the city centre. Morgan's night school exerted a major influence on Bristol engineers early in the present Century, and Roy attended his classes on automobile engineering and internal-combustion engines throughout his three indentured years with

Bristol Motor and for a further nine months afterwards.

Unlike many, Roy believed that the motor car had come to stay. He carefully studied the cars on sale and noted that they seemed to be unnecessarily large and expensive. All appeared to be designed upon the assumption that the customer would be wealthy, and would employ a chauffeur. Roy questioned this policy. He could see no technical objection to designing a car that was smaller and cheaper. If the owner drove it himself it would still be useful even if it had only two seats. Such a car ought to be within the financial reach of a vastly increased number of people; thus the size of the motor industry could be increased. In 1906 he decided he would attempt to design such a car.

His father took a keen interest in his son's work, but just at this time had much on his mind. Early in the Century the old *Formidable* had been condemned. Henry Fedden was sent official letters expressing thanks and saying in glowing terms what a fine job he had done, but he refused to give up. With the financial help of two of the most famous Bristol families, Wills' tobacco and Fry's chocolate, he drew up plans for a great school on land, and on 5th May 1906 the Princess Christian opened the National Nautical School at Portishead. The school has flourished ever since. In its later years it was nobly served by Vincent Fedden, and in 1939, two years after Vincent's death, the Bishop of Malmesbury dedicated a stained-glass window in the memorial chapel which Roy gave in his brother's memory.

In 1906, though Roy had little spare time, his car design made good progress. At the end of the year, as his apprenticeship was coming to an end, he obtained an introduction to John P. Brazil, who was both a qualified engineer and a dynamic businessman. In 1893 an engineering works had been established at St Phillips Marsh, Bristol, under the name of Owen, Brazil & Co to make German Bonzac cigarette machines under licence, Djinn marine engines, hydraulic presses, perforated plates for Spencer Moulton rubber railway buffers and a range of castings and forgings. In 1897 Holborow, an experienced West Country engineer with a flowing white beard, turned the company into Owen, Brazil and Holborow. Meanwhile, Sidney Straker Ltd, a Blackfriars, London, firm of motor agents, had collaborated with Bayley's, an old firm of boilermakers and wheelwrights, to make a steam tractor. Straker had an interest in the Bristol company and subcontracted them to make the cast and machined parts of his patented engine and chassis. In 1901 Owen retired from the Board, and Straker came in to make it Brazil, Holborow & Straker, and the firm extended its St Phillips works (the Vulcan Iron Works in Chapel Street) and opened new premises in Grafton Street and Albert Road.

One product of the Bayley-Straker team was the steam "lurry", entered in the Liverpool trials of 1899, with a Bayley boiler made to De Dion design

A Wesleyan Sunday School outing on 1 July 1912. The three buses leaving Bishop Sutton are Brazil Strakers of Bath Electric Tramways. (Mike Tozer)

and a Straker compound engine. Production was centred at the Bristol works, but servicing and selling was handled by the Straker Steam Vehicle Co formed by Straker and his London partner L R L Squire. The Straker Squire marketing organisation also bought the licence for the German Büssing motor bus. This famous design was adopted by the London General Omnibus Co, and went into production at Bristol in 1906, at what had become Brazil Straker & Co, no fewer than 1,000 of the London buses being produced by the end of 1909. Brazil Straker then thought about motor cars, and in 1906 Mr Brazil decided to market a fine four-litre French car, the CSB (Cornilleau et Ste Beuve). The expanding firm quickly built a new production factory at Fishponds, Bristol, which was not only large by 1906 standards but also lavishly equipped. To meet the severe Scotland Yard limitations on road-vehicle noise, which applied to London buses, Brazil Straker installed such unfamiliar machine tools as Gleason gear shapers and Reinicker gear grinders, to make accurate and smooth gear teeth. Roy saw these, marvelled, and so made up his mind to approach Mr Brazil.

Aged about 40, Brazil was a stocky and clean-shaven Irishman, who, unlike practically every other man in England, appeared never to wear a hat.

In January 1907 RF completed the design drawings and specification of his two-seater car, which he named the Shamrock in view of Brazil's nationality. He visited Brazil at his house in Belgrave Road and showed him the drawings. Brazil was intensely interested, thinking the young Mr Fedden had come with the right product at the right time. He said he would seek the technical opinion of his design staff. In the meantime he invited Roy to join that staff as a junior draughtsman; he was very taken by the attractive young man and considered he could be useful to the flourishing firm.

As Brazil had hoped, the design staff reported favourably on the Shamrock. Brazil Straker decided to go ahead, and try to make one in time for the annual motor show at Olympia, London, in November 1907. Brazil placed absolute trust in his young employee – unwisely so, Fedden thought – and gave him freedom to manage the design staff. The unknown and inexperienced 22-year-old had the stature, the character and yet the essential humility to make the tricky situation work. He settled down to run a team of busy and experienced engineers who perhaps themselves wondered that they

The Shamrock, which caused such a stir at the 1907 London Motor Show. (Author)

did not think of young Fedden as an upstart. The design flourished, Brazil became enthusiastic, works manager C B Westley gave Fedden unstinted support, and swiftly not one but two Shamrocks were taking shape.

The original Shamrock had an engine of clean design, with "square" cylinders of 85 mm (3.35 in) bore and stroke, cast in pairs, giving a capacity of about two litres and with an RAC tax rating of 12-14 horsepower. A bevel gear on the rear end of the camshaft drove a vertical shaft with the oil pump at its lower end and the ignition distributor at the top. The stiff crankshaft drove through double universal joints and a leather-faced cone clutch to a gearbox with sliding spur gears offering two forward speeds and one reverse, selected by a radial arm below the steering wheel. The open propeller shaft drove a novel back axle. The crown wheel and differential were mounted from the rear in a casing clipped to steel tubes surrounding fully floating live half-shafts driving the wheels through jaw clutches. Without using a jack, either half-shaft or the differential could be removed in minutes, an unheard-of capability in an age when back axles broke frequently. Other features included V-type torque rods and radius rods, and double band brakes on the rear wheels.

Fedden accompanied the little car to Olympia to explain it to prospective purchasers. The price had been set at £250, and though this was a large sum in 1907 it was about half the price of the average car and less than one-quarter the price of the better models. Many rivals had a close look at the Shamrock, and expressed the view that if the production model was made to the same standard there would be precious little profit for Brazil Straker. The little car was an immediate success, and received such acclaim in the press that it drew the visiting crowds like a magnet. A typical report appeared in the *Bristol Times Mirror* for 15 November 1907: "To find a real novelty at the motor show grows more difficult every year, but ... I came across a sensational novelty today in the shape of a 12-14 hp four-cylinder car, with body, for £250. This little car, called the Shamrock, is certainly a marvel, of which the British industry has reason to be proud ... The popularity of the car during the coming season is beyond question, for while I was examining it an agent, who had placed an order for a dozen light cars of a world-renowned make, informed me that he had cancelled that order and substituted the Shamrock in its place." Other writers referred to "This little gem of a car", which was "the centre of interest" about which "From all quarters splendid accounts are constantly being received" – which may have been over-enthusiastic as so far nobody had had time to try it out on the road.

Such a reception was more than Brazil or Fedden had dared hope for. In a matter of days the little car became a major project. At the age of 22 Fedden changed from being a mere enthusiast, who read in the car magazines about the doings of others, into the chief engineer of Brazil Straker, a man of authority and even international fame. The key to his success, and a feature that subsequently characterised his whole career, was his ability to gather round him a superb team. Leader of the team was little L F G "Bunny" Butler, the chief designer and a fanatic for painstaking detail. George Murray came from the Arrol-Johnston Co in his native Scotland to be chief draughtsman. Sidney Ware became works manager and also designed what became the standard production carburettor. Fred Whitehead specialised in machine tools and became probably the leading man in Britain on mass-production of metal parts. R S Witchell came to run the Experimental Department, and F C Clement took over Road Testing.

While preparations were made for production, the car was modified in detail – engine stroke was increased to 87mm – and subjected to exhaustive testing, most of it initially by Fedden himself. So in its report on the 1908 Motor Show the London *Daily Telegraph* provided a reminder of the state of the automotive art: "This year the car has had its compression increased, giving the engine greater power; the high-tension magneto is now used ... a foot accelerator is also fitted; lever and rod control in place of Bowden wires; radius rods fitted in addition to the torque rods; and larger wheels are carried, running on ball-bearings throughout. The price has also been slightly increased, which is a very good thing, as the new 14-16 hp Straker Squire (as it is now called) is figured at a very moderate price even now. At the last Brooklands meeting this year this little car – tuned up, of course, but not otherwise altered in any way – won its heat, averaging a speed of over 64 miles an hour from a standing start over about five miles. So its designer has justified himself". The new price was £315.

In its first selling season, 1908-09, about 150 Straker Squires were produced, with rate of manufacture rising fast. Fedden drove at Brooklands, and in the Irish, Scottish and 2,000-mile Trials, with encouraging success. H F Smallwood, whom he met in the 2,000-mile event, joined the company as manager of the running shop (later he became chairman of Dorman Engines). Competition results in 1910 were further improved by increasing the stroke to 100 mm (almost 4 in). Finally in 1911 Fedden introduced an entirely new 3-litre engine with four 90 x 120 mm cylinders cast in one block, driving an oval-webbed crankshaft running in five bearings. His streamlined PDQ (pretty damn quick) racing model gained several successes at Brooklands, and for two years held the record for climbing the test hill there. This so-called 15 hp Straker Squire gained hundreds of column-inches of glowing publicity and added further to the reputation of its young designer, who the previous year had achieved the honour of being elected a Full Member of the Institution of Mechanical Engineers. Over the remaining years of peace this single model remained the most important of all the company's products, output being kept at 12 or 13 a week and the total sales

RF on a stripped 1910 racer on the test hill at Brooklands. (Peter Ware)

amounting to about 1,300 – which with an embryonic market and *more than 200* rival British car makers was outstanding success.

Thus by 1908 Roy Fedden had "arrived"; indeed, he was almost a household word. But what was he like as a person? Superficially the answer is simple. He was tall and well-built, good looking and extremely fit, and a more attractive bachelor would have been hard to find. Though clearly from a good family he was very much one of the boys, and he had yet to become devoted to the serious matter of work. He no longer lived at home, but was one of a group of lively young fellows who shared a delightful rented house at Nailsea, aptly named The Nuttery. Those who squeezed the huge bulb-horn that served as front door bell – with the instruction HONKEE KINDLY – included many of the early motoring and flying men in Britain. The residents, apart from RF, were Ware, Witchell and Smallwood, all at Brazil Straker, and the famous aviator Howard Flanders. A good time was had by all.

RF with Sidney Ware in a 1910 racer. (Peter Ware)

Yet deep inside, RF was already totally single-minded. Later Sidney Ware was badly hurt while testing a Brazil Straker chassis. Though solicitous, RF instantly realised he was no longer useful to the company and so had no more time for him. As Ware's son Peter recalls, "Roy's ruthlessness was not something that came with maturity – he had it there from birth on his punchcard. After all, you don't rise so swiftly in management just by being a nice chap". Yet, single-minded as he was, social injustice upset him terribly. One day Brazil called him in and said – and RF never forgot his exact words – "It's ten to three. I'm afraid we've lost that order for 400 lorries for the Crown Agents for the Colonies. Pay off 280 men this afternoon". In later life he would have had the instinctive experience not to get involved, but at 26 he was overwhelmed. The first thing he did was rush to the washroom and be sick. What he had to do was like passing a death sentence. Indeed, some of the families did lose children through starvation, though Roy with his mother tried to visit all the stricken homes with baskets of food – an act which 1911 society would have thought most irregular. Many of the men were out of work more than a year, and had no income at all apart from the few who belonged to the Royal Ancient Order of Buffaloes who got 8s 6d. This was the way life was, and it was a way that Henry Fedden was fighting to change.

In 1911 Roy was injured playing football. The injury evidently exerted a strong emotional effect on him, and he refused to discuss it, but it was serious enough to cause him to take a year's leave from Brazil Straker and recuperate in South Africa. At this time he was 26 and Norah Crew 22. They were deeply devoted, and in view of his meteoric rise to fame the Crew family now regarded him as very much more than "some kind of plumber". Had they married it would probably have been an ideal match, but it shows something of Fedden's character that he talked earnestly with his sweetheart and told her he had put off all thought of marriage, and was going away from Bristol. The result was that, though she did not love him, Norah Crew married an Army officer. He was a hard and austere man, though capable and brave, and his career was distinguished. He became a pilot in the Royal Flying Corps and later an air marshal in the RAF; but it was never a happy union, and about 20 years later Norah and Roy began to meet again.

When Roy returned from his rest in South Africa he was reappointed chief engineer at Fishponds, though he did not go back to The Nuttery but instead

RF first studied aircraft at the 1912 military trials at Larkhill, Salisbury Plain. One participant was a Bristol-Coanda monoplane generally similar to this one (No 132). (Rolls-Royce plc)

stayed more quietly with an aunt at Royal York Crescent. By this time he was no callow youth but an experienced practical engineer and leader of men. He kept an eye on possible future markets for Brazil Straker, and increasingly studied the field of aviation which, like motors, he was convinced had come to stay. He added *Flight* and *The Aero* to his regular list of motoring papers. In 1912 he attended the Military Aircraft Trials on Salisbury Plain, he went to Hendon to see Howard Flanders' new monoplane, and he often thereafter went to see races at Hendon, and to chat with pilots and aircraft engineers at *The Blue Bird* restaurant on the flying field in the centre of Brooklands race track. In 1912 and 1913 he accompanied Brazil on visits to French aviation firms. A particular objective was to explore the possibility of making rotary engines under licence from the Société des Moteurs Clerget in Paris, but the terms offered were not attractive.

In early 1914, at 29, Fedden was appointed the company's technical director, with a seat on the Board. By this time the War Office had at last noticed that there were no aircraft engines available in Britain capable of rivalling those on the Continent, and it organised a Naval and Military Aeroplane Engine Competition. Fedden decided his company had insufficient experience to enter, but he carefully studied every submission. One engine made a deep impression on him. The Scottish motor firm of Argyll had used the patent for a sleeve valve jointly held by their compatriot Burt and the Canadian McCollum to design an excellent 125 hp six-in-line engine. RF was delighted when this engine was pronounced the winner, and puzzled when the outbreak of the First World War was given as the reason for abandoning any thought of making it in quantity! For the next two years British aero engines continued to be either rather poor or of foreign design.

In 1913 Straker Squire cars were continuing to sell well and flourish in competition, with Witchell and Clement doing most of the driving. It was perhaps inevitable that the little 2-litre Shamrock should, over the years, have become larger and more powerful; this is a trend from which cars have found it hard to escape. For the 1914 market Fedden planned an even bigger and better 4½-litre engine of 100 mm bore and 140 mm stroke mounted in a fine new chassis. Among many novel features were spring-damper timing gears, a short and stiff gear lever to a four-speed box with flame-hardened and ground gears, enclosed caliper drum brakes, and quickly detachable wire wheels. At all times the company strove to excel not only in detail design and finish but also in modernity. In May 1914 Fedden went to Stuttgart to finalise arrangements for fitting his cars with the new Bosch electrical system, serving powerful headlights and a self-starter. One afternoon he was driven over to the nearby Mercedes plant to see a car with the whole system fitted. Wandering off inquisitively, he suddenly found himself in a big assembly shop. In various stages of erection were serried rows of big six-in-line water-cooled engines. With a thrill of excitement Fedden saw that these were not for cars but for aircraft. The Mercedes production line was many times bigger than anything Fedden had dreamed of in the world of aviation. Quite obviously he was not meant to see it. For the past several years the threat of war had been in the atmosphere; his elder brothers' friends, politically well informed, took it for granted that open conflict with the Kaiser was only a matter of time. He came away from Stuttgart profoundly concerned.

RF on a 1914 Straker Squire competition car. (Peter Ware)

Back at Fishponds he plunged straight into the final preparations for one of the classic motor races of all time, the 1914 Tourist Trophy. Six years had passed since the last TT race, and the technical advances that had been made were astonishing. Nobody rated the Straker Squires as likely winners, although the car's reputation was second to none. But Fedden had designed a 3.26-litre overhead-camshaft engine that had delivered 80 hp on the bench, and decided to mount the best challenge he could. In February he had been over to the Isle of Man, with Witchell and Clement, to study the course. In June, they went over for the race. With a week to go they suffered the crushing disappointment of discovering carburettor and induction-pipe snags in the new engine installation that were not manifest in bench trials, and when the race began on 10th June both Strakers had the ordinary "15 hp" under the bonnet. Even so, the car could do 90 mph and the 39-mile course demanded frequent and heavy application of the brakes. In 1914 roads were not designed for motors. Almost all of the course was unpaved, and it abounded in hairpin bends and narrow stone bridges which called for extreme care and precision. Even at a mere 30 mph the wickedly hump-back bridge at Ballig made cars leap several feet into the air, and it was obvious that to finish at all would be a major achievement.

In the event the two Guinness brothers, driving Sunbeams, led almost all the way. They were pursued by the Belgian Minerva team; but, to the surprise of many, Dick Witchell came next. Clement unfortunately broke a tappet finger on the second of the two afternoons, but Witchell hung on, gained on the Minervas and even passed Molon and the Champion Porporato. Then, on the very last of the 16 laps, he was flagged down and spent six minutes crawling behind a doctor's car summoned to a stricken Vauxhall. This cost him third place, by 30 seconds – but the Straker Squire won the prize for the most consistent performance up Snaefell mountain, at a steady 55 mph. Winner Kenelm Lee Guinness later lent his initials to a

The 1914 Straker TT team included – from the left: F C Clement (driver), E Winstone, anon, Preston, Rudman, anon, Brown, RF, R S Witchell (driver) and Wiltshire. (Peter Ware)

famous make of sparking plug. Witchell was soon a pilot in the RFC, and survived the war to work on aero engines under Fedden, on cars under W O Bentley (who finished sixth in the 1914 TT) and finally on gearwheels as a director of the ENV Company.

One of the few notable absentees from the 1914 race was Mercedes, which had become a world leader in racing. The French Grand Prix of 1914 was won by a Mercedes of advanced design. The car was promptly bought by an English brewer and taken to London. This was of no small interest to one of Fedden's sailing friends, Cdr Wilfred Briggs RN. He was Head of the Royal Naval Air Service Engine Division. His office over Admiralty Arch radiated ceaseless activity, and his deep concern over Britain's apparent lack of good aero engines finally burst into effective action. On the Sunday following the declaration of war on 4th August 1914 he had the Mercedes racer taken from the showroom in Shaftesbury Avenue where it had been stored. He then hitched it to his own car and personally towed it to Derby, where he invited Rolls-Royce to use the Mercedes cylinder, and any other of its features they thought desirable, as the basis for a series of powerful aircraft engines, to be produced to the fastest possible schedule. In fact, though the German engine was carefully studied and test-run, it was in no way copied, and particular care was taken not to infringe any Mercedes patent. Before the end of August the basic design of the big vee-12 Rolls-Royce Eagle engine was on paper, thus starting a famous family of engines that in the course of time were to give Fedden his most severe competition.

In the first week of war Fedden tried to enlist, but was turned down because of his old footballing injury. Henceforth a khaki armlet with a red crown testified to the fact, shielding him from the stigma of the white feathers that zealous women gave to able-looking men not in uniform. He managed the Fishponds works as it grew to over 2,000 workers, an increasing proportion of them female, and soon they were delivering more than 50 staff cars and 4-ton lorries a month to the War Department, plus artillery shells and other stores. The design staff, depleted by the war, used their TT experience in creating an outstanding 3½-litre car with cantilever springing which performed superbly. But the war was not "over by Christmas" as had commonly been supposed.

In the autumn of 1914 Briggs decided to test Fedden and his team by seeing what they could do to rectify a situation which had become serious. Most pupil pilots for the Royal Naval Air Service were being trained on the Curtiss JN-4 "Jenny", an American aircraft being made in vast quantities for the Allies. There was evidence that these machines, supplied for cash, were not subjected to a satisfactory standard of inspection before delivery. In particular, their 90 hp vee-8 Curtiss OX-5 engines were proving most unreliable and suffering breakdowns due to numerous causes within an average life of less than five hours. RNAS pilot training was in a bad state, with frequent fatal crashes and poor morale. Fedden was sent more than 300 crated OX-5 engines, told some of the faults that had been found – for example, the crankcase often broke – and then given a free hand.

RF welcomed the chance to work on an aero engine, but no special skill was needed to spot some of the faults. Several of the engines had flown, and a few had crashed and been embedded in earth. According to Fedden, "Nearly all were filthy, and many had in their crankcases solid rubbish which might have been put there deliberately had it not included at least one dollar bill. Even the cleaner and better-looking specimens contained examples of bad workmanship such as a broken drill-bit jammed in a crankshaft oil-hole". But Fedden soon came to the conclusion that the engine needed to be redesigned. By December 1914 he and Butler had drawn an improved OX-5, with revised crankcase, valve tappets, induction and ignition system. The first engine was built within a month and performed excellently on test. The redesigned parts, amounting to almost half the engine, were put into production at Fishponds. From then onwards the RNAS training scene was transformed, and the redesigned engines ran up to 200 hours before overhaul.

This Curtiss OX-5 rebuilt by Brazil Straker is in the American Air Museum at Duxford. (John Scott)

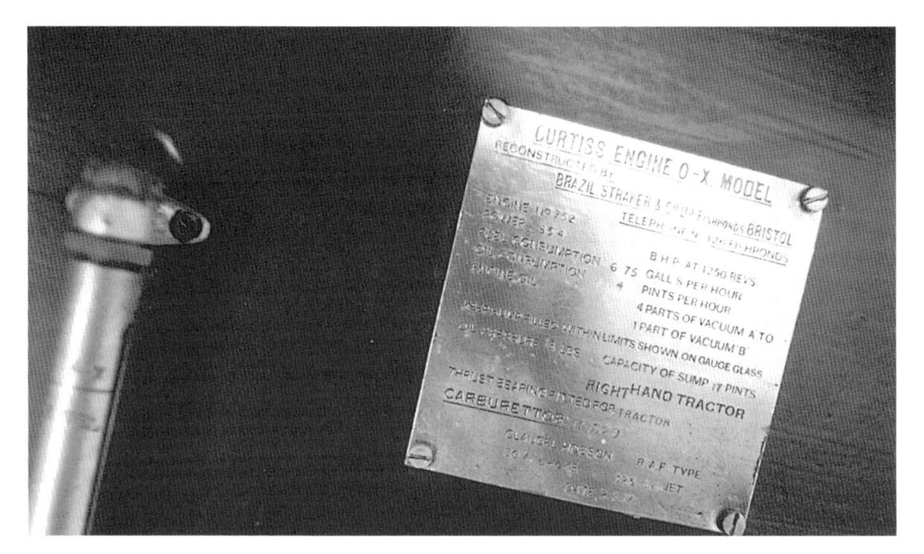

Manufacturer's plate on the OX-5. (John Scott)

RF was at once in great demand. The Admiralty took over the Fishponds works in January 1915 and put it totally on to war production. Sir William (later Lord) Weir, Director of Aeronautical Supplies at the Ministry of Munitions, suggested that Brazil Straker should make the newly designed Rolls-Royce aero engines, and Briggs drove Fedden up to Derby to see the firm that was already a household word. Rolls had been killed flying at Bournemouth in 1910, but Henry Royce was very much alive at St Margaret's Bay, Kent, with a small nucleus of design staff around him. The general manager was Claude Johnson, the highly cultured former Secretary of the Royal Automobile Club, who had his office in Conduit Street, London. Derby was in the charge of the works manager, Arthur Wormald. RF was glad to be acquainted with these famous men, and with young Ernest (later Lord) Hives, who ran the Experimental Shop. But the meeting was by no means a one-way adulation. Young Fedden was already held in respect at Derby, and because of this Brazil Straker was the only company in the First World War allowed to manufacture Rolls-Royce engines under licence. Indeed, in 1917, when Sir William Weir wished to rationalise the British aero engine effort and get everyone from knitting-machine makers to small jobbing workshops acting as suppliers of parts for Rolls-Royce engines, Claude Johnson did not merely emphasise the futility of such a plan, "which would yield nothing but mountains of scrap", but said he would go to prison rather than agree to it. What finally tipped the scales was his decision to call in Fedden to give evidence on the quality of workmanship needed.

The first Rolls-Royce engine to be made at Fishponds was the six-cylinder Hawk of 75hp. The parent firm did not want to be bothered with this small engine which was needed mainly for RNAS non-rigid airships, and Brazil Straker delivered the main run of about 200 of them. In 1916 RF made a seven-hour operational sea patrol, from Plymouth round Lands End to Bude, in an airship powered by one of these engines. Although the visit to the Cornish RNAS base was instructive, being the first of many such visits to users of his aero engines, RF found that not even gripping a Lewis gun did much to remove a pervading feeling of vulnerability. In contrast the 240-280hp Falcon vee-12, almost a doubled-up pair of Hawks, was made by Brazil Straker to power the renowned Bristol Fighter, which was anything but vulnerable. Brazil Straker also made components for the big Eagle, which by the end of the war was giving 360/375hp, but they did not assemble complete Eagle engines. In addition to these three engines of Rolls-Royce design, the Bristol company also made over 600 French Renault 80hp vee-8 air-cooled engines, bringing their total output to rather more than 1,500 complete engines, plus a much larger quantity of spares, as well as the staff cars and trucks and over 750,000 artillery shells.

Brazil Straker-built Rolls-Royce Hawk in SSZ-class airship gondola. (Rolls-Royce plc)

Brazil Straker-built Renault air-cooled V-8, with detail of plate on the crankcase.
(Calgary Aerospace Museum).

Rolls-Royce Eagle VIII, incorporating Brazil Straker-manufactured parts. (Rolls-Royce plc)

By the middle of the war the air-cooled rotary engines, which were predominant on the Allied side in 1914, had shown themselves incapable of being developed sufficiently to stay in the battle. The whole burden fell on in-line water-cooled engines such as the Rolls-Royce designs, but the Admiralty became increasingly concerned at the fact that at least one-quarter of the service failures were due to faults in the water cooling system. Thus began an enduring conflict between the proponents of the liquid-cooled aero engines and the air-cooled type. In 1916 RF had experience mainly of the former, and was aware of the popular trend among RFC and RNAS aircrew to chew plenty of gum so that they could plug the frequent leaks in the Rolls-Royce welded-steel water jackets – especially in the case of the big Handley Page bombers whose engines were accessible in flight to a man with good nerves. As the pros and cons figured so prominently in Fedden's career it is worth stating the bones of the argument here.

The liquid-cooled in-line or vee engine tended to have small frontal area and to look more streamlined when installed in an aircraft in a smooth cowling as was done after 1925, but account must be taken of the bulk, drag and (in the case of military machines) vulnerability of the water circulating system and the radiator placed in the air stream. Some racing aircraft had liquid cooling circuits with flush wing-skin radiators or self-contained ice boxes, but such arrangements would have been impractical for military or commercial machines. Moreover the in-line engine was usually long, heavy and relatively difficult to make, and its length increased the moment of inertia and reduced the manoeuvrability of the aircraft, which was serious for fighters. A further consideration is that the cooling system worked well only between strict limits of temperature. In extremely cold conditions the liquid could freeze, especially when plain water was used, while in hot climates there was a reduced margin between the coolant temperature limit and the temperature of the air.

Air-cooled engines can be of various arrangements but the favoured configuration for high powers was the radial, in which the cylinders are arranged like the spokes of a wheel, with all the connecting rods driving a single crankpin. This very fact of itself shows better economy of material, because the crankshaft and crankcase are shorter and stiffer than in the liquid-cooled engine. The complicated cooling circuit and radiator are eliminated, or replaced by simple cowls and baffles. Drag of the engine itself is generally higher than that of the rival form, but the installed drag allowing for cooling is sometimes less, and the aircraft performance gains from the reduced weight. The air-cooled engine usually comprises a fewer number of more compact parts with an aggregate cost substantially less than that of the liquid-cooled engine. It is supreme in harsh service use, and especially in extremes of climate. The argument can go on and on; and it did, from 1916 until after the Second World War, with RF right in the middle of it.

During 1916 Commander (later Admiral Sir) Murray Sueter, Director of the Air Department at the Admiralty and Briggs' immediate superior, decided to draw up a specification for an ideal engine for the RNAS. It was drafted in early 1917 and called for a static radial, with air cooling, having a diameter not greater than 42 inches, a weight not greater than 600 lb and a maximum power of not less than 300 hp. Fedden decided to enter the competition. Soon he and Butler were fired with enthusiasm. By now they were a great partnership, Fedden the creator scheming new things "on the back of an envelope", and Butler the superb detail designer converting the sketches into beautiful engineering drawings. Already the code-letters "FB" on every drawing had a significance far beyond Fishponds; the two men's initials also preceded all the Brazil Straker part numbers.

Soon the small design staff were practically working day and night. Swiftly they created the Mercury, an engine of 20 litres (1,223 cu in) capacity having 14 cylinders arranged in what looked like two rows but was actually an unusual helical configuration. There were two crankpins each driven by seven narrow roller-bearing connecting rods fitted in side-by-side. In a remarkable 5½ months the prototype was running – in Butler's words "Like a sewing machine". The Mercury showed promise, and Fedden was given an immediate order for an initial batch of 200. A rival 14-cylinder design, the Siddeley-Deasy Jaguar, derived from the earlier RAF 8 by the Royal Aircraft Factory at Farnborough, was likewise successful. But almost at once the apple cart was upset by ABC Motors, whose chief designer Granville Bradshaw was a persuasive salesman. His Dragonfly engine promised to do all its rivals could do, and do it more cheaply as it had only a single row of nine cylinders. Weir overruled the Admiralty and decreed that the Dragonfly should be the standard engine for all British fighting scouts. It was ordered in unprecedented numbers – more than 9,500 within six weeks, in five big contracts.

Had the war continued beyond 1918 this decision would have thrown Britain into a monumental crisis. The Dragonfly was one of the classic failures in the history of aircraft engines. Not only was it 56 lb overweight and 13 per cent down on power (295 hp instead of 340) but it overheated badly and happened to have been designed to run just at its principal torsional frequency. Resonant vibration was so bad that wooden propeller hubs became charred with the heat, and no crankshaft could last more than an hour or two. Amazingly, this was not fully discovered until production was in full spate, with over 1,000 engines delivered!

The prototype 14-cylinder Mercury on test at Fishponds. (Rolls-Royce plc)

Towards the end of the war RF's private life was profoundly changed by two events. One was the loss of his father on 6th April 1917. With his passing Roy lost a mighty prop on which, in times of particular stress, he had not hesitated to lean. It may have been partly due to this that he became strongly attracted to a woman rather older than himself. She had been on the stage, was very much

The one that didn't work: the ABC Dragonfly. (Rolls-Royce plc)

a woman of the world, and had been married and divorced – so she hardly stood a chance in polite society. Yet in 1918 she and Roy announced their engagement, much against the wishes of his mother, and they later married and set up a fine home: Widegates, Westbury-on-Trym. Her son Tony was at Clifton. His new stepfather kept him there, doted on him and lavished on him everything he would have wished for a true son of his own. As for the new Mrs Fedden, she was no delicate flower to be trampled on by the giant she had married. She appears to have been the only person ever to speak sharply to RF and, indeed, to cow him. His colleagues were used to hearing her powerful voice approaching his office during late management sessions. "Come home, Roy", she would shout, "come home this instant!" It was not unknown for her to switch all the lights out. Fedden would look cross – once he said "I don't like her doing that" – but he would follow her out. In the inter-war years the storms got worse, culminating in a climax of pure melodrama, as we shall see.

Although the Mercury had shown itself to be a smooth runner, it was not an unqualified success; in any case, RF could see by the middle of 1917 that future aircraft would be served better by a simpler and more powerful engine. Talks with aircraft designers convinced him that 300 hp was not enough, and to meet future needs the little Mercury would have to operate at a brake mean effective pressure (a measure of the average combustion pressure in the cylinders) beyond the limits of available fuels or the engineering state of the art. He looked carefully at what his rivals were doing. Rolls-Royce had a fine engine in the Eagle, but showed every sign of devoting most of their energies to cars as soon as the war was over. Like almost all other good businessmen they thought little of the future of aviation, but a great deal about the future demand for cars. Siddeley-Deasy, soon to become Armstrong Siddeley, had the 14-cylinder Jaguar which looked good for an eventual 400 hp or more. Most potent competitor of all seemed to be D Napier & Son, for whom A J Rowledge had designed the Lion, with three blocks of four water-cooled cylinders arranged in "broad arrow" formation and already giving 450 hp. Many believed Napier's claim that the Lion would meet all aircraft needs for many years. Even more widespread was the belief that it would be foolish to try to rival it with an air-cooled radial.

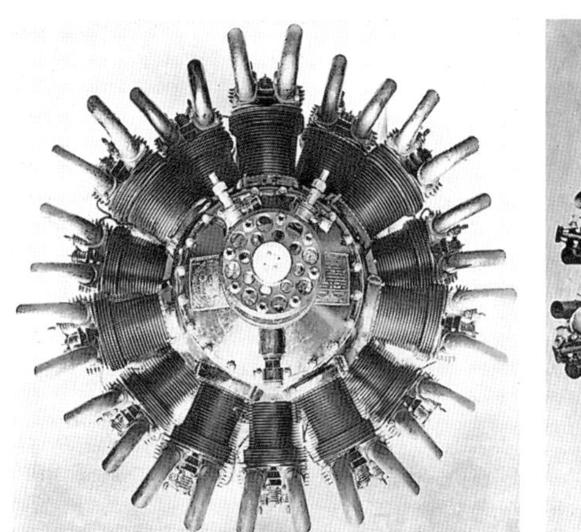

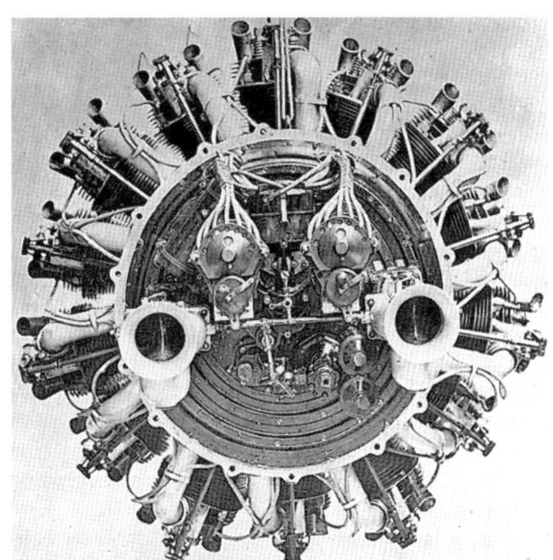

The Cosmos Mercury had 14 cylinders in an unusual helical configuration. (Rolls-Royce plc)

In the middle of 1917 RF took the most important decision of his life. He decided to go ahead with an air-cooled radial, having nine cylinders in a single row, to deliver 500 hp. He called it the Jupiter. Today it is hard to appreciate the tremendous boldness such a decision meant in 1917.

He and Butler finished the design in early 1918. They had no contract for the Jupiter, but increasingly believed that it represented the optimum design of aero engine for the foreseeable future. The big cylinders had a bore of 5¾ in (146 mm) and stroke of 7½ in (190.5 mm), giving a capacity of 1,753 cu in or 28.7 litres. The engine was straightforward and clean in design. Fedden was anxious not to push his luck. He used a split master rod on a one-piece crankshaft. He also decided to use a "poultice" head. Each cylinder was a steel drum closed over at the end, with machined apertures for the inlet and exhaust ports; then a finned head of aluminium was fixed on the end to dissipate the heat. The Royal Aircraft Factory at Farnborough had shown that poultice heads could suffer from poor heat transfer, but Fedden had yet to be convinced of the integrity of the open-ended cylinder closed by a separate head fastened on. On the other hand, he unhesitatingly took the unusual step of fitting the head with four valves (two inlet, two exhaust) to provide good breathing at the higher engine speeds he was sure would be needed in future. Another unusual feature was that on the rear cover were three carburettors, side-by-side, feeding the nine cylinders via a spiral deflector guide.

The Air Board accepted the design of the Jupiter in July 1918, and the first experimental engine ran on the bench on 29th October, before the end of the war. It ran well. Though it would have been hard-pressed at that time to deliver its rated power of 475 hp, it weighed only 662 lb in running order and thus set a world record for a completely equipped engine at about 1.4 lb per hp. Early in 1919 a second Jupiter was made with an epicyclic reduction gear, of 0.656 : 1 ratio, which weighed 757 lb but reduced the propeller speed at full throttle from 1,800 to only 1,200 rpm. During the 1920s geared engines became common, driving larger propellers at lower speed for greater propulsive efficiency, with the engine running faster to give higher power.

In 1918 and 1919, to Fedden's distress, the Brazil Straker group was progressively dispersed. Brazil himself went with the Bonzac machine business to Imperial Tobacco, and a shipbuilding firm bought the Djinn engine business. The Fishponds works was bought by a newly formed Anglo-American financial group called Cosmos, which had big interests in shipping and coal. Fedden was instructed by letter that his works was henceforth the Cosmos Engineering Co, and that he should carry on as before (no Cosmos director came to see what was being done).

Fedden and Butler were in fact busy getting back in the private car business. Though Fedden had been legally prohibited by Rolls-Royce from designing a water-cooled in-line aero engine, he was free to do as he wished with cars and he soon planned a first-class car – in no way inferior to a Rolls-Royce except in price – with a 4-litre engine having six Rolls (née Mercedes) style cylinders. Later, in March 1919 he cast caution to the winds and planned a new little car that seemed to him superior to what had become the accepted norm. At that time car design was still fluid, and the public could readily be "sold" on something completely radical so long as it seemed to make sense. Fedden's baby, a true successor to the Shamrock, had a three-seat body made of the nearest 1919 equivalent to modern plastics: layers of brown paper bonded with a special seaweed and moulded in cement tooling. This rode on coil springs, and the lightweight car went like the proverbial bomb on a 1.2-litre engine with three air-cooled cylinders arranged at 120° with horizontal crankshaft. Perhaps surprisingly the roadholding was outstandingly good, and the motoring press (who had been all set to scoff) went into raptures. At the 1919 Olympia Motor Show Fedden's sales staff booked over 2,000 orders, with cash deposits.

The 3-cylinder engine for the 1919 car on test at Fishponds. (Rolls-Royce plc)

Fedden could undoubtedly have become once more a leader of the motor industry, but his emotional attachment to aircraft engines had become exceedingly strong. He was also officially encouraged to believe in the Jupiter. Though its design had been accepted by the Air Board of the Ministry of Munitions, under Sir William (later Lord) Weir, this did not imply that any Jupiters would be bought. The Armistice of 11th November 1918 had resulted in slashing cutbacks in aviation orders, and a general air of retrenchment. But in December 1918 Brig-Gen J G Weir, Technical Controller of the Ministry of Munitions, wrote Fedden a letter that exerted a profound impression on its recipient:

MINISTRY OF MUNITIONS OF WAR.
AIR GROUP.

TECHNICAL DEPARTMENT,

KINGSWAY, LONDON, W.C. 2.

December 3rd, 1918.

Messrs. Cosmos Engineering Co., Ltd.,
Lodge Causeway,
Fishponds, Bristol.

For the attention of A. H. R. Fedden, Esq.

Gentlemen,

Re Experimental Work on Aero-Engines.

With reference to your Aero-Engine Work, I wish to impress upon you that the changed conditions due to the Armistice, do not affect the importance of your experimental and development work in connection with engines and it is most desirable that you should continue with your efforts in this direction.

I need not enlarge upon the success of your work nor upon the high hope which this Department has regarding the "Jupiter," beyond stating that it is of very great importance to the Nation, as far as aircraft is concerned, that you should press on in all haste to perfect the "Jupiter," which I feel sure has a considerable future in front of it in commercial aviation.

I shall be glad if you will communicate to your staff my very great appreciation of their efforts and my strong desire that they should continue to apply themselves to this work as effectively as during the period of hostilities.

Yours truly,

J G Weir.

Brigadier Gen. R.A.F.
Controller Technical (A.P.)

The 1918 letter from Brigadier General Weir to AHRF instructing Cosmos Engineering to continue the work on aero engines. (Rolls-Royce plc)

"I wish to impress upon you that the changed conditions due to the Armistice do not affect the importance of your Experimental and Development work in connection with engines, and it is most desirable that you should continue with your efforts in this direction. It is of very great importance to the Nation, as far as Aircraft is (sic) concerned, that you should press on in all haste to perfect the Jupiter which I feel sure has a considerable future in front of it in Commercial Aviation". This was vastly encouraging, because many in high places did not believe in commercial aviation at all. In the same month Fedden was elected to Associate Fellowship of the Royal Aeronautical Society, along with aircraft designers Sydney Camm and Harry Folland.

The Cosmos Board viewed peacetime markets differently from the other engineering firms that had been impressed into war production. Instead of discarding aviation and concentrating on cars, they sold the car business in 1919 to Straker Squire Ltd at Edmonton, North London. This company failed to produce new designs and in 1923 went out of business, though one or two Straker Squires can still be found on the road today. Instead, Cosmos kept Fedden and his team working on aero engines, possibly because the organisation had so many interests it had no time to bother about the Fishponds works. Had they visited the factory they would have discovered not only the Mercury and Jupiter but also a little 100 hp engine called the Lucifer. Fedden and Butler had produced this for hardly any outlay at all, by designing it around three cylinders similar to those of the Jupiter but with shorter stroke. At speeds seldom exceeding 1,500 rpm the Lucifer ran with a distinct succession of separate firing strokes, but it was a much better design than the old wartime engines in this power class.

The prototype Lucifer on test at Fishponds. (Rolls-Royce plc)

Fedden would actually have welcomed some attention being paid to Fishponds, because though he and Butler had gained for the works a reputation for first-class engineering, he had no immediate saleable product. Rolls-Royce had taken back the parts and spares for their engines, and the wartime contracts had been terminated. Fedden became increasingly certain that the Jupiter was exactly what both civil and military aviation would need, but he was concerned at the fact there was nothing he could sell to cover the Jupiter's development cost. Knowing this, rival companies put out feelers to see if they could entice him away from Bristol. Some bluntly offered him more money. Rolls-Royce sounded him out with more finesse. On his final trip to St Margaret's Bay, where the design office under A G Elliott had grown to 17, he was asked by Mr Royce to stay behind after the business had been completed. "I've watched your engineering closely", said the impressive man, "I like it, and I think you're a pretty good engineer. But for Heaven's sake, why do you have to design a radial, with everything acting on one crankpin? You would have better success with our engines." Fedden politely declined, and refrained from commenting that Ernest Claremont, the Chairman of Rolls-Royce, had been instructed to write a clause into Brazil Straker's wartime licence forbidding Fedden ever to attempt a rival in-line engine. (Nine years later Sir Henry Royce, as he had then become, called Fedden to his company's marquee at the RAF Pageant, beneath a sky echoing to the sound of squadrons powered by Jupiters. He shook his hand, saying "I really must congratulate you; I am delighted that you have proved me so wrong.")

149,380. Fedden, A. H. R., Butler, L. F. G., and Cosmos Engineering Co. March 12, 1919.

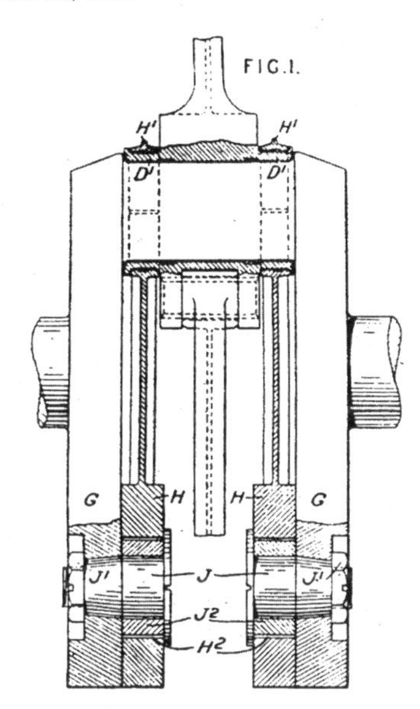

Radial-cylinder engines; balancing moving parts in engines of unspecified type.—A crank-shaft is provided with balance weights which act directly on the big end of the connecting-rod and not through the intermediary of the crank-pin. In the example shown the big end of the master connecting-rod of a radial-cylinder engine is formed with flanges D^1 on which are pivoted bearings H^1 at the ends of shanks carrying balance weights H. The latter are slotted to receive square blocks J^2 which are secured to the balancing extensions G of the crank webs by bolts J, clearance H^2 being left to allow for wear in the bearings.

An example of one of many patents raised by Fedden and Butler as part of Cosmos Engineering. The patent is for improved balancing of a radial engine (not put into practice). (Rolls-Royce plc)

But in 1919 the prospect was bleak. Apart from the moral boost of General Weir's letter, Fedden was encouraged only by the way his engines performed. The first to fly had been the second prototype Mercury. This particular engine had reached 347 hp on the test bed, and in July 1918 was approved for flight at a preliminary rating

A group of Brazil Straker workers outside the Motor Works at Fishponds and a drawing by Mervyn Bracey showing a 'Shamrock' outside the gates.

of 315 hp. It so happened that Capt Frank Barnwell, chief designer of the British and Colonial (later Bristol) Aeroplane Co, was looking for a good air-cooled radial to replace the Sunbeam Arab in the Scout Type F, and Fedden was equally keen to get the Mercury into the air. The engine was neatly installed in the third Scout, B3991, converting it into the Scout F1 or Bristol Type 21A. It flew, probably in the hands of F P Raynham, on 6th September 1918. On 25th October the Bristol company took on an officer seconded from the RAF, F/Lt (though he preferred his old RFC rank of Capt) Cyril F Uwins. He became one of the world's first full-time company test pilots, and he flew the Mercury-Scout on the following day. In April 1919 the aircraft was tested by P W S Bulman at the Royal Aircraft Establishment (previously Factory) at Farnborough, setting unofficial records by climbing to 10,000 feet in 5.4 min and to 20,000 feet in 16.25 min. It also astonished Bulman by reaching 143 mph.

Captain Barnwell heard about the Jupiter before the first engine was built. In the summer of 1918 he secured Air Board permission to fit one of the first experimental Jupiters in the second of three Badger two-seat fighters, the others having the Dragonfly. He was painfully aware of the shortcomings of the ABC engine, and was pleased and relieved when the Jupiter-Badger, F3496, at last flew in Uwins' hands on 24th May 1919. The new engine had

Bristol Scout Type F B3991 (Cosmos Mercury engine). This aircraft set records for rate of climb and speed at altitude that stood for seven years. (Ken Wixey)

been taken from Fishponds to Filton by W Jefferies, who upon demobilization had first been sent to Farnborough to look after the Mercury-Scout. He then supervised the installation of the Jupiter in the Badger by Freddie Mayer and R N Swinchatt, both of whom soon afterwards left the British and Colonial Aeroplane Co and joined Fedden. When Jefferies was satisfied, and had test-run the engine, he telephoned Fedden and said that Capt Uwins would fly after lunch. That afternoon the directors of both the aircraft and engine firms, and the Press, gathered to witness the first flight of a Jupiter. To Jefferies' horror the engine would not start. When everyone had departed he discovered that, since the morning test run, someone had tampered with the main fuel cock so that when it was in the ON position it was actually "off". Though it was a very undeveloped installation, the Badger set further excellent figures for climbing and reached 137 mph (later, with small changes, 142 mph). The third Cosmos Jupiter was fitted to the Sopwith Schneider seaplane, G-EAKI, said to be capable of 165 mph and almost certainly the fastest entrant in the 1919 Schneider Trophy race at Bournemouth. Pilot Harry Hawker was very impressed with the Jupiter, which ran faultlessly at full power during the race, but the event was abandoned due to dense sea mist.

Flight development of the Lucifer was done with an Avro 504K trainer, G-EADI, bought from the Disposals Board. With this aircraft Cosmos probably had the world's first engine test-bed aircraft, and the first flight-test department. The Avro was flown on 11th December 1919 by Capt Norman Macmillan. Later the role of flight test observer was filled either by Swinchatt (later chief production development engineer for many years) or Fedden himself. An order was placed with Westland Aircraft at Yeovil for a passenger transport to test and demonstrate the Jupiter. W Jefferies had just arrived at Yeovil to supervise the Westland engine installation when the shocking news came through that Cosmos had gone into liquidation.

The cause was a wild financial gamble on a colossal scale involving the export of household goods to White Russia. Goods and ships were seized by the Bolsheviks, and Fedden suddenly found himself holding the Fishponds works for the Receiver. It was a priceless national asset, but although he managed to get the Bristol Aeroplane Co, Vickers and Sir John Siddeley interested, nobody was prepared to take a decision. Fedden was impatient to get on with developing the engines he believed in, and thought it might spur interest if he got the Jupiter put through the new official Type Test schedule under the supervision of the Aeronautical Inspection Directorate (AID). He obtained the Receiver's permission to do so, but, when more than half of the schedule had been successfully completed, the Receiver saw the Bristol Corporation's bill for electricity for the test-bed cooling fan, and the test was promptly stopped.

Siddeley's nearly took Fedden on, but his implacable rival Major F M Green quashed the suggestion. Throughout the early 1920s the two men were bitter business competitors, although on the best personal terms. General Caddell, head of the Vickers Aircraft Works at Weybridge, considered it too much of a gamble to try to produce both aircraft and engines under one roof. The Board of the Bristol Aeroplane Company at Filton House had alone obtained first-hand experience of the Cosmos engines, and were deeply impressed; but they cannily professed to be far from enthusiastic. Fedden's reputation was already such that the government then brought pressure to bear. Air Marshal Sir Robert Brooke-Popham came down from Air Ministry and threatened that, if Bristol did not buy the Cosmos team, the Ministry itself would. After keen negotiations the sharp Bristol Board obtained a bargain. For £15,000 they purchased Fedden and whatever members of his engineering team were left, plus the goodwill, a promised Air Ministry order for 10 Jupiters, all drawings, patterns, tools, five Jupiter engines, numerous parts, and 50 sets of raw material with a book value of £60,000. But when the Engine Department

Bristol Badger F3496 (Cosmos Jupiter engine). Vickers guns retained. (Rolls-Royce plc)

of the Bristol Aeroplane Co was founded on 29th July 1920 the Board were wondering what sort of cuckoo they were letting into the nest.

It was the nephew of Sir George White, the founder and Chairman, who made the move. Sir Henry White-Smith, who had been knighted for having in 1917 founded the Society of British Aircraft Constructors and steered it with distinction, offered a seemingly fair deal. Fedden had proposed to develop the Jupiter to give 500 hp for a weight of 650 lb in two years and for a cost of £200,000. White-Smith, a great asset to the Bristol Board, got his co-directors to accept. "But", he said, "if the work does not go well, we must cut our losses and get out of engines". It was to be "a damned close-run thing".

Later, the Badger was fitted with a new propeller and a cowl over the crankcase. Note the intake pipes to the three updraught carburettors. (Rolls-Royce plc)

Sopwith Schneider (Cosmos Jupiter engine). (Rolls-Royce plc)

Advertisement similar to one that appeared in 1919 Jane's All the World's Aircraft.
(Rolls-Royce plc)

CHAPTER THREE

Bristol engines

July 1920 was the happy month when Fedden knew the Jupiter was not only going to continue but would stay in the city of its birth. From Fishponds to the village of Filton, which in those days had yet to be swamped by the spreading city's development, is less than five miles as the crow flies, but to the little team of engineers it meant a marked change. Everyone in Bristol knew about the White family. In 1920 the Master and the Man were so dissimilar they might have belonged to different species, and where the Whites were concerned – said Fedden – "everybody bowed the knee to a quite extraordinary degree". In his view, from one end of Britain to the other, it would have been impossible to find a more autocratic rule than that of the Whites. Odd, because they had made their money "in trade".

Patriarch of the family had been Sir George White, Bt, born in 1854, who had died suddenly in 1917. One of his many enterprises was the Bristol Tramway & Carriage Company, which by 1914 had given Bristol the finest public transport system in Europe, with a city-wide network of bus and tram routes and large numbers of powerful Charron taxicabs. Another was the British and Colonial Aeroplane Company, set up in 1910 as a result of Sir George happening to witness a French flying meeting at Pau the previous year. With his son George Stanley (later Sir Stanley) White as managing director, the company swallowed at least £500,000 – a vast sum for those days – before it saw much return; but the First World War happened at just the right time. By 1916 Capt Barnwell had achieved a major success with the Bristol Fighter, powered by a Falcon engine often made at Fishponds. The Bristol Aeroplane Company, as it was then known, had become one of the big names in British industry. It had already dabbled in aero engines, Wilfred Reid having in 1917 planned a design with 12 horizontally opposed water-cooled cylinders, and run a two-cylinder unit that gave 65 horsepower. Reid later went to Canada to build his own lightplanes, and helped form the Curtiss-Reid company.

Despite this prior venture into engines, the proud Board of the family-owned Bristol company looked on their acquisition from Cosmos as being something of an ugly duckling. The reasons were varied. One was a straightforward matter of business. Though superficially the £15,000 deal was a bargain, the White family sometimes wondered if it had not made a crass error. The war was long since over. Nobody wanted new aero engines, because the face of the land was disfigured by thousands of airframes and engines surplus to requirements. Powerful and experienced aero engine companies, such as Rolls-Royce, Armstrong Siddeley, Napier, Sunbeam and

Wolseley, were finding it exceedingly hard to stay in business. Many were the experts who thought the Bristol Board mad to launch into this field. But a less obvious reason was RF himself. The Whites knew the Feddens. RF was from a stock as good as their own; indeed his family had been famed in Bristol for at least 100 years longer, which in 1920 was important. RF himself, at 35, was not the sort of man who could be "put in his place" as the Whites were accustomed to do. Not only was he physically large, but he had an intense personality, a powerful and articulate voice, and an apparent belief that he was their social equal (which, of course, he was). He had, incidentally, lately been made a Member of the Order of the British Empire for his wartime achievements. So the Whites, having discussed the matter, agreed that the team from Fishponds, and Fedden in particular, must be watched like hawks and never given an inch of latitude. They judged that Fedden might have one eye on their boardroom in august Filton House. Not one of them could have tolerated such a thing for an instant. Not only was he not one of the family, but he was far too powerful a character. This was the way Fedden saw it, and to some degree he was right.

The relationship between the Bristol Aeroplane board and Fedden was truly something to ponder. Fedden had the whole thing buttoned up with crystal clarity. To him the inbred, family Board typified the British tradition of the aristocratic and cultured amateur. He, Fedden, could never be ONE OF THEM. He was a mere employee, and had to touch his forelock with all other employees. In his view he was appreciated to the extent that he remembered this fact. Though he never wasted much time bothering about it, his mental picture of the Board was of their unanimous agreement that in Fedden they had got hold of a man with such drive and enthusiasm that he had to be "kept down".

In fact, the true picture was a little different. It is probably fair to claim that Fedden actually got a mixture of backing and restraint that were both essential for his own success. The Board were not afraid of him, nor did they despise the cuckoo in their nest (though, as Cosmos had virtually been foisted on them by Brooke-Popham, they at least had an excuse for not welcoming the new venture). Perhaps their main sin was that not one of their number was an engineer, and this made it impossible for them to exercise the correct decision-taking which they knew to be their main duty. Sir Stanley White, as Managing Director, showed great patience in trying to understand each fresh argument Fedden sought to put across. Usually there would be a request for an increased budget – to support a new development or clear a new difficulty – and the Board did their best to come to a correct decision. But on the one hand they were technically illiterate business men; on the other side was a man who quickly became impatient when he was misunderstood and who, instead of conveying the information in the simplest words possible, was prone to turn in desperation to ill-advised lobbying.

It was a vicious circle, caused by a problem in communications that was wholly predictable and which ought never to have been allowed to mature. Fedden already had a reputation not only of being a hard worker – in an age of hard workers – but also of being an enthusiastic visionary. At Brazil Straker and Cosmos he had never had the time or opportunity to do much about this, apart from letting off steam in the lecture theatre; but at Bristol it was abundantly clear that he simply had to be "kept down" if the firm was to survive. This was not for the reasons Fedden supposed. Too great an enthusiast will ruin any business, and in the 1920s it was the bounden duty of the Board to husband the company's resources to the best benefit of the stockholders. After the tragic departure of Sir Henry White-Smith in 1926, for personal reasons, the problem of communication between Fedden and the Board intensified. By 1930 he had run the Board into so many problems through over-running budgets and failing to meet over-optimistic delivery schedules, that the relationship deteriorated. An impartial observer would surely have agreed that it was grossly wrong to keep Fedden off the Board; he was the most important man in the company. At the same time, the picture as Fedden saw it was not a true one.

RF himself was too overwhelmed with work to bother about his fancied station as a mere hireling. He had an objective, and money with which to attain it, and if his team could do the job then it would be done even if it meant working day and night. Afterwards he considered their position had really been hopeless, but that they were pulled through by their enthusiasm, gross overconfidence, and lack of time in which to reflect on how heavily the dice were loaded against them.

With RF, the team numbered 32. In addition to Butler, Swinchatt, Stammers, Jefferies, Richardson, Damsell, Price and Vowles, who had stayed to the end at Fishponds, 23 former Cosmos engineers rejoined RF, as well as Norman Rowbotham, the AID inspector who decided to throw in his lot with them rather than be transferred to Armstrong Siddeley at Coventry. In early July 1920 the tedium of waiting at the silent Fishponds factory was finally broken. A letter delivered by a messenger instructed Fedden urgently to prepare a Jupiter, a Mercury and a Lucifer as exhibits for the first exhibition ever to be held by the SBAC. When the show opened at Olympia, London, on 9th July 1920 the three Cosmos engines, clean and polished, were on the stand of the Bristol company. Considered just as engines they were outstanding, but most of the informed comment was disparaging or even hostile. Some prophesied doom for this foolish marriage of airframes and engines under one roof. Others were merely cross that Fedden and his team had been saved. As there was nothing like enough new work to go

A 1937 gathering of some of the original Cosmos team who stayed on at the Bristol Aeroplane Company. From the left: H V O'Gorman, S Damsell, G J Gulliford, W Stammers, G Bennett, A J Cox, R Williams, RF (with H Wills behind), F Collett, A G Adams, L F G Butler, F Powell, A Houlson, R N Swinchatt and B Brown. (Rolls-Royce plc)

Often the source of much confusion – two photographs were taken on different days in 1937 of some of the original Cosmos team. The lower photograph includes W Jefferies on the extreme left as you look at the photo next to Swinchatt. (Rolls-Royce plc)

round, the fewer people competing for business the better.

On 24th July Capt Uwins flew the Bristol Bullet racer, which Barnwell had specially designed for the Jupiter, into second place in the Aerial Derby. This trim machine (not to be confused with the Bristol Scout of 1914, which was unofficially called the Bullet) was the first aircraft ever designed to have a Bristol engine. Five days later the Bristol Engine Department officially came into existence. In the first week of August the move began from Fishponds. Sir Henry White-Smith, the only director who had any personal contact with Fedden, suggested the new department should take over some of the empty hangar and sheds up on the hill around Filton House. Fedden surprised him by disagreeing, though with great respect. The new man preferred instead to take his men a mile to the north, to the far corner of Filton aerodrome which the company had bought from the Air Ministry the previous year. Here, near the village of Patchway, was adequate accommodation adjacent to the flight sheds that were still in use. RF thought it important for the pilots to appreciate the painstaking care needed in making and testing engines. He wanted to be amongst the aircraft to speed up installations and flight testing. And he wanted his engineers to spend more

Filton aerodrome in 1931, showing the old hangars occupied by the Engine Department. The white building amidst them is the new Engine Department office block and on the right is the new canteen and other units which were the first to be built on the east side of the A38 Gloucester road, which runs across the centre of the picture. In the background is the Bristol Flying School. The Aeroplane Company is a mile off to the left. Today, Rolls-Royce European Military Aero Business occupies the entire area in the foreground. (Rolls-Royce plc)

time in the air, and learn at first hand of the difficulties and problems in aviation.

The geographical location was important. Though it did prove to be beneficial in allowing constant and intimate contact between engines and aircraft, in the long-term it accentuated the chasm between the company's aircraft side and engine side, and made proper union impossible. Over the years, while the aircraft business stagnated, Fedden's Engine Department grew and prospered, creeping out across the green fields on both sides of the road to Gloucester until it had become a mighty factory, bigger than the aircraft plant up on the hill. But Fedden considered the 'us' and 'them' attitude died hard, and the suggestion even lingered in his mind that his engines were in some way considered uncouth.

Fedden could hardly visualise all this on 29th July 1920; he had more immediate problems. He had ample floor space, but his buildings had high Belfast roofs, with felt covering which leaked badly. Though they had been designed as aircraft shops, they were devoid of all essential services. And, before anything else could be done, they had to be cleared of tons of rubbish. In one hangar bay was a dismantled Porte flying boat, which was scrapped. In another shed were dozens of aero engines; Gnome, Le Rhône and Clerget rotaries, Anzani and Salmson radials, a flat-four Darracq and many other types. Some time was spent stripping these and examining their design minutely, in the course of which Butler – who always had a twinkle in his eye – asked, "Can't think why they needed to buy us as well!" The piles of engine parts then made heaps beside the Porte's ashes on the waste land across the airfield. There followed a scrupulous spring-cleaning operation, after which Fedden had the shops partitioned and given water, gas and electricity. Then lorries shuttled to and from Fishponds bringing machine tools, test gear and raw material. Only rarely did RF sanction outside purchases. He was determined not to overstep the allowed budget.

Though they were young in years, his team were likewise schooled in the harsh world of business, and they knew how to make every penny count. But Gavin Grieg, the company secretary, paid particular attention to the new intruders. Grieg was a reserved and canny Scot, who wore a cap so constantly he was reputed to go to bed in it. Often he seemed never to go to bed at all, for in the dead of the night he would silently visit the Engine Department to study the written records and then count the items in the stores – and never realised that Fedden watched him!

In such a stringent environment the answer seemed to be hard work. On the whole people worked very hard in 1920, but RF's team regularly put in 90 hours a week because they believed in what they were doing. There was nobody to tell them not to, there was a strong wish to survive, and RF's own leadership inspired confidence. At first motivated by the need to keep the department in being, the team later continued to work under the most intense pressure for different reasons. They did it because they wanted to beat the competition, or because they were proud of their products, or simply because it was natural to give one's all in the ceaseless struggle against engineering problems – especially in aviation. Gradually, however, society's values have changed, and Fedden regretted it. For all his well-developed social conscience, he came to regard the notion of a Welfare State, in which everyone is "looked after", as a stark tragedy. In his view, a world in which children could be unpopular because they want to learn, and workers ostracised because they want to work, was more like a nightmare than Utopia. His Utopia was toiling day and night, as in 1920. This was not a posture, but a deep conviction.

Unlike the other 31 men, RF had a burden of worry as well. He needed to go out and sell his engines. All he had was the promised Air Ministry order for 10 Jupiters, and when this materialised in August 1920 the £25,000 payment was for five engines brought from Fishponds (at an inflated price, to help cover development) and only five new ones. With the prototype this

This may have been taken to emphasise the Jupiter's modest weight, but each shoulder still had to support nearly 200lb (91kg), including the beams. (Rolls-Royce plc)

made 11, beyond which there was an apparent desert. The world was full of surplus engines which could be had for next to nothing. Fedden was constantly sustained by the unshakeable belief that, eventually, airlines and air forces would judge the Jupiter to be, in modern parlance, cost-effective. But would this day come too late?

He intended the Jupiter to be the best engine in the world. He filled his nights writing papers and giving lectures explaining why the air-cooled radial was inherently preferable, from the structural and mechanical points of view, to the long water-cooled engine. It was clearly lighter and simpler, and because of its shape could improve the manoeuvrability of a fighter. Only in one respect did he have any real struggle. The water-cooled engine could be (and later was) streamlined into a pointed nose. In special racing aircraft, it could outpace the bluff air-cooled engine, and this was most apparent in the Schneider Trophy contests which from 1919 to 1931 dominated the thinking on fast aircraft by the European air staffs. But in a practical fighter or bomber the water-cooled engine had to have a large cooling radiator which, as related earlier, added cost, weight, drag and vulnerability in combat. In very cold climates the coolant froze (until new liquids were introduced before the Second World War). In very hot climates the radiator boiled and the engine overheated, while air-cooled radials still dissipated excess heat straight from their cylinder heads which were far hotter even than the tropical sky. In the long term the superiority of the air-cooled engine gradually eliminated liquid cooling, but it fell to Fedden to have to fight not only Rolls-Royce, which in the 1930s became a formidable competitor, but also entrenched opposition to air-cooled radial engines based on mistaken beliefs.

In 1920, however, this was a side-issue. The central problem was that there seemed to be no customers for new aero engines of any sort, and the only good things from Bristol's point of view tended to be rather negative. One was that the Engine Department was smaller than the rival organisations, and appeared better able to weather a lean period that nobody expected to last for ever. Fedden was building an efficient design, development and manufacturing organisation in a way that would have been more difficult with an established factory. An impartial observer in 1920 would probably have concluded that the Jupiter was indeed the best aviation engine in the world, and that Fedden's organisation would be able to build it for a keen price. It obviously looked that way to the other leading engine firms, and it is significant that before 1920 was out Fedden had been offered jobs on tempting terms by his three main rivals. Spriggs of Armstrong Siddeley, Vane of Napier and Wormald of Rolls-Royce all came to Bristol to see him, quite independently, and offered him salaries even higher than he was getting at Bristol, plus considerable fringe benefits, if he would join their own organisations as chief engineer. Fedden did not doubt that they meant to offer him an assured career, and did not merely hope to bring about the closure of the Bristol Engine Department; but acceptance never crossed his mind.

In his view his loyalty to his team was absolute; and he was also becoming emotionally attached to "his" engines. The Mercury continued to run sweetly at Bristol, on the bench and in the Scout F, but Fedden knew in his heart it was not a winner and did not demur when the Board sent all three Mercuries to the USA in an inter-governmental deal. Fedden felt strongly he must concentrate his efforts on the Jupiter, but he first allowed his enthusiasm one final fling. In 1919 he and Butler had completed preliminary design of an engine that was almost a twin-Jupiter, and in 1920 he could not resist getting most of it drawn. It was the 18-cylinder Hercules, and Fedden was stopped in his tracks only by the fact that he simply could not design an elegant valve gear. He resisted the easy way out of using only two valves per cylinder, and it was with reluctance that he abandoned this 1,000 hp design. (He did not need to feel sheepish; nobody ever did design an elegant two-row engine with four-valve cylinders, though the question was to arise again and again). Wisely, Fedden decided to put everything on one side for the time being, apart from the basic ungeared Jupiter and the simple Lucifer.

Even so, it was no easy task for a mere handful of men to set up not only the Bristol design and development organisation but also the only post-war engine factory in Europe, if not in the world. The simplest part was the mere acquisition of manufacturing capacity. British aero-engine firms were either desperate for work, and prepared to undertake intricate machining at cut-rate prices (as was the case with the Liberty-engine plant at Bookham, Surrey), or they had gone into liquidation. Fedden was able to buy excellent machine tools cheaply from the defunct British Le Rhône factory at Blackhorse Road, Tottenham, London. What was much more difficult was building a foundation of sound engineering practice, and ensuring a future supply of good engineers. Fedden was constantly reminded of the fact that in making aero engines it was necessary to fashion metal in such a way that the parts would stand up to prolonged use, over many years, in the most severe conditions it was possible to imagine. Non-aeronautical engineers could make their parts with a very generous "factor of safety" – more truthfully a "factor of ignorance" – in the hope that they would thus stay intact. But in aviation weight has to be pared to the bone. There is no room for any "fat", and every component has to be designed so that the material is worked really hard. The pioneer flyers and wartime squadrons had not needed to bother about parts having a long life; yet, despite this, frequent crashes due to mechanical failure were accepted as inevitable. In 1920, the scene had become quite different. Air forces and airlines were emerging which wanted their equipment to fly safely, and to go on doing so for many years. This was

This model of the projected 18-cylinder Hercules has Jupiter-type cylinders, with provision for four valves which, on this two-row engine, RF found too difficult! (Rolls-Royce plc)

quite impossible with wartime engines, but Fedden was utterly determined that the Jupiter should meet the new need in full.

This at once highlighted the fact that engineers did not know why parts failed. Sometimes there was clear evidence of poor design or faulty workmanship, or incorrect assembly or maintenance, but what was much more disturbing was that components often just broke for no apparent reason. It seemed that if a part was used over a period it could suffer a malady called "crystallisation". In some way the very make-up of the metal became altered so that it was unable any longer to bear the working loads. At the end of the First World War important research on what is now called fatigue was begun by the Aeronautical Research Council. In the absence of their findings, all one could do was either design the part so that it was far stronger than need be, or, in aero engines, just keep one's fingers crossed. Today we know very much more about the various kinds of fatigue, but in 1920 Fedden organised some of the first research ever done in this field, because he meant to prevent the dreaded "crystallisation" from ever happening.

It seemed prudent to call in expert help. On this vital subject there were hardly any experts, but Fedden had the good fortune to know Professor Leslie Aitchison. This metallurgist had set up the Materials Department for the wartime Air Board, had helped the Aeronautical Research Council in pioneer fatigue research, and had written a monumental series of specifications for aeronautical materials and test procedures which were far ahead of anything in any other country or branch of engineering. He came down to Bristol, installed machines to test specimens from the 50 sets of Jupiter raw material, and discovered that almost all of it was below standard. It had been bought at a difficult time just after the war and, even though it had been passed by the AID, Fedden had to throw almost all of it away or use it on jobs around the factory.

Aitchison then not only went through the Jupiter's mechanical design in great detail but also outlined almost all that was then known about fatigue. Fedden and Butler spent many hours with him studying the design of every part of the Jupiter, and Aitchison showed how fatigue failures can stem from even the most microscopic local stress concentration. What is needed, he explained, is a part with smooth curves, generous radii, carefully blended fillets, a complete absence of sudden discontinuities or changes in section, and overall a smooth polished surface with no dents or scratches. He had devised a method for testing parts for fatigue by bending them to and fro for days or weeks, and reported that the safe fatigue limit load for the steels used in aviation was just under half the ultimate stress. This took fatigue out of the realm of "crystallisation" mythology and, for the first time, enabled engineers to think of it in numerical terms. Aitchison later let Fedden have

RF pioneered engine endurance running. This was the first fully instrumented Jupiter test bed, first run in 1921. The single-cylinder rig is in the right background. (Rolls-Royce plc)

The first single-cylinder test bed. (Rolls-Royce plc)

his assistant, Leslie Johnson, who devised the Bristol/NPL combined stress and fatigue testing machine which over the next 50 years gradually permeated universities, technical colleges and industry throughout the world. It was Johnson's reluctant departure to Mond Nickel on financial grounds, that finally made the Bristol Board yield to Fedden's incessant request that the staff should have a pension scheme, which in the 1920s was something almost unheard of.

Fedden tackled a number of key materials suppliers by going with Aitchison to their works, thus creating another precedent. Before long he had established a reputation as the most difficult possible customer; indeed many suppliers agreed that he was a good man not to do business with. Yet very gradually these firms realised that difficult customers, provided they knew what they were talking about, were just what they needed in order to improve their own standards and stay in business. But at the start Fedden had an uphill struggle in his great long-term fight for quality. There were even times when he had to admit failure. One of these times was his inability to find a British company that could supply anything but porous cylinder-head castings. Eventually he decided to set up the department's own foundry on the waste ground across the aerodrome, and this was producing perfect castings within three months. Later he tried to do away with castings altogether, and in any case usually preferred to draw upon the resources of a wide range of specialist suppliers. In 1920 few people consciously considered the possibility of another war – if they did it was against France – but in the back of Fedden's mind was the wish to set up an overall industrial structure that could not be disrupted by the failure or destruction of any one link in the chain. Like everything else it became a passionate crusade.

Soon after his team had been taken on by Bristol, Fedden went to the Air Ministry to introduce himself to Maj G P Bulman. Bulman was then Chief Inspector of Engines, and in 1923-44 was to have the key post of Director of Engine Development. He recalls "We became the closest of personal friends, and withal bitter opponents....In 1923 I solved the enigma of Roy's personality. While he was in his teens he developed a serious illness which caused him to be sent to Switzerland [not quite right, BG]. No improvement appeared, and he returned home, with an ominous prognosis. On the journey back he fell in with a most earnest Christian Scientist practitioner. From this casual meeting Roy became a convinced believer. He arrived home and recovered completely!

"It dominated him for the rest of his life and all his actions, but he never referred to it and few had any knowledge of it. Years later I ventured to discuss it with him, and he left me deeply moved and understanding. It explained his dedication and singleness of purpose. Perhaps unknowingly, he regarded himself as a 'chosen vessel' of enormous driving power, certain always that his own convictions were quite incontrovertible. Thus, those who didn't agree were either stupid or malicious. Hence derived his ruthlessness to his devoted staff, and the recklessness of his accusations against imaginary enemies. Yet away from his engines Roy was always a charming companion, unfailingly kind and sympathetic."

In the long term he was also deeply worried at the absence of any kind of training scheme. One of his earliest major battles with the Board was to try to get them to accept that there was a need for an apprentice department. Sir Stanley White found it hard to understand how Fedden could have the temerity to argue with him. Fedden was able to do this largely because, he said, "I was not scared of being sacked; I would not starve, and had no need to pull my punches. In the end the shocked Board gave way. I brought in an old Fishponds craftsman as supervisor, and was able to attract a large number of keen young fellows who subsequently became the backbone of the Engine Department. Without them it would have been impossible to grow in the way the department did. Very soon the aircraft side of the company took to poaching my apprentices, until I suggested they might run their own scheme". Long before the Second World War a Bristol engine apprentice could pick and choose his employment wherever he wished, so high was their standing, and many of them became top names in the aircraft industry. But in 1921 an apprentice scheme seemed presumptuous. If the Engine Department was to be closed down it would not need one.

CHAPTER FOUR

Survival

Fedden and Butler had planned the Jupiter as the most powerful engine they could conceive with a single row of air-cooled cylinders of what seemed to be a reasonable size. The resulting engine was a technical success from the start. It could run for brief periods at something like its design figure of 450 horse-power, and was undoubtedly sound and a good basis for development. By 1921, however, there were plenty of things Fedden wanted to do to make it better. Since Cosmos days he had regretted the split master rod, and planned to introduce a one-piece unit running on a two-piece crankshaft. But first he had to do something to improve the valve-gear, which, as the engine warmed up, began to clatter noisily and cause severe wear and spoil the timing efficiency. In the spring of 1921 the Jupiter II ran with valve gear which, for the first time, automatically compensated for expansion of the long cylinders and thus maintained the correct clearance under running conditions. This gear ran quietly and efficiently, and was retained ever after. As there seemed to be no military customers, the Jupiter II was planned as a long-life trouble-free unit with the conservative rating of 368 hp for the airline market that was supposed to be emerging. In September 1921 the Jupiter II became the first engine ever to pass a type test to the Air Ministry post-war schedule; indeed it was the first air-cooled engine ever to be subjected to such a severe test.

This was a very big step-forward indeed, but before the month was out Fedden was summoned to a Board meeting and told that the close-down he had feared was not far off. Sir Stanley White appreciated how hard the team had worked – indeed they had earlier heard that the Board were perturbed at their rate of progress! – "but the £200,000 has nearly all been spent. In 15 months we have sold eleven engines and delivered two. There does not seem to be any prospect of further orders, and this is not the kind of business we find attractive". He told Fedden he could do anything, within reason, to try to improve matters, but that unless he had changed the order-book position by the end of the year the Engine Department would be shut down. Fedden had to accept this, but asked permission to take the Jupiter to the Paris Air Show the following month. This was granted, and versatile Bob Williams and his staff worked feverishly preparing several engines as exhibits and backing them up with pictorial displays. The result was most effective. Whereas other engine firms were again showing their wartime products, the Bristol company had completely new engines with better ratio of power to weight (about 1.4 lb/hp) than had been seen before. People from all over the world showed intense interest, and the French Gnome-Rhône company decided to acquire a manufacturing licence. It was a very large deal, and brought Bristol a considerable sum.

It looked as if the department was going to survive. Though the British Government steadfastly found reasons for not giving it a production order for either military or civil engines, it was clear by the end of 1921 that the Jupiter ought to be able to find customers in many countries. For the moment, the directors stayed their hand. The one firm customer already gained was Gnome-Rhône, and Fedden soon saw a great deal of them. He found them an odd mixture. They had an impressive Paris factory, well equipped with American machine tools. The management could only be described as individualists – one of them carried around a small suitcase specially fitted to house objects which Fedden gradually realised were for use in sexual activities – but the senior foremen and toolroom men were charming. Virtually all the unskilled employees were what Fedden called "negroes"; the plant was filthy, and the toilets indescribable. Their methods of testing were rudimentary, with no attempt to measure torque or consumption, and oil leaks were ignored. On the other hand they subjected engines to a lot of very hard running, and most of the really important things were paid proper attention. The Jupiter III, which incorporated small alterations, some of them at French request, had to be subjected to prolonged official testing by the Service Technique. Swinchatt patiently looked after it for months, often working day and night and finding the licensees less than helpful. Then one day he met a big man in oily leathers who tested the flat-twin motor-cycles that were one of the firm's major products. He was an Englishman, Ken Bartlett by name. A strict Roman Catholic, and brother of a priest, he went out of his way to help Swinchatt get the tests done. Later he joined Bristol, spearheaded the sales force on the aircraft side, and became a member of the Board.

It was not until the end of June 1922 that all the French tests were completed. One of the schedules was a 100 hr test at up to 90 per cent power, with non-stop runs of 35 and 45 hr, which for 1922 was regarded as extremely severe. On the other hand the French schedule allowed any part to be replaced if this could be done during one of the timed shut-down periods. With the Jupiter this concession was never needed. In contrast, the new British official type test permitted no maintenance or repair at all. This was based on a 100 hr schedule intended to simulate the most arduous Service flying. In 1923 a Jupiter IV, with further small changes and rated at 436 hp, successfully passed this gruelling test, with an average mechanical wear afterwards measured at less than 0.0005 inch. This showed a standard of reliability and quality unapproached by any previous aircraft engine. During 1923, after a series of discussions at Air Ministry by Sir Henry White-Smith

The Jupiter IV on its 100-hr test. (Rolls-Royce plc)

Bristol's Engine Department was saved from extinction by an order for 81 Jupiter IV engines for 62 Hawker Woodcock II fighters. (Rolls-Royce plc)

and Fedden, the great news emerged that the Jupiter would be adopted by the RAF. It was still having a stern fight with such established engines as the Jaguar and the Napier Lion, but at last, after years of minuscule defence votes, the RAF was saying it could not go on for ever with surplus wartime equipment. New aircraft would be ordered, and some would have Jupiter engines. At last, in September 1923, an order came through from the Air Ministry for 81 Jupiter IV engines. From that day the department never looked back.

The first Service aircraft to fly with a Jupiter was J2405, an RAF Nieuport (later Gloster) Nighthawk. In November 1922 its Dragonfly was replaced by a 385 hp Jupiter II, one of the original batch of 10. Two more Nighthawks were fitted with Jupiter IIIs, being renamed Mars VI, and sent to 1 Squadron at Risalpur on the North-West Frontier for trials. Two Nighthawks were also fitted with the neat little Armstrong Siddeley Jaguar, which though only rated at 325 hp had a smaller diameter. From the start Armstrong Siddeley made it clear they wanted to drive Fedden's department clean off the map, and the competition remained intense. In the early years it was the Jaguar that pushed Fedden the hardest, though from 1925 the Jupiter slowly but surely drew ahead in power, economy and overhaul life.

One of the Jupiter-Nighthawks flew at the Hendon Air Display of 1923, and both aircraft then underwent a period of tropical trials at Hinaidi, Iraq. The big batch of Jupiter IV engines was destined for the first production machine ever designed for the Jupiter, the Hawker Woodcock fighter. Prior to this, Barnwell had designed several machines for the Jupiter. The first was the Bullet racer already mentioned. In 1921, when Barnwell had left in a huff to seek a new career in Australia, W T Reid modified the Bullet until it flew at 170 mph. In the following year Reid produced the outrageous Racer (Bristol Type 72) by adding behind a Jupiter IV the minimum barrel-like body and thin stubby monoplane wings, with fully retractable undercarriage. Uwins succeeded in flying it long enough to discover that the ailerons twisted the wings to give complete reversal of lateral control. The top speed, which not even Uwins dared to attempt, was estimated at 220 mph. A much better Reid design was the Bullfinch fighter, which was really a monoplane but could have a lower wing added to please the anti-monoplane officials.

All these Jupiter installations provided valuable experience. Fedden was fortunate in adding to his growing department Freddie Mayer, who soon made a name for himself as head of installations. Indeed he had his own Installation Department, which in 1923 was completely novel. Previous engine firms had sold engines to airframe companies and then let them get on with it. From the start Fedden could see that the two sides ought to work as the closest possible team, and he set up this special department to work out the best ways of installing his engines. One had to take into account aerodynamic drag, air-inlet and exhaust systems, all-round access for servicing or repairs, the fuel and lubrication systems, the ease of removal and replacement, and, by no means least, the proper cooling of the cylinders. Mayer kept in close touch with every customer for Bristol-built engines, and he not only avoided countless difficulties but was instrumental in gaining new business in the years to come. Early installation experience at Bristol also helped with the first real outside customer. H G Hawker Engineering was the successor to the renowned Sopwith firm, and the Woodcock was their first fighter. The assistant designer was young Sydney Camm, who had just joined the firm. Fedden was to have the pleasure of 20 years of close collaboration with him.

In 1923 Barnwell asked Sir Stanley White if he might come back, complaining "the biggest job I have had to do in Australia is to redesign the tail-skid of a 504". Back at Bristol he quickly did a Jupiter conversion of the Bristol Fighter. This was logical, because, though large numbers of Falcon-engined Fighters were available for next to nothing, the new engine transformed the performance and the reliability. The Jupiter Fighter was not adopted by the economy-minded RAF, but a batch was sold to Sweden where the water-cooled Falcon was unable to operate in winter without a long ritual before and after each flight to prevent the water from freezing. This Swedish

In 1924, the engine assembly shop at last had something in it: Jupiter IVs and the first Lucifers. (Rolls-Royce plc)

The Bristol M.1D, the second aircraft to be powered by the Lucifer. (Rolls-Royce plc)

installation afforded experience at temperatures far below 0°C and set in motion trains of thought which led to improved ways of starting engines quickly and of taking off without having to warm-up the engine. Barnwell also produced a more extensively modified version which the Bristol Flying School adopted as a standard dual-control trainer. Many Second World War leaders of the RAF were taught to fly on the Jupiter School Machine, as it was called, which throughout the inter-war period ensured that Fedden could usually hear a Jupiter overhead.

He also increasingly heard the distinctive grumbling sound of the three-cylinder Lucifer. In January 1920 a Cosmos Lucifer had been earmarked for one of the beautiful little Bristol M.1C monoplane fighters, in place of the usual 110 hp Le Rhône rotary. The result was G-EAVP, the M.1D sports machine, which flew in September 1920. The main problem with the Lucifer was torque-reaction from the firing strokes in the three big "pots", because in itself it was robust and reliable. Barnwell's team made a most satisfactory installation with a thick plywood bulkhead. Uwins flew the M.1D to first place in the 1922 Croydon Whitsun Handicap, and L L Carter won the 1922 Aerial Derby Handicap with it at an average of 109 mph. This was the first time Bristol engines made headlines. In the same year the Lucifer II was type-tested at 118 hp, and it was chosen by Reid (in Barnwell's absence) for the Lucifer School Machine, which was used by the Bristol School for many

A feature first seen on the Jupiter-engined Brandon and Ten-seater, the Lucifer of the Taxiplane could in minutes be swung round on hinges for access to the rear.
(Rolls-Royce plc)

years, and for the Taxiplane, which was the smallest and most economical three-seater Reid could devise. Both retained the multi-ply bulkhead mount. By 1925 the 140 hp Lucifer IV had become available, by which time the engine had been sold in Holland, Spain, Russia, Chile, Norway, Japan, and, above all, in Germany. The first major air race permitted in Germany by the Allies, the 1925 Rundflug, was dominated by Lucifers. It was won by a Heinkel, and Junkers, Caspar and Albatros were also important Lucifer customers. By the end of 1925 the Lucifer was cleared to run 250 hr between overhauls, which was several times as long as any rival engine in the same power class.

Great interest was shown in light aircraft in the period after the war. Eventually the Air Ministry two-seater Light Aeroplane Trials were held in 1924 at Lympne, Kent, in an endeavour to choose the best design for private owners, clubs, schools and similar users. The officials stipulated stringent limits for weight, power and performance – for example, the unladen weight could not exceed 500 lb – and though some excellent little machines were entered it was eventually agreed that the restrictions had been a mistake and that a practical light aircraft needed greater power. But Fedden never regretted the little engine he and Butler designed for this competition. The 32 hp Cherub was a flat-twin of just over 1 litre (61 cu in) capacity, with

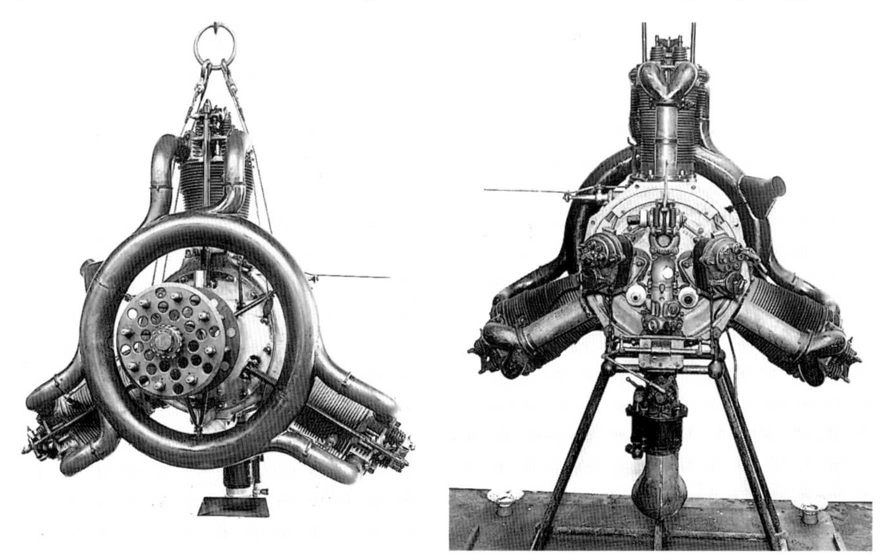

Front and rear views of a Lucifer IVA. The exhaust system was beaten out by hand – a job which, from 1927, was given to Bill Lyons (later Sir William Lyons of Jaguar Cars).
(Rolls-Royce plc)

connecting rods having big-ends with roller bearings working on a one-piece crankshaft running in four ball bearings. Bristol made 25 Cherubs (or should the plural be Cherubim?) for the competition, some of them having a geared drive to the propeller because on paper one could get better aircraft performance with a larger propeller turning more slowly. Only when they were fitted to competing aircraft was it discovered that the torque recoil of the geared engines made them very rough during acceleration, and they began to break their mountings. Butler, Swinchatt and a few other enthusiasts spent an entire night in a shed at Lympne converting the geared engines back to direct drive so that the aircraft could compete.

The original 32hp Cherub had a single carburettor. Note the two FB numbers, 5483 on the front cover and 5512 on the square plate over the front bearing. (Author)

The Parnall Pixie IIIA of September 1924 had the 32hp geared Cherub I with twin carburettors. (Rolls-Royce plc)

The Cherub III of Hawker Cygnet G-EBMB, photographed at Dunsfold in 1961. (Rolls-Royce plc)

Twin pusher Cherubs powered the Johnson 60 made at Dayton, Ohio. (Rolls-Royce plc)

Barnwell had designed the little Brownie for this contest. Not only was it that great rarity a low-wing monoplane – without any external bracing, to boot! – but its structure was largely of steel tubing in such a thin gauge that it was damaged by knocking out the ashes of a pipe against it. Seeing this, the authorities would not allow the Brownie to enter until Barnwell himself had pluckily taken one up, looped it and demonstrated that it would not fold up. Cherubs powered six of the seven prizewinning machines (the Brownie was placed second), and was the engine in all the first awards. In 1925 the Royal Aero Club held a three-day race meeting for these ultra-light machines, and the Cherub powered eight of the ten prizewinners. In 1926 the capacity was increased to 1.228 litres, raising the horse-power to 36, for a *Daily Mail* competition. This was won by a beautiful little biplane designed entirely by Camm (now chief designer), the Hawker Cygnet flown by P W S Bulman. Another Cygnet came second, and Uwins flew a Brownie into third place. In 1927 the little Cherub carried all before it in a stiff competition in Germany, and it also won the most important lightplane race at Dayton, Ohio. In 1928 the son of a rich Augsburg wine merchant made Mercedes-Benz very cross by fitting the lightplane he had built with a Cherub instead of one of the special engines the German firm had made for the contest the previous year. The tall young German constructed his little monoplane in one of his father's cellars and then made an outstanding non-stop flight of 375 miles from Munich to Rome, reaching 14,750 ft in crossing the Alps and Apennines. Fedden little knew what he was starting by selling him the 36 hp engine; his

Willi Messerschmitt with the Cherub-engined M 17 Ello, with airline entrepreneur Theo Croneiss in the rear cockpit. (Rolls-Royce plc)

name was Willi Messerschmitt.

Fedden would have been delighted if he could have foreseen that in 1998 several Cherubs would still be in use in Britain and New Zealand. He learned much from the Cherub, one lesson being that such engines are best produced by a separate division with small overheads and not mixed with engines for big aircraft. Bristol put in a lot of effort and did not see much return, apart from an abundance of that intangible commodity called prestige; but they did have a chance of big orders from an unexpected quarter. During the 1924 Lympne trials Mr Morgan, the Malvern light-car maker, came up to Fedden and said he had been impressed by the Cherub's good running and low fuel consumption. He requested a quote for 500 engines. Fedden's team went to a good deal of trouble on this, and did wonders in getting the selling price down to £63. But Morgan wasn't interested. He got his existing engines from Switzerland for £27, and the whole three-wheeler sold for £92 retail!

By 1923 Gnome-Rhône were getting into production with the Jupiter, and one of the first French-built engines was fitted to a Gourdou-Leseurre racer of extremely advanced design. The Jupiter was completely enclosed in a tight-fitting "helmeted" cowling, with cooling-air slits on the front of each helmet, and the main landing gear could be cranked backwards into the body. Its small size, great power and narrow track made it a tricky machine, but what did this matter if it could set a world record for the 50-kilometre closed circuit at a speed of 224 mph? This was twice as fast as typical fighters and bombers, and spurred French constructors to use the Jupiter in almost every one of their new military or civil transport designs. Indeed from that time onwards the Jupiter totally dominated the aircraft-engine scene in France, to the extent that after the 1929 Paris Salon the influential newspaper *L'Aéro* had two-inch headlines shrieking SCANDALE JUPITER because the Jupiter had been found to power almost 80 per cent of the military and commercial aircraft on show.

Lt Gardin of the Swedish Air Force about to average 124mph over the 800 miles from Kiruna (where the Bristol Jupiter-Fighter G-EBHG had been undergoing Arctic trials) to Malmslätt in November 1923. (Rolls-Royce plc)

But in 1923 the Engine Department still had a long way to go. The nagging problem Fedden could never get out of his mind was that the Jupiter's master rod was split and the two halves held on the crankpin by bolts. He felt he had to make the crankshaft in two parts to fit the crankpin through a one-piece big-end, a technique which had first been done early in the First World War. It was the first major change he had sanctioned. Butler had the drawings finished in June 1923, the new parts were made in October and the engine incorporating them ran in November. This was ahead of two American claimants to have been first with a one-piece master rod, George Mead of the Pratt & Whitney team (which did not exist until two years later) and Arthur Nutt of Wright Aeronautical. Fedden was delighted with the one-piece master rod, which ran on a fully floating big-end bush. The two parts of the crankshaft, with the master rod in place, were secured by a maneton coupling, the end of the crankpin being pinched between the split halves of the web which were tightened on it by a bolt. Fedden decided to use a smooth crank-pin with no splines or keyways, and to rely solely on the squeeze of the bolt, an accurate jig being used to ensure a precision assembly. From the start the improved engine, the Jupiter V, performed admirably. In 1924 it accomplished an excellent Air Ministry type test to an even more severe schedule, with a rating of 500 hp at 1,900 rpm.

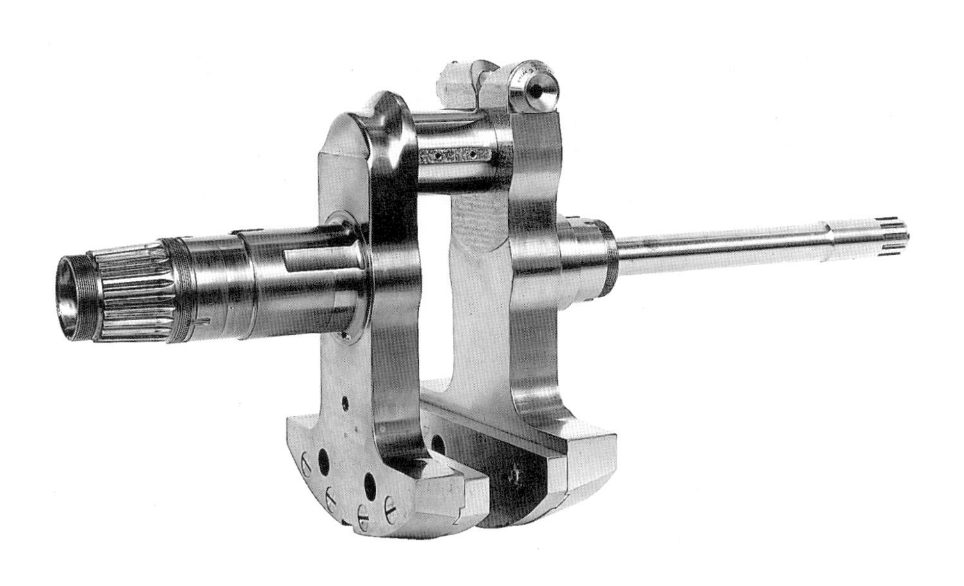

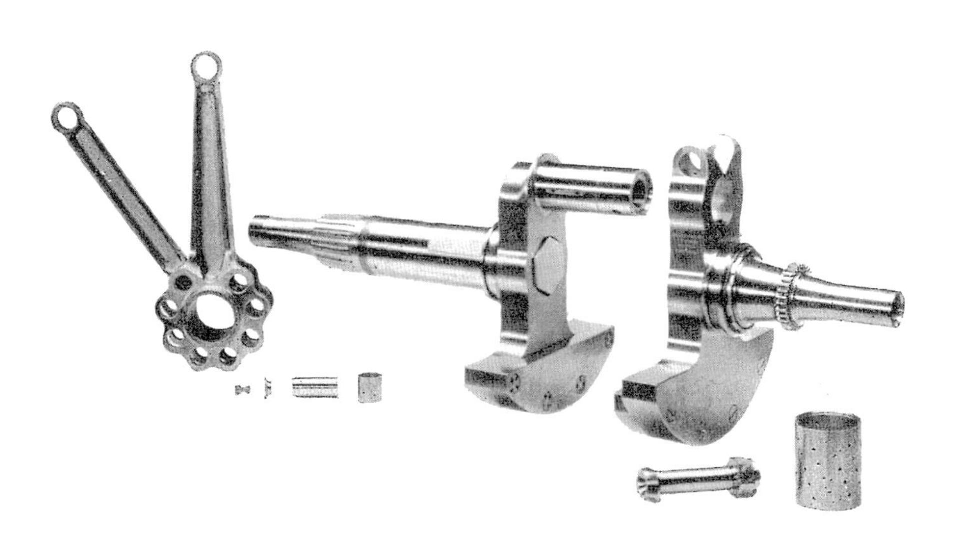

Fedden was pleased to switch to using a split crankshaft and one-piece master rod.
(Rolls-Royce plc)

Yet there was still much to be done, over and above the ceaseless quest for reliability. Fedden was determined to make the Jupiter the pre-eminent engine in the world, and keep it in that position. The Bristol Engine Department was making engines in fives and tens, whereas during the war Fishponds had worked in hundreds. While this allowed hand-built quality, it made it more difficult to achieve perfect repeatability and standardisation, even in the material specifications. Almost every day Fedden introduced something new to try to make his engines to a higher standard, until visiting engineers were not sure whether they should be deeply impressed or regard him as a lunatic.

For example, whereas during the war a failed engine was merely a nuisance to be pushed on one side, the team at Patchway in the early 1920s became desperate to discover causes. The instant anything broke, men would be working like mad to open up the engine and plunge hands into scalding oil to fish out the parts. They would not walk but run. They would examine failures with microscopes and with what were then completely new kinds of test equipment, and conduct detailed detective work to satisfy themselves exactly what had gone wrong and why. Fedden assigned a room near his spartan office as the Chamber of Horrors where every failed part could be re-examined. Close by was the Model Room. Originally this had been just a viewing room for a chief inspector, but it was gradually made apparent that there are many things on a drawing that cannot be inspected, and that the three-dimensional shape, polish, surface quality and "feel" of a part can best be appreciated by having a copy of the real thing, so the Model Room contained just that. It gradually also acquired a carefully selected collection of faulty parts, some of which were acceptable on concession and some of which were scrap. Only a skilled engineer could appreciate the differences. Whereas in the Chamber of Horrors a senior engineer or young apprentice could get an understanding of how parts of an aero engine can break, what sort of energy can be released, and of the vital importance of microscopic details, in the Model Room he could pick up every component, either faulty or in perfect condition after final inspection.

The Model Room was one of Fedden's many innovations in the early 1920s that later became common practice. He started it so that it would be possible to demonstrate on every part what the chief inspector can never show or prove by his function, but soon found that it was constantly being used for other purposes. Not least of these was just to refine and sharpen one's mental image of exactly how the engine worked, where the stress paths lay, and where one might encounter trouble. From his teenage evenings under Professor Morgan, Fedden had learned avidly of the rather heady brew that is the highest grade of mechanical engineering. To claim that designing a machine in the class of an aero engine is an art, rather than a science, is nothing more than the truth. There are so many variables – so many stresses, so many manufacturing processes, so many possible materials, so many conceivable variations in temperature or temperature gradient (hot one end, cool the other), so many things that can go wrong in the air, and so little margin to work with because of the need always to pare down the weight – that one could spend hours considering the simplest-looking component.

Fedden found the best drop-forgings came from the Belgian Derihon Company. J D Julien, Derihon's fine old forgemaster, would never look at a drawing for an important new part until he had taken the finished prototype component, which might be a gearwheel or a master rod, and spent from 10 to 30 minutes examining it with his finger-tips, with his eyes tightly closed. This was not mere showmanship but the best way of putting himself right inside the part to understand its design completely and decide how the metal in the forging would flow, and in which directions and at what speeds, and how the forging dies could be arranged to give the best possible fatigue-free product. In 1940 Julien escaped to England, and helped set up the valuable Firth-Derihon Stampings Company at Darley Dale and Sheffield on which most British piston and gas turbine engines have since relied.

At first Fedden's struggle for better quality was almost a lone one. Other engine firms had not yet moved far down this road, and did so only when the Jupiter began to hurt their business. Airframe constructors still worked by the old wartime design methods, were happier with wood than with metal, and seldom took fatigue into consideration at all. One of Britain's great engineers, A A "Soap-bubble" Griffith (so-called because of his classic discovery with G I Taylor that soap films can provide an analogy of a rod or tube in torsion), was making real progress in fatigue studies until his department at RAE Farnborough was told to stop thus wasting its time because there were no fatigue problems in aircraft! Even Frank Barnwell, whom Fedden admired as an aircraft designer, thought his colleague's preoccupation with raw material, the Model Room, and the urgent examination of any fresh fracture surface was all "poppycock" (Barnwell's word) and totally unnecessary. Fedden suspected the Board thought so too; but perhaps thinking their difficult engine chief would kick up a great fuss if they forbade such practices, they chose to humour him, without having the slightest inkling of how vital it all was to their future prosperity. (Again, Fedden possibly under-rated them).

Most firms were concerned simply to save pence and shillings wherever they could. They would scout around, like a modern housewife, for the "best buy", which simply meant the cheapest. In the motor-car industry this is commonly supposed still to be true. Rolls-Royce were always an exception, though they often spent their money on what seemed to be wilfully uneconomic methods which did little for the car or its customer. A more significant exception was the Daimler company. This firm, which had its roots deep in Germany, was a ceaseless fountain-head of new methods for combining high quality with economic production. From it came a number of top engineers who played a great part in injecting better attitudes into the British car industry. One of the greatest of these was F ”Pop” Nourse, whom Fedden secured from Daimler in 1924 to fill what was then a completely new kind of appointment; today it would be termed a Quality Manager. He was a tower of strength and played a leading part in interpreting his chief’s ideas. Almost every week he installed some new device to help in the search for quality and reliability, which Fedden had come to regard as goddesses. Until the Second World War Bristol never lost its commanding lead in the size, scope and facilities of its Engine Laboratory, under E R “Jim” Gadd. In 1937 the work-load on the PTR, the Physical-Testing Research Lab, was so great it was moved to new premises much larger than those of the original Engine Lab itself. Day and night the fatigue tests would click up their millions of reversals, while in daylight hours the Amsler repeated-impact machine, the abrasion tester, the 50-ton Avery universal tester, and many other devices would subject specimens to every kind of treatment, with or without lubrication, and at room temperature or dull-red heat, to give the answers needed. The significance of all this is that 60 years ago nobody else did it on such a scale, and most people thought Fedden mad to bother.

In the early days, before he had built up an overseas licence business other than in France, Fedden stayed at the works about 12 hours a day, except when Mayer thought he ought to go and see an aircraft company about a possible contract or some thorny problem. Fedden’s day would begin at 7.00 am with a quick conference in Butler’s office. Little Butler was RF’s ideal partner, a man totally dedicated to perfection. Then RF might visit the inner sanctum of the select team working on new projects under Frank Owner. (Owner, a gangling and gregarious pianist and the company’s very first university graduate, came as the department’s stressman in 1922. Young and enthusiastic, he later initiated several successful developments, and became chief engineer in 1947). Fedden would then go round the drawing office on one day and the production shops on the next, knowing everyone personally and what he was doing. George Adams, Butler’s faithful watchdog, was usually on hand to look up any drawing or technical detail, and it was said that he never failed to recall the FB-number of every component of every engine – certainly up to No. 20,000. Fedden would also try to see how things were going on the test rigs. From 1922 a growing number of rigs were constantly running to test bearings, con-rods, impellers and other dynamic parts without having to run a whole engine. Fedden also advanced the technique of making and running single-cylinder engines to prove the design before making the complete new engine.

Cross-section of the Jupiter V dated 15.4.25. (Rolls-Royce plc)

Though there undoubtedly may be flashes of true inspiration in the original layout of an engineering design, the main burden of the work is development. This meant blood, sweat and tears – often the first two, and under Fedden the third was sometimes close. The main purpose of development is to refine the design so that it is easy to manufacture, gives the highest possible performance, and has the highest attainable reliability. The three objectives often pull in opposite directions, and it is part of the art to strike the best compromise. Other compromises must be struck between achieving these objectives and cutting down the cost of running rigs and engines, using up man-hours and breaking costly components. Fedden had the innate ability to gather around him men who possessed not only consummate mechanical skill but also the sixth sense needed to predict and avoid trouble.

Increasingly, engines became more difficult to make. Cylinder pressures and temperatures went up, materials became harder to machine, and the machining needed became more intricate and to finer tolerances. In 1922, searching for skilled staff, Fedden wrote to Fred Whitehead, who had been at Brazil Straker but spent the war at Vickers, Crayford, where he had done wonders on munitions production. In reply to the request for the names of two or three good production men he said he would come himself. Fedden rated him, along with young Leonard Lord (later Sir Leonard, of British Leyland), as the best man in the country on modern machine-shop work. Subsequently he and Butler appeared at times to design parts that would challenge Whitehead's ingenuity to make them, but in fact the three worked closely together. Whitehead's forceful energy kept the machine shop hard at work, and often converted tools to operate in a completely new way, turning out parts at low cost that would have defeated many engineers to make at all. Fedden sometimes wondered if such virtuosity was bad, in that it almost encouraged the Fedden/Butler duo to seek the impossible; yet Whitehead's amazing skill stood up not only to tiny batches of Jupiters but also to the demand 20 years later for much more powerful engines by the thousand.

Whitehead had not been at Filton very long when he and Butler pondered on Fedden's question "What single thing will do most to advance the Jupiter?" They chose to do something which had never been done before and which, had it not come off, would have delighted their host of rivals who were always seeking to find some way of "knocking" the Jupiter. They took six engines accepted off the production line, ran them in the presence of AID inspectors, brought them back into the shop, stripped them completely, stamped an identifying number on all the parts, mixed them all up and then rebuilt them into six "mixed-up" engines. These all ran perfectly, to the genuine surprise of Lt Col H W S Outram, head of the AID, who had earlier shaken his head at such a "very bold undertaking". This gave the Jupiter a tremendous fillip, and it was an obvious testimony to Whitehead's tooling. Today such a thing is taken for granted, but in 1923, with a rate of output of about one engine a week, it was almost unbelievable.

In the middle of the decade Fedden started an extended programme of bench and flight tests at higher duty and for longer periods than any aero engine had ever been subjected to before. On the whole the results were very satisfactory, and did the engine a great deal of good. One of the most important tests was that flown by the Jupiter Express Freighter. Like several other firms the Bristol company had tried to get airline costs down by making large single-engined machines, and the first all-Bristol civil transport was the Type 75 10-seater of 1924 (G-EBEV).

Like its rivals it was damned by the inherent inability of a single-engined aircraft to be at once economical to run and also have power in reserve for emergencies, and even with a Jupiter there are advantages in having more than one engine when flying over the sea or rugged terrain. So the 10-seater was modified into the Express Freighter, which was chartered for a long period by Imperial Airways and used with complete success carrying freight between London, Paris and Cologne. It was no easy matter installing the Jupiter IV in the nose of so large a body, which extended well beyond the overall frontal area of the Jupiter, and still preserve good cooling. This

After the 225 hr 54 min endurance flying of the Bloodhound (Jupiter V). (Rolls-Royce plc)

installation was notable in that the entire nose of the aircraft could be hinged to one side to give all-round access to the engine, a feature also of the Brandon military transport, and Lucifer machines (page 74).

The second, and greatest, flight trial was one in which access to the engine was prohibited. The aircraft was the Bristol Type 84 Bloodhound, intended as a successor to the Fighter but made only as a one-off (G-EBGG). Early in 1926, in foul weather, the Jupiter V of this aircraft was officially sealed so that any attempt to tamper with it would have been obvious, and Lt-Col Frederick Minchin then took off from Filton to fly to Croydon, with Bristol engineer Griffiths in the rear cockpit. Minchin and Capt F L Barnard kept up a regular shuttle between the two airfields until 25,074 miles had been flown in 225 hr 54 min. The engine had given no trouble whatever, and once the AID representative had broken the seals Bristol stripped the engine and found it in perfect condition apart from one slightly corroded exhaust valve. Later Minchin made a high-speed tour of the main European capital cities, with Freddie Mayer as passenger. The faithful Bloodhound then continued with intensive development at Filton. It made the first flights of the Hele-Shaw variable-pitch propeller, which Fedden was later instrumental in getting put into production by the specially formed Rotol company.

G-EBGG also flew 6,000 miles to Cairo and back in just under 60 hr flying time, which in 1926 was not a journey to be undertaken lightly. But before this flight the story of the 25,000 miles with a sealed engine had finally ensured a marketing success so great that the Jupiter became almost the standard big aviation engine in a score of countries. It eased the path of the Jupiter into many types of fighters, bombers and other aircraft for the Royal Air Force, and it also gained for Bristol the highest accolade of all. The special trial had been conducted on behalf of Imperial Airways, Britain's national airline, and its complete success confirmed de Havilland's choice of Fedden's engine for Imperial's DH.66 Hercules 14-seat airliners. For the next 10 years the Jupiter was the most important aircraft engine in the world.

CHAPTER FIVE

Building on success

It is not generally known that Owner's work in 1924 included an examination of the possibilities of the gas turbine, in its turboprop form, as a long-term replacement for the piston engine. At the time Fedden was obviously right to study it, and equally right to drop it, because with the cycle efficiencies and blade temperatures that seemed attainable there was not much power left to be usefully employed. Bristol later took a careful look at gas turbines before and during the Second World War, and decided reluctantly to become involved. But the 1924 study reflected RF's long strategic vision.

More than 70 years ago the main problem, if one had a piston engine that was already powerful and reliable, was to maintain power as the aircraft climbed into thinner air. To a first approximation the power is proportional to the mass of air drawn into each cylinder on each induction stroke, so climbing to 22,000 ft, where the air density is half that at sea level, results in the engine losing half its power. There were several possible answers, but the problem was a big one and Fedden talked at length with the helpful Engine R & D team at the RAE at Farnborough. Led by Major Norman, an

In 1928, the Engine Department got a proper front door with the addition of this office block. (Rolls-Royce plc)

experienced engineer, they included such enthusiasts as Jimmy Ellor, "Jock" Taylor, "Snowball" Taylor and B C Carter; in 1928 Fedden was able to hire several first-class men when Norman's operations were drastically (and foolishly) curtailed by the Government. They agreed that there were four methods of attacking the altitude problem: use of higher compression with a bi-fuel system; variable inlet-valve timing; a mechanical supercharger; or a turbo-supercharger. Bristol was the only company in the world to try all four.

The first was explored by raising the compression ratio of a Jupiter IV to 7:1, and providing the aircraft with an additional small tank of alcohol fuel. This fuel, with its greater resistance to detonation (or anti-knock quality), was used only at take-off and for the initial climb. At altitude the engine could be opened to full throttle on regular fuel. When the system was tried on the Bloodhound it cut no less than 10 minutes off the time taken to climb to 20,000 ft, and also increased the speed on the level, but nobody liked the complex fuel system or the possibility of dangerously selecting the wrong fuel.

A simpler system, which gave quite good results with no extra complication, was to increase the compression ratio and then "gate" the throttle at low altitudes to restrict the power output in dense air. Even better results were obtained with variable timing. Again using the Bloodhound, a worm-gear (later, a crank) was added to allow the pilot to rotate the fixed outer annulus of the cam-drive epicyclic gear. The pilot took off with the high-compression engine at full throttle, but with the inlet timing so far retarded that part of each fresh charge was expelled back into the induction manifold, thus reducing volumetric efficiency and restricting the power. As height was gained, the pilot progressively returned the valve timing to normal to give full power at altitude. The results surprised everyone. Eventually a timing schedule was devised that cut 11 minutes off the climb to 18,000 ft and increased speed at that height by 11 mph. The concept was strikingly successful, yet in his heart Fedden knew the right answer must be some kind of supercharger to blow a greater mass of air into the cylinders.

At first sight the most attractive scheme is the turbo-supercharger, because instead of extracting useful power from the crankshaft this is driven by harnessing the considerable energy that would otherwise thunder out into the atmosphere from the exhaust pipe. Obviously there were severe problems in doing this, but Ellor, the supercharger wizard at Farnborough, had made and run a turbo-blower in 1916 which had then been successfully flown in an S.E.5a. This showed that turbine blades could be made to withstand the white-hot exhaust gas and the severe centrifugal pull when spinning at about 15,000 rpm. In 1923 Bristol added an improved RAE turbo-supercharger to the Jupiter IV which had been fitted to the Bristol Seely Tourer. It added 140 lb to the installed powerplant weight, and there were plenty of fairly minor snags – the cylinder and exhaust-valve cooling was simply not up to the increased exhaust back-pressure and greater power – but it soon achieved excellent results. The service ceiling was increased by more than 10,000 ft, and the speed at critical altitude (the height to which the supercharger can maintain sea-level manifold pressure) was increased by more than 40 mph. Surprisingly, there was no breakdown or major failure, but Fedden judged such a system ahead of its time. With sufficient development effort the rather ungainly installation could have been made trim and neat, and eventually the Americans showed what could be done. In 1923, however, there was no development money and no obvious customer, so Bristol shelved the exhaust turbo for four years. This simply reflected the complete short-sightedness of the Government in not appreciating the importance of such work. In the Second World War the exhaust turbos in operational aircraft were all American.

Though large numbers of Service machines flew with the higher compression ratio and either the gated throttle or the retarded inlet timing, both systems fairly soon gave way to mechanical supercharging by a blower driven at high speed by step-up gears from the crankshaft. The first practical mechanical supercharger was again a child of Ellor's fertile brain at Farnborough in 1916. He had looked at reciprocating and Roots-type

The Seely is seen here with turbocharged Jupiter III and Leitner-Watts steel propeller.
(Rolls-Royce plc)

blowers, but got the best results from a small centrifugal impeller mounted concentrically with the crankshaft on the outside of the crankcase rear cover, delivering its air through curved manifolds. F M Green and S D Heron helped supercharger development, and discovered that the drive had to incorporate centrifugal clutches if it was to avoid stripping its gear-teeth. The first engine to put this development to use was the Jaguar, the rival from the Armstrong Siddeley company, which went into production with the Ellor/Heron/Green supercharger in 1925. But the Bristol Engine Department was close on their heels, and in 1926 ran a Jupiter with a geared supercharger.

The main Jupiter development in 1925 was the Mk VI, which eliminated the old cast crankcase. The new case was machined from two forgings of Duralumin. In 1971 Fedden wrote to what is today the British Steel Corporation's River Don and Associated Works and found that they still remember parts FB5606 and 5607, the front and rear forgings. They were hot-soaked for 24 hours and then brought up to forging temperature, the skilled foreman judging the temperature by whether or not a piece of paper placed on the billet smouldered! About 120 blows were then given by a 7½-ton drop hammer, forging continuing as long as the tallow lubricant burned between blows. Today this sounds like primitive witchcraft, but in fact in 1925 the know-how and leadership of this works – then the English Steel Corporation – was, in Fedden's words, "Terrific … Mr Clarke was managing director, Mr Williamson forgemaster and Mr Wilkinson the metallurgist. Williamson used to take me up to Mr Clarke's office whenever I offered them a severe challenge. Clarke would read the riot act to me, which seemed an odd way to treat a customer, but always finished up with something like "Williamson was quite right to bring you to see me, as our business is to make money; but this time I will forgive you, as, surprisingly, most of your pedantic ideas have paid off". ESC did very well out of Fedden; when the Jupiter went into licence-production around the world, few licensees could do better than buy stampings from the Yorkshire firm.

Changing to a forged crankcase not only made for a superior case but also, with other small changes, saved 80 lb weight and enabled the frontal area of the engine to be reduced by 12 per cent. Another change was a switch to a triplex carburettor with three barrels in a single easily adjustable unit. It was a Jupiter VI which flew the 226 hr sealed trial, and the same type of engine was selected for the six DH.66 Hercules for Imperial Airways. The civil Jupiter VI had a compression ratio of 5:1 and was rated at 460 hp. The Hercules went into service between Cairo and Basra in 1927, and in 1929 went on to serve Karachi. In 1932 they were transferred to the new African route between Kisumu and Cape Town. By mid-1931 each engine had run about 2,000 hours and had the world record time between overhauls of 555 hours. When they were withdrawn in 1935 the average flight time was about

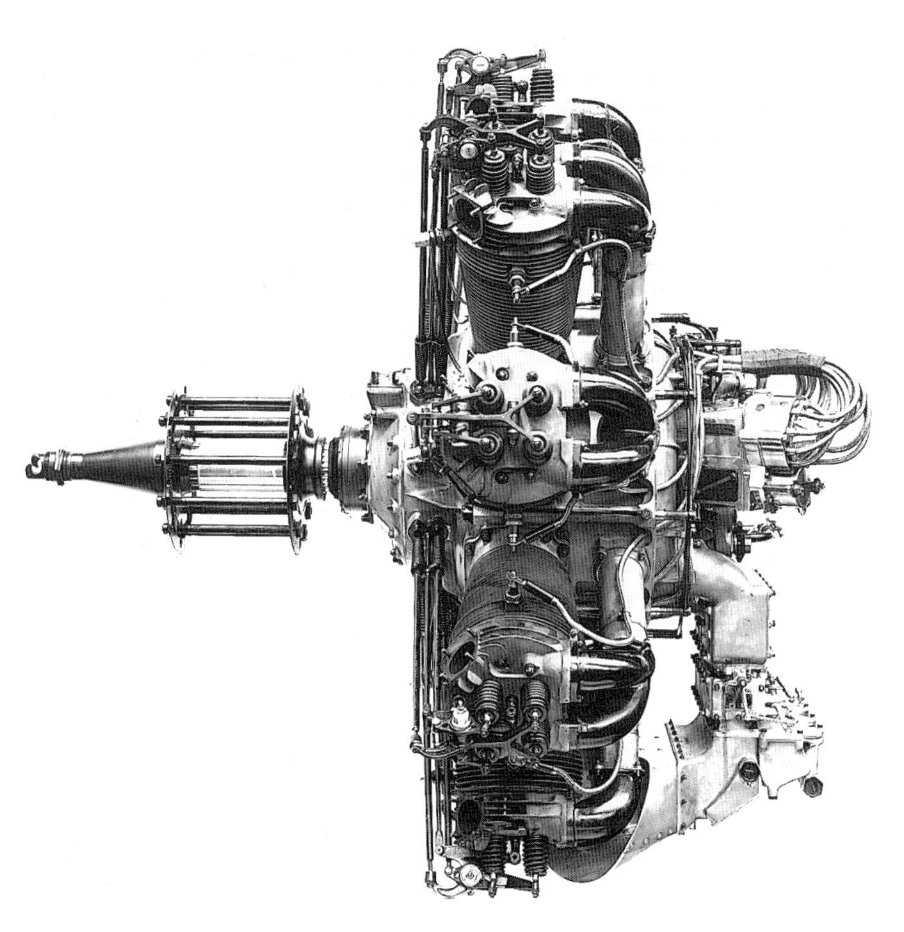

The Jupiter VI introduced the forged crankcase and triple carburettors in one unit. (Rolls-Royce plc)

2,600 hours. Today an airline engine may reach 2,600 hr in six months, but in the 1920s these were marvellous figures. Large numbers of the military Jupiter VI were also made, with higher compression of 5.3 or 6.3:1.

Seemingly trivial changes can be of great importance in such advanced engineering. There had been a few cases of broken Jupiter valve springs, and Owner criticised the way the four-lobe cam rings were made. In a radial engine the cam ring rotates inside the crankcase and its raised portions operate the valve push-rods. The Jupiter ring was forged and machined and then coated with blue marking-out ink. The cam profiles were scribed on the

Air Minister Sir Samuel Hoare and Lady Hoare and their staff about to leave Croydon for Delhi on 27 December 1926 in the second DH.66 Hercules G-EBMX. (Rolls-Royce plc)

ink by striking a series of arcs of half-inch radius from a template, the ring finally being filed as accurately as possible along the top of the arcs. Whitehead suggested the ring should be made automatically to a tolerance of "half a thou" by using a surface grinder with a wheel kept dressed exactly to one-inch diameter, the curve being generated by a dividing head and a roller follower to get the correct cam lift. The first ring made by this method not only made the engine quieter, and broke no springs, but it raised the output on type test of a Jupiter IV by no less than 12 hp. This was unexpected, and thereafter Whitehead sat in at the project stage of all new or revised engines, whilst maintaining a wholly amicable relationship with the designers.

In the 1920s very few British businessmen had any direct contact with the United States, and this was even true of the aviation industry. Fedden became the outstanding exception. In 1925 Guy Vaughan, vice-president of Wright Aeronautical, came to Patchway with his chief inspector and went through Fedden's operation in great detail. In the same year Major J R McCrindle, an ex-RFC officer who represented Bristol interests in the USA, forwarded a firm order for a Jupiter V for the US Government. Fedden mentally pictured

Jupiter features appearing freely in rival American engines, but the Board overruled him. Fedden then told the Board he would like to visit the US engine firms. Sir Stanley White held that "Dagoes start at Dover", and would have been horrified at the thought of going to such a foreign place as America, but said Fedden was welcome to go if he could do any good there. In February 1927 Fedden made the first of more than 50 transatlantic trips, becoming the best known and most respected British engineer to everyone in US aviation. Such people as Nutt and Jones of Wright, Rentschler, Mead and Willgoos of Pratt & Whitney, and Luke Hobbs, the Army Air Corps carburettor expert at McCook Field who later became chief engineer of Pratt & Whitney Aircraft, became Fedden's close friends as well as keen commercial rivals. In 1931 Hobbs was asked "Why haven't you made a two-row engine?" and he gave the oft-quoted reply "Because Fedden hasn't". But on the very first trip, in 1927, the thing that stuck in Fedden's mind was that in Pratt & Whitney's experimental shop he found the bits of his Jupiter V – the one sold to the US Government – scattered around as if they had been keenly studied. His conclusion was obvious, though it was not correct. He repaid the compliment by closely following each new development by his US rivals.

On his early visits to the United States, Fedden became particularly interested in American progress with such engine-related devices as variable-pitch propellers and engine starting systems. In the early days of aviation, engines were "swung" by hand, which is hard and potentially dangerous work. During the war B C Hucks had devised his method of using a special starting vehicle – often basically a Ford Model T – which could be backed up to the engine until a belt-driven output shaft, which could be adjusted in height, engaged with drive dogs on the front of the aircraft propeller hub. The engine could then be rotated by the Hucks vehicle's own engine. But this was a tricky method, and in any case could not be used on the largest aircraft where the propeller was out of reach. In their case each engine had to be swung by ropes thrown up across the propeller blades. Fedden gave much thought to the problem. Aircraft had no electrical system, apart from simple windmill-driven supplies just powerful enough for a wireless set. The best answer seemed to be that of Major Norman at Farnborough. This used a small auxiliary engine, usually a flat-twin of motor-cycle size, with one cylinder for motive power and the other serving as a pump supplying fuel-rich mixture which could be piped, by rotating a selector cock, to the engine in the aircraft.

Norman's gas starter system fed the combustible mixture under pressure to each cylinder in turn, causing the engine to rotate as if it was running. The ignition was then switched on, firing the rich mixture and starting the engine, and the cycle repeated. Four engines could be started in less than a minute, and the RAE appeared to have a practical method, but it had several drawbacks. One problem was that the aircraft engine had to have a special non-return valve at the end of the gas pipe in each cylinder, and this valve, projecting into the combustion space, caused detonation. This problem, which is explained later, reared its head whenever the combustion pressure or local temperature became too high, and could be overcome only by reducing compression ratio or adopting a different kind of fuel with higher anti-knock qualities. In the early 1920s there were no anti-knock fuels, but fuel specialists devised a scale of anti-knock performance in which one particular fuel, isooctane, was rated at 100. Thus, typical motor fuels, which were the same as those then used in aviation, had octane ratings of around 70. Fedden was keen to learn all about detonation, and the need for high-octane fuels, and increasingly fought for such fuels to be made available. He also tried to overcome the shortcomings in the RAE gas starter.

Between February and May 1922, two Jupiters had been fitted to a civil Handley Page O/10 transport, G-EATK. This belonged to Handley Page Air Transport, and it gave Fedden his first experience of a multi-engine

The first Jupiter multi-engined aircraft was the Handley Page O/10. Fitting the air-cooled engines in early 1922 saved over 900lb (408kg). (Rolls-Royce plc)

installation. It revitalised the Handley Page, raising top speed from 100 mph to over 140, though at the conclusion of the trials one crankshaft was found to have developed a perfect spiral torsional-fatigue failure which was on the verge of the final break! Fedden developed a Bristol gas starter system which overcame the main faults of the RAE method and installed it in the O/10. The gas starter was gradually perfected, and late in the decade it went into production for several types of multi-engined machines in which hundreds of installations gave good service. This was the world's first multi-engine starting system.

By 1925 the Jupiter had fulfilled its promise as potentially a world-beating engine. It was almost impossible to fault. In only one respect did Fedden have to admit it was less than ideal: it had a large frontal area, and Rolls-Royce, Napier and Fairey (who wanted to make the American Curtiss D-12 engine) lost no opportunity of emphasising this fact. Even the Armstrong Siddeley Jaguar radial was noticeably smaller in diameter, and during 1925 Fedden and Butler sought to rectify the position by designing a special highly rated short-stroke Jupiter for fighters and racing aircraft. By November they had completed a scheme for an engine with the stroke reduced by 1 in to 6.5 in, the capacity being reduced from 28.7 to 24.9 litres and the overall diameter being brought down from 53 to 47.6 in. As this was the biggest change Fedden had sanctioned since 1920, he went further and introduced several other bold innovations that had been germinating in his mind. A new separate cast cylinder head was specified, with sloping ends housing two pairs of inclined overhead valves, which suggested the name of "penthouse". This looked far superior to the old poultice form, and Fedden no longer doubted that a reliable barrel/head joint could be made. New pistons were made of drop-forged Hiduminium, one of the alloys of the new company High Duty Alloys. At the back was a mechanically driven supercharger, with spring-drive gear and centrifugal clutches to give smooth torque without shock. It was different enough to be judged a new engine, and Fedden revived the name of Mercury, though it had little in common with the 1917 engine.

In early 1926 Hugh Dowding, the RAF Director of Training, showed great interest in the Mercury. He considered it had potential for the 1927 Schneider Trophy race as well as for fighters, and shortly Bristol received a £13,000 contract for three prototype engines and the Type-Testing of one. The chosen airframe was the Short Crusader racing seaplane. Fedden was determined to achieve a really streamlined installation, and wanted a long extension shaft to drive the propeller so that the whole front end could continue the line of the spinner. This raised the prospect of severe "whip" of the long shaft. P Salmon at Farnborough said, "It won't be able to accelerate beyond 1,600 rpm; all the energy will then go into torsional vibration, and the prop will fly

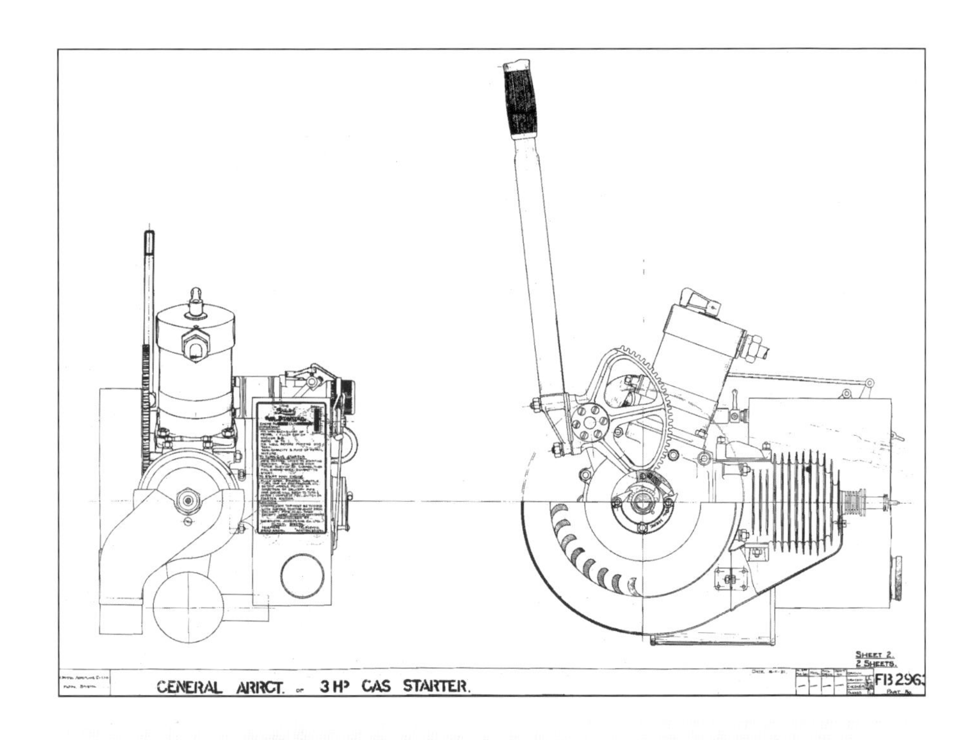

Drawing of the gas starter, dated 15.11.21, and photograph. (Rolls-Royce plc)

off". Owner looked up from his calculations and said, "I can't extend it more than an inch or two". Fedden, who was sensitive to criticism about draggy radial engines and had made up his mind, vehemently replied "I want it a foot longer". Owner schemed a shaft with a 3/16th inch wall thickness, too thin for a keyway, and calculated there would be a critical whirling mode at just under 1,600 rpm. The design limit speed of the engine was precisely twice this, and when the first engine was ready for bench testing Harry Powell was told "Open the throttle as hard as you can between 1,200 and 2,000 revs!" Powell did so, and nothing broke. In fact this was a much less critical engine than an American one in airline passenger service immediately after the Second World War which had only three safe speeds at which sustained running was allowed.

Powell was one of those whose devotion to Fedden extended into his already limited "spare time". Fedden kept him constantly on the go in the evenings and at weekends, either getting all manner of jobs done at

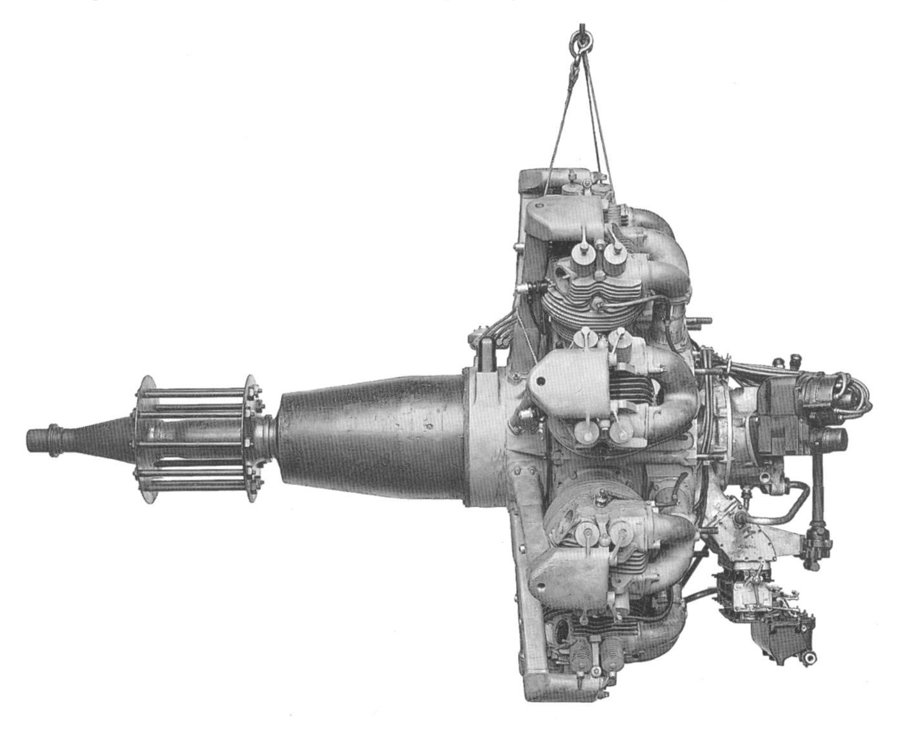

The new Mercury of 1926, with a long drive shaft to the Crusader's propeller.
(Rolls-Royce plc)

Widegates or looking after the well-being of his speedboats, their transport, crew and mechanics. Together with Eric Turner (from 1936 Fedden's private secretary, as related later) Powell was instructed to organise three big staff outings by boat down the Bristol Channel. Turner recalls "Harry, with megaphone and 'hymn sheet', led the community singing, while I played the accordion. It mattered little that poor Harry was tone deaf!"

Fedden delivered the first Mercury in January 1927, having achieved during bench testing the sustained power of 808 hp, with about 960 hp available on experimental 100-octane fuel for five-minute sprints at 2,400 rpm. To reduce weight, several parts, including the whole crankcase, were made of magnesium. Fedden disliked this metal, which he considered was liable to harbour unpredictable and dangerous flaws which could not be detected (this was before the development of modern methods of non-destructive testing), but the RAE was eager for it to be used in order to gain experience.

The Crusader flew in May 1927 and its behaviour was encouraging. Though the cylinders had no exhaust manifold and were almost completely enclosed by long streamlined "helmets", cylinder-head temperatures stayed acceptably low and the drag appeared minimal. During pre-race trials at Venice the Crusader reached 271 mph, with the prospect of doing

A Fedden boat trip – known today as "team building". (Mrs Elizabeth Thomas)

N226, the Mercury-engined Short Crusader. (Rolls-Royce plc)

appreciably better in the race after small modifications; then disaster struck. The ailerons were incorrectly re-rigged, with the wires crossed. The pilot Schofield survived the ensuing crash, but the Crusader was demolished. It was three weeks before the wreck was raised from the Adriatic, and Fedden saw that the magnesium crankcase had corroded completely away to leave the pistons carrying loose cylinders.

Over the following three years Fedden's team converted this outstanding racing engine into a reliable engine for Service use, without magnesium parts and with a rating starting in the region of 500 hp. In the second half of the 1920s he at last considered that the sweeping success of the Jupiter provided a sure enough foundation for the development of other engines. Some of the new engines were improved Jupiters. The Jupiter VII, in production for military use in 1928, incorporated what was probably the world's best mechanical supercharger at that time, making use of experience with the racing Mercury. It was rated at 460 hp at 12,000 ft, and in the report of its Type Test it is recorded that there was "a complete absence of measurable wear" on the supercharger gears, and that the power curves (graphical plots of power against rpm) at the end of the test were at levels higher than those recorded at the start. The Jupiter VIII, run in April 1927 and Type Tested at the end of that year, was the first to have a geared propeller drive since the Cosmos prototype of 1919. That early Jupiter had straight spur epicyclic gears, but the Mk VIII had a bevel epicyclic gear of 0.5 : 1 ratio, which Fedden thought compact, light and well suited to different ratios. He regarded the Mk VIII as the first of a new family of civil and military engines all able to run at 2,000 or more rpm yet driving large and efficient propellers at about half this speed.

Another new Jupiter even bore a new name. The Orion, basically a Jupiter VI, was designed against an Air Ministry contract to incorporate the RAE turbocharger which Fedden had already run and flown in 1923 as a crude lash-up on the Seely Tourer. In contrast the Orion was neat, with the exhaust collected in a small front ring and piped at the 6 o'clock position to the turbo on the rear cover. The Orion ran in 1928, and late in the year took a Gloster Gamecock fighter to 20,000 ft in 12¾ minutes and held 495 hp at that height. But the cooling problems were severe, and when the turbine casing distorted, and caused the impeller to rub, the programme was again abandoned by the Air Ministry. In retrospect it may have been a mistake to give up so easily. Fedden had too much on his plate, and in any case could not fund development himself, but at the national level a fully developed turbocharger would have been a great advantage in the Second World War. As it was Fedden then had to begin again with turbos and still find success elusive, but his team was the only one in the world to complete significant development in this field apart from General Electric in the United States.

The first Jupiter with a mechanically-driven supercharger was tested in 1927. This shows the steel impeller, with surrounding guide vanes. (Author)

The neat bevel epicyclic reduction gear introduced on the Jupiter VIII. (Author)

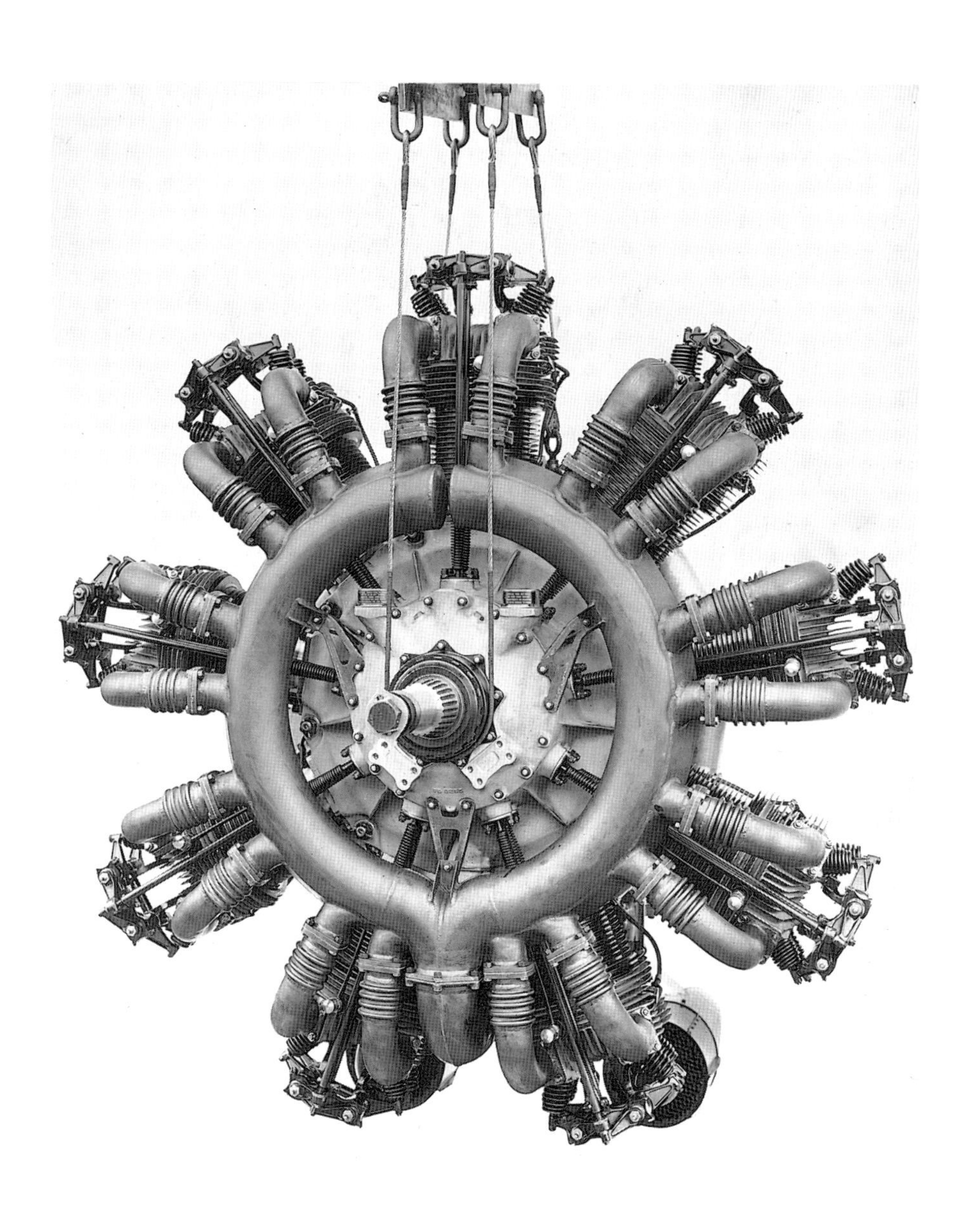

The turbocharged Orion. (Rolls-Royce plc)

One of the few Bristol-made Neptunes. (Rolls-Royce plc)

Avro 504N G-EBKQ had a most varied career, including testing startling wings of RAF 30 profile and experimental floats. Here it is seen, with normal wings, serving as the Titan test bed at Filton in 1928. (Rolls-Royce plc)

Fedden also decided to do something to fill the gap between the 130-140 hp Lucifer and the Jupiter of steadily increasing power beyond 450 hp. In 1927 the Titan was produced, with five Mercury-size cylinders and a capacity of 13.8 litres. It ran well and was offered in competition with the Wright Whirlwind (which gained enormous publicity in 1927 from Lindbergh's solo transatlantic flight). At first the Titan gave 200 hp, but by 1929 it had been Type Tested at 220 hp. In 1929 the seven-cylinder Neptune appeared, with 19.1 litres and a rating of 315 hp. Though there was little demand for these engines in Britain, Gnome-Rhône made both in considerable numbers for use in many important European aircraft. Unfortunately the French licensee had for some years been seeking ways of evading the terms of the original 1921 licence, and this was finally achieved with the K-series of engines similar to the Jupiter but with two-valve cylinders. Fedden took a poor view of this evasion, and the agreement was not terminated without acrimony. Norman Rowbotham and Roger Ninnes returned to Bristol from Paris in the early 1930s, and Bristol's French business waned until it was revived by the sheer technical superiority of Fedden's later engines.

When relations with Gnome-Rhône turned sour, this was no longer of great importance. By the end of the decade Fedden's personal leadership and salesmanship had secured manufacturing licences for the Jupiter in 17 foreign countries. No other aero engine has ever been so widely made, and it is doubtful that one ever will be. Unlike Rolls-Royce, which at that time

Close-up of the Titan in G-EBKQ, in which it was rated at 210hp. (Rolls-Royce plc)

professed to think licence deals degrading and certain to lead to an inferior product that would harm a good name, Fedden actively encouraged licensing and eventually was earning the Bristol company a million-pound royalty annually, besides the considerable extra business due to support equipment, training, accessories and many other peripheral items. In particular, "Dev" (Col Wallace Devereux, of High Duty Alloys) made it a practice to tour overseas markets with RF to supply special light-alloy forgings and, in many instances, to supervise the establishment of a local factory to produce Hiduminium alloys and make forged pistons and other crucial components. Between 1925 and 1935 RF and Dev jointly concluded licensing deals worth tens of millions of pounds, which in those days was business on an astronomic scale.

Fedden was a stickler for proper organisation. He saw there was a need for a self-contained technical group to solve licensing problems, and in 1927 established a Licence Drawing Office – the first in the world – under a versatile Belgian, Emil Lavrillé. He learned the hard way, in advance of any other organisation, just what is involved when a complex product made by precision engineering is manufactured under licence in many countries. While some metric conversion was easy, other conversions raised great difficulties with the licensee's available stocks of raw material, sizes of ball bearings and other bought-out parts. For example, changing gearwheels from the British diametral pitch to a metric module led to changes in distances between shaft-centres and thus to a vast amount of detailed redesign. Often parts had to be restressed, owing to small differences in dimensions and strength, and in many cases a great deal of work had to be done to match the engine to foreign auxiliaries, propellers, fuel and oil systems and gun-synchronising gear, or to change the direction of rotation. Laboratory tests, changed tooling, training courses, and advice on changed detail design, all became a matter of routine.

It was very much worth while. It was the sale of the licence to Gnome-Rhône that put the Bristol Engine Department on its feet. In the course of the subsequent decade the Jupiter became the standard high-power aircraft engine in most countries that had an aircraft industry. Licences were sold to: Gnome et Rhône, Paris (France); E W Bliss Co., Brooklyn (USA); Nakajima Aircraft Co., Tokyo (Japan); Italian government, SA Italiana Alfa-Romeo, Milan, and Societa Piaggio, Genoa (Italy); Swedish government and Nydqvist & Holm (Nohab Flygmotorfabriken), Trolhätten (Sweden); Siemens und Halske, Berlin (Germany); S. A. Saurer, Arbon (Switzerland); Soc. J. Walter a Spol, Prague (Czechoslovakia); SABCA, Brussels (Belgium); Industrya Avijonskih Motora, Rakovika (Yugoslavia); SA des Acières Manfred Weiss, Budapest (Hungary); Sociedad Union Naval Levante, Madrid (Spain); Parque de Material Aeronautico d'Alverca,

Alverca (Portugal); Trust d'Etat de l'Aviation, Moscow (USSR); Polish government and Skoda Co., Warsaw (Poland); Bristol Engines of Canada, Montreal (Canada); and Linne-och Jern-Manufaktur AB, Tammerfors (Finland).

Indeed until 1927 it looked as if nearly all the Jupiters would be made outside Britain, but in that year the Jupiter was the engine chosen for the two most important programmes for new RAF aircraft since 1918. One was for a new fighter. The Air Staff had long regarded France as the only likely enemy, and in view of that nation's lumbering heavy bombers had complacently thought it could manage with uninspiring fighters. Fedden was one of the few who thought otherwise, and argued that a 250 horsepower fighter would be inadequate. Eventually the F.9/26 specification for a new fighter was won by one of Barnwell's masterpieces, the much-liked Bristol Bulldog, flown by Uwins in May 1927. Its only serious rival was the Hawker Hawfinch, whose designer, Camm, was a bad loser. He angrily complained that Barnwell got a better Jupiter engine than he did. Fedden had many such scrapes with rival planemakers, which were usually more good-natured than they sounded, but on this occasion he had to produce the log-books and test records to prove that the engine sent to Hawker was up to standard. The other big win for the Jupiter was the Westland Wapiti. In 1926 the RAF decided its D.H.9a – the

Bristol's first real production aircraft since 1918 was the Bulldog; this is a Mk II (Jupiter VIIF). (Rolls-Royce plc)

wartime day bomber used for policing the Empire – needed to be updated, and ran a contest for a new multi-role machine which used as many D.H.9a parts as possible, yet made the greatest advance in performance and efficiency. Westland chose the Jupiter for their winning design, which, like the Bulldog, was made in what were for those days immense quantities over more than eight years. The RAF alone bought 312 Bulldogs and 507 Wapitis, and many more were exported.

Another major customer for Jupiters was Westland Aircraft: these are Mk IIAs with the Jupiter XFa. (Rolls-Royce plc)

Most Bulldogs served at home, while the Wapitis went almost everywhere the Union Jack flew. Fedden enjoyed visiting RAF units, but regretted the fact that he received no information on how his engines stood up to operational service. Such knowledge, he said, would be of the greatest value in improving the product. No machinery existed for feedback to the manufacturer, and Fedden was for a long time unaware of the fact that, in the harsh conditions of Iraq, Wapiti engines were breaking their con-rods. The Chief of the Air Staff, Sir John Salmond, wanted to "throw the Jupiter out" (though there was no evidence that any other engine could even do as well), and Maj G P Bulman, Deputy Director of Engine R & D at Air Ministry, had to fight hard to save the situation. Slightly modified rods were already being intensively bench-tested at Bristol and these withstood the Iraqi environment successfully, but Salmond's precipitate decision would, if carried out, have hurt the RAF very badly and also provided the one big bit of ammunition Fedden's many rivals – real and imagined – were constantly seeking.

Rolls-Royce still have the original of a memorandum sent to Derby by Henry Royce on 3 June 1926, in which the firm's patriarch proclaimed "The Jupiter may be considered to have definitely beaten the watercooled engine, except for its one disadvantage of too much head resistance...Should we decide to build an air-cooled (radial) engine, as I strongly recommend...I think this matter is more urgent than would at first appear, owing to the loss of trade we have experienced in this country and abroad through the success of the air-cooled engine..." In fact, after wondering how to design a superior aircooled radial, the next Rolls-Royce engine was the water-cooled Kestrel.

Fedden never for a moment let up in his drive for air-cooled radial engines in general, and for the Jupiter in particular. He did not play golf, but loved to get away on fishing trips with aviation friends or foes, and which were really conferences conducted at high pressure whilst thigh-deep in a river. One way in which he could do better was improve the basic engine, and when Harvey Mansell arrived from the axed team at Farnborough in 1928 he was put in charge of running the growing array of single-cylinder test engines, on which new or improved features could be run under overload conditions day and night before being committed to a complete engine. The other way to improve aircraft performance was to install the engine better. Fedden was sensitive to the parrot-cry that radials meant high aircraft drag. Eagerly he read in 1926 the first report by Dr. Townend at the National Physical Laboratory of research into improved radial installations with a surrounding ring, like a circular mudguard, round the cylinders. The ring behaved as an annular wing, giving an effective lift (thrust) pulling the aircraft along. The American National Advisory Committee for Aeronautics (NACA) advocated a similar but even better idea which was extended back to cover the engine completely, leaving just an annular gap at the rear (later filled by adjustable "gills") where the cooling air could escape.

In the mid-1920s production Jupiters were uncowled, but fitted with a small exhaust manifold round the front of the crankcase with a sloping outer surface to deflect cooling airflow past the cylinders. By 1929 a Jupiter VIII was flying in a Wapiti with a streamlined exhaust ring of increased diameter forming the front section of a Townend ring. In the same year a Bullpup flew with a Mercury surrounded by a close-fitting Townend ring. It was a time of hit-and-miss experimentation, and a profusion of new ideas. A young engineer at the Gloster Aircraft works had the idea of discharging the exhaust to give the maximum jet thrust, and Fedden's office checked and agreed his figures in August 1926. A few months later Fedden was walking round the Gloster drawing office with chief designer Folland. They stopped at the same young man's drawing board and Fedden criticised his answer to

A 1929 installation of a Jupiter XIF in the Bristol Type 109 – an aircraft built for long-range flying. (Rolls-Royce plc)

a problem met with the Gloster F.9/26 fighter submission. To Fedden's amazement the junior draughtsman looked up and said, "With respect, I don't agree with you Sir; you see ..." Nobody ever disagreed with Fedden on technical matters, and what made it even more of a shock was that the young fellow was clearly right. Thus did Fedden meet the man who 30 years later was to be his last employer: George Dowty.

Exhaust problems brought him to another man who later became famous. Ducting white-hot gas was no easy matter in the first quarter of the Century. By 1925 improved stainless steel was available, but Fedden was ceaselessly tormented by manufacturing defects, by weld failures in service and by the swift deterioration even of the few acceptable exhaust systems. In 1927 he was recommended to see a man up in Coventry who had a reputation for "bashing" such difficult material as Armco stainless, and who might be able to deliver exhaust systems at the rate needed by the greatly increased Jupiter production schedules. Fedden found him in his shirtsleeves beating out the panels of a sidecar body, with two Austin Sevens next in the queue. He listened to the problem and carefully studied the pressings Fedden had brought. Then he quoted a price for 50 sets per month. He delivered every set on schedule for a year and then met an increased rate of 20 sets per week. Fedden found that he could place complete trust in Bill Lyons, later Sir William Lyons of Jaguar Cars.

Fedden was constantly thinking up ways of adding fresh jewels to the

A 1930 installation of a geared Mercury IV in a helmeted cowling in Bulldog II J9591.
(Rolls-Royce plc)

A 1932 installation of a Mercury IVS2 in a Townend ring in a Bulldog IIIA; the exhaust pipes fed a front collector ring from which two pipes discharged underneath. (Rolls-Royce plc)

A 1934 installation of a Mercury IVS2 in an Italian Breda 27 with individual aft-facing exhausts. (Rolls-Royce plc)

On test in February 1928, G-EBVG, the first Short Calcutta had emergency long-wave radio masts above the upper wing. (Rolls-Royce plc)

In the Rochester erection shop, the port engine of the first Calcutta still has its installation derrick attached overhead. Note the strut-mounted instruments. (Rolls-Royce plc)

G-EBTS, the Fokker F VIIA Princess Xenia was owned by "All-Weather Mac" (R H McIntosh) and had an eventful career. Originally, it had an ungeared Jupiter VI driving this inefficient-looking propeller. (Rolls-Royce plc)

G-EBTS took on a new lease of life as *The Spider* (so named because it kept on trying), powered by a geared Jupiter XI and four-blade propeller. (Rolls-Royce plc)

Jupiter's crown by setting records in the air. It came as a shock to find someone was a jump ahead of him. On 26th May 1929, Willi Neuenhofen in Germany set a new world absolute altitude record of 41,790 feet, using a Junkers W.34 monoplane. Its engine was a Jupiter VII, not made by Siemens but purchased from Bristol, driving a Bristol metal propeller. The Bristol company had no foreknowledge of the attempt, and were delighted to learn that the Jupiter ran perfectly at the top of the climb with an outside air temperature of minus 55°C. Thus began a series of altitude records that made Fedden's engines supreme in this field up to the Second World War.

In 1929 Imperial Airways put into service its first large type of flying boat, the Short "Calcutta" class, powered by three Jupiter XI (later XI.F) engines. Initially used on the Mediterranean sector of the long route to India, the five boats were based at Alexandria and in the first three years each flew an aggregate distance of 100,000 miles in 1,000 hours, which at that time was an outstanding performance. In 1931 the Calcuttas operated down the Nile, chiefly between Khartoum and Mwanza, returning to the Mediterranean in 1935. Also in 1929 the German Dornier company flew a flying boat which was by far the largest and heaviest aeroplane attempted up to that time. The Do X, powered by 12 geared Jupiters built by Siemens, first flew on 12th July 1929 and later in the year carried the unprecedented total of 169 passengers. Fedden was not prepared to sanction the use of six push-pull nacelles, considering the rear motors to be likely to overheat, but in fact Dr. Claudius Dornier confirmed that the Jupiter was satisfactory and used numerous pusher Jupiters in Wals and Super-Wals. The reason they were later replaced by American Curtiss Conquerors was twofold: the US engine was more powerful, and enabled the giant flying boat to be freely imported for revenue service into the United States. All 12 engines could be reached by an engineer in flight, and all were started by a Bristol gas system.

To show what a single Jupiter could accomplish in effecting rapid communication within the Empire, the Duchess of Bedford flew to India and back in eight days in August 1929, roughly halving the Imperial Airways timing. Her pilot was Capt C D Barnard, the navigator R F Little, and the aircraft a Fokker F.VIIA built in 1925 for the Amsterdam-London service of KLM. The F.VIIA was used by airlines all over the world and was perhaps the most important civil airliner of the 1920s. For this flight the original ungeared Jupiter was replaced by a new Series XI driving a large four-blade propeller. The journey from Lympne to Karachi and back worked out to about 9,000 miles flown at just under 100 mph. Between 10th-30th August 1930 the same aircraft and crew, accompanied by the stalwart duchess, flew to Cape Town and back at 96 mph in 195 hours. Capt Barnard emphasised the "perfect" running of the lone Jupiter throughout the 20 days. Total cost of replacement parts on the subsequent strip was under £4.

This Jupiter was one of the first to have a forged head. It was in 1928 that Fedden at last decided to throw away the poultice head. In eight years his team had pushed up the rated power of the Jupiter by 50 per cent, from 368 hp to almost 550. The nine cylinders were having to work harder, the geared engines put out greater torque, and the introduction of peripheral cowlings (and, in particular, installations on the noses of large fuselages) did nothing to alleviate matters. The limiting factor was cylinder-head cooling, and with the poultice head it seemed impossible to increase the area of cooling fins from which the surplus heat could be dissipated. Whitehead did wonders contriving to make cast poultice heads with deeper, closer-pitched fins, but these could not be made without the scrap rate, which was already high, becoming intolerable.

Casting appeared to be a difficult art for British industry to master. As related earlier, at first the Bristol Engine Department had been forced to do its own. The racing Mercury of 1926 had at last escaped from the old poultice head only by having excellent cylinder heads cast at the RAE at

The F-series Jupiters had a forged steel barrel and forged head of Y aluminium alloy. More than half the material was machined away during manufacture. Today such a development seems obvious but, at the time, a British engineering magazine called it "ridiculous" (RF said this article "was used by our competitors to some effect".) (Author)

Farnborough under the expert eye of Gladding, foreman foundryman. But Fedden was unable to get any British company to produce an equally good and repeatable cast head for the Jupiter – though there were plenty in the United States – and it could hardly be assigned to a government research establishment. Eventually, after many fruitless discussions at casting firms all over the country, Fedden sat down with Butler in September 1928 and designed a head made by drop forging, which Whitehead could machine with deeper and closer cooling fins. The forged head was mechanically far superior. When finished it was screwed and shrunk on to the cylinder barrel in the way that Fedden had doubted could be done reliably in 1918. The new F-type Jupiter ran in March 1929. By the end of the year the entire range of Jupiters was available with the magic F added as a suffix to their series numbers.

Fedden was also constantly improving engine peripheral items. In 1929 the F engines introduced two important automatic features. A centrifugal ignition control adjusted the ignition timing, and, in partnership with an added acceleration pump in the triplex (three-barrel) carburettor, augmented the fuel supply whenever the throttle was suddenly opened, greatly improving engine response to changed throttle settings. The other device was the first automatic boost control (ABC). In a supercharged engine the pilot must take note of the pressure in the manifold delivering the mixture to the

Celebrating the first Jupiter F in March 1929; in the centre are Butler and RF and Damsell is on the left. (Rolls-Royce plc)

cylinders, and avoid over-boosting. Fedden's device did this automatically by sensing the boost pressure with a barometric aneroid capsule and using an oil servo to magnify the output so that it could continuously command the correct throttle opening. Like several other Bristol developments the ABC was patented, but widely copied. With automatic advance/retard and a separate acceleration pump it gave better engine response, reduced weak-mixture cruising fuel consumption, and substantially reduced pilot work-load.

Pilot work-load was something that in 1930 had not even been identified or named, but Fedden recognised its importance. In its first decade his department had produced the world's finest aviation engine, turned it into the best-selling product in the history of peacetime aviation, and seen his little team grow from 31 to over 1,900. Fedden remained absolute king of the engine side of the company, managing not only design and development but also basic engine policy, production, advertising, publicity, licensing, technical records and several other functions which, incidentally, often had no counterpart on the aircraft side. But he was not offered a directorship.

It was an extraordinary situation. Fedden and the Bristol Aeroplane Company were essential to each other. Fedden was by far the dominant character, and in executive matters the leading member of the company, yet the Board judged that keeping him off the Board was the lesser of two evils.

Late-model Jupiters in production in about 1930. (Rolls-Royce plc)

The following photographs show a selection of foreign aircraft powered by the Jupiter:

(France) A Gourdou-Leseurre GL-812 catapulted from cruiser Duquesne.
(Rolls-Royce plc)

Loire-Gourdou-Leseurre LGL-32 fighters. (Rolls-Royce plc)

Farman F168 torpedo bombers. (Rolls-Royce plc)

Wibault-Penhoët RP. (Rolls-Royce plc)

(Germany – built clandestinely in Sweden) Junkers K37 bomber. (Rolls-Royce plc)

Potez 25 of the Estonian Air Force. (Rolls-Royce plc)

Junkers K47 dive bomber (again clandestine). (Rolls-Royce plc)

(Italy) Caproni Ca 50. (Rolls-Royce plc)

(Japan) Nakajima Army Type 91 fighter. (Rolls-Royce plc)

(USA) Keystone Patrician of Transcontinental Air Transport, (Rolls-Royce plc)

(USSR) Tupolev ANT-14. (Philip Jarrett)

(Germany) Dornier DoX. (Rolls-Royce plc)

Two Gnome-Rhône GR9 Jupiters powered the terrifying Aéroglisseur designed for 100 knots!
(Rolls-Royce plc)

CHAPTER SIX

Pegasus and Mercury

After 10 years with the Bristol Aeroplane Company, Fedden still had only one major product, the Jupiter. But he had made this the most important aircraft engine in the world. Including the 17 licensees the cumulative output of Jupiters at the end of the first decade was approximately 7,100, and they had powered an incredible 262 different types of aircraft. Yet the Jupiter could not go on for ever. A new aero engine, even then, took several years to design and develop, and was not a task to be accepted lightly. The Jupiter had shown remarkable capacity for improvement, and Fedden could see much further along the same path; but one can only do just so much with 1,753 cubic inches in nine cylinders. In 1930 he was looking hard at various ways of making a more powerful engine with two rows of cylinders, such as the stillborn Hercules of 1919. He was also looking at diesel engines, at direct fuel injection and at the sleeve valve. What he would have found physically impossible would have been to rest on his Jupiter laurels – as Napier had rested on the Lion, with near-fatal results for that company. Frank Owner enquired rather testily one day if he was ever satisfied, to be told "Certainly not, Owner; that would be a terrible state to be in!" Those who suffered in the proximity of the man still found lasting delight in that reply.

In 1930, though for the long term the need for research was never relaxed, in the short term the Jupiter was just what the market wanted. As the main high-power engine of Imperial Airways, it was specified to power the Handley Page 42 ordered in 1929 for the route to India. At first only a prototype of this huge biplane was ordered, but before this flew a small fleet was bought, including a high-density 38-seat version for Europe. The first HP.42 flew at the new Radlett works on 14th November 1930. It was like a great silver galleon in full sail – though when it entered service at Croydon someone called it "The flying banana" because of the slender, slightly curving fuselage – and it will forever epitomise Imperial's policy of ignoring speed and devoting its entire attention to reliability, comfort and impeccable service. The six "42E" (Eastern) aircraft, named *Hannibal, Horsa, Hanno, Hadrian, Hengist* and *Helena,* were powered by four 555 hp Jupiter XI.F engines disposed in an odd way with two on the lower wing and two on the upper. A lock on the throttle quadrant prevented the pilot from opening up the top pair until the lower engines were at full power. This ensured there would be enough slipstream over the biplane tail to prevent the giant from being pulled over on to its nose. Novel features included a gas starter in a small compartment between the passenger cabins, rubber shock-absorbing engine mountings, and airframe-mounted auxiliary gearboxes providing drive faces for all accessories. These aircraft went into operation in June 1931 on the Paris service, and in November began their proper role between Cairo and either Karachi to the east or Kisumu to the south. The HP.42W (Western) type, of which there were two, *Heracles* and *Horatius,* operated to Paris, Zurich, Basle, Cologne and Brussels. These were powered by the Jupiter X.FBM moderately supercharged engine, which at 4,900 ft could give 600 hp at the maximum rpm of 2,200. The big Handley Page cruised at 100 mph, consumed only about 21 gal/hr per engine, and could fly on any three (with one of the huge wooden four-bladers gently windmilling). It was to become Imperial's proud boast that the great Handley Pages never hurt a passenger.

In May 1931 the airline commissioned three Short flying boats roughly as capable as the Handley Pages. The "Kent" class, *Scipio, Satyrus* and *Sylvanus,* incorporated all the lessons learned with the successful "Calcuttas" and carried 7,500 lb payload instead of 4,429 lb. Powered by four Jupiter X.FBM engines, they operated between Genoa or Brindisi and Cairo or Alexandria (with, of course, numerous intermediate stops).

Thus did Britain's national airline choose the new forged-head Jupiter as its principal engine. Fedden wanted one of the engines to be subjected to a

G-AAGX, the prototype HP.42, seen in November 1930 before being named *Hannibal.*
(Rolls-Royce plc)

All three Short Kent-class boats, and a Calcutta, at Alexandria in 1932. (Rolls-Royce plc)

spectacular test, and suggested that the Bristol 109 long-range biplane should undertake a sealed-engine voyage to Australia and back. This was not agreed, but in September 1930 a Jupiter XI.F ran over 337 hours in that aircraft, including a 300 hr sealed trial flying from Farnborough. At 232 hr there was trouble with a magneto (not a Bristol product) and at 262 hr a valve-rocker tie-rod broke and had to be replaced, but at the conclusion of this severe trial in March 1931 the engine stripped well and no parts needed replacement. In August 1930 Fedden subjected an XI.F to an unprecedented Air Ministry type test with ten 10 hr runs made not at the regulation 90 per cent power but at 100 per cent. Afterwards the plotted curve of power of this engine was found to be well above the published and guaranteed figure. The following month a X.FBM completed the same test, the maximum (4,900 ft) power being almost unchanged at 622 hp throughout, again well above the "brochure" figure.

In 1931 Imperial's chairman, the Rt Hon Sir Eric Geddes, announced "We are now getting three times the mileage between flight cancellations or abandonments that we were getting five years ago. Much of this improvement is due to adopting air-cooled engines". On the Eastern Route the regularity in the first year (1930) was 99.7 per cent, and when Geddes spoke in October 1931 the second year had yet to fall below 100 per cent. Every engine on this route was a Jupiter. Between May 1931 and August

1932 the "Kent" boats ran individual distances of 98,270, 90,565 and 77,484 miles without a minute's delay due to the engines. By 1935 Imperial's Jupiters – augmented by two landplane versions of the "Kent" boats, the 40-passenger *Scylla* and *Syrinx* (see page 171) – had run some 3,500 hr each. At about 1,800 hr they had been fitted with new valve seats and guides, but the original pistons, cylinders and other moving parts remained. Even the ball bearings for the 13,000 rpm superchargers showed the same long life. By 1939 almost every Imperial Jupiter was close to 10,000 hr, comfortably in excess of any other aviation engines in the world. This also testifies to Imperial's own standards, because a single vicious run-up with very cold or incorrectly chosen oil, or detonation due to the wrong fuel, could have caused severe damage in minutes.

This unprecedented record was gained by single-minded effort. Whenever Fedden found a perfect supplier of materials or parts he clung to him, and any lesser supplier was soon rejected. For example, after near-catastrophic troubles, Jupiter valve springs were eventually made from ingots of special high-tensile steel from a particular steelworks in Sweden, fabricated by a long series of high-precision processes. In 1929 the Aeronautical Inspection Directorate put pressure on Fedden to try to do away with all such "exotic" practice and use more readily available British supplies. Fedden had always appreciated that in any future war this would be essential, and he intensified his campaign to pull British industry up to the perfect standard he demanded. No longer would Bristol themselves tackle the tasks, such as fine non-porous casting, that British firms were unable or unwilling to do. With the backing of the AID Fedden constantly campaigned, not in vague after-dinner speeches but in heated discussion at the firms concerned, to build up a big and broad British industrial base for highly rated aero engines.

Fedden was also the industrial leader of a parallel effort to improve fuels and oils. The power that a spark-ignition engine can generate is limited by the mean effective pressure permissible in the cylinders, which in turn is dependent on the compression ratio. But attempts to increase the compression prior to spark-ignition of the mixture soon become thwarted by detonation. The mixture virtually explodes inside the cylinder, instead of being consumed in a controlled way by a flame-front which spreads outwards from the plug electrodes. Detonation, commonly called "knocking" or "pinking" by motorists, makes an unmistakable noise like knocking a china basin. It causes gross local overheating and overstressing, and can ruin an engine in hours or even minutes. For the Schneider races F R (later Air Cdre Rod) Banks of the Ethyl Company had helped to concoct witches' brews which began in 1927 with petrol having a high lead content and finished in 1931 with semi-synthetic fluid in which plain petrol was replaced by other carefully blended hydrocarbons with a high proportion of tetra-ethyl lead (TEL) to give extreme resistance to knocking. With a mixture so rich that unburned fuel streamed from the exhaust stacks, this gave tremendous power – but it was impractical for the RAF. Fedden collaborated from 1930 with the Air Ministry to upgrade regular aviation petrol to enable a given size of engine to develop higher power.

He was also the first man in industry to appreciate that the vegetable oils (mainly castor oil) used in British engines would have to be replaced by mineral oil, which could better withstand long storage and would be available in the million-gallon batches that would be demanded by a war. While other engine designers dug in their heels and bitterly fought the Government, Fedden saw the need for mineral oil, forced through a programme of minor engineering changes and special tests, and began to qualify his engines on mineral oil as early as the winter 1930-31. (Maj G P Bulman disputes this, despite abundant evidence that the above is correct. In his view, Fedden "was merely following the Air Ministry's decision to bring in the new DTD.109 oil by a certain future date.") He also hit on a simple scheme for recirculating hot oil so that, even in the Arctic, it would be safe to fly within a minute or two of starting a cold engine.

In 1930 the Jupiter was at its zenith. It was the principal engine of nearly half the world's airlines and more than half the air forces. It had done more than any other engine to turn even the fastest military fighter into a safe and reliable vehicle. Whereas in 1920-23 not one of the scores of aircraft flown from Britain to Spain, for use in the Rif war in Morocco, had reached its destination without at least one forced landing, by 1931 the Polish Air Force could send a fighter regiment of 29 PZL monoplanes powered by the supercharged Jupiter VIII.F on a long formation flight to Bucharest, covering two weeks of intensive flying and including a breathtaking aerobatic display for King Carol of Romania, without once opening their crate of spare parts. But Fedden drove himself even harder. The most important immediate task was to get the Mercury into service – without, of course, the long propeller shaft of the 1927 racer. Geared Mercury III and IV engines flew in prototypes before 1930, and in 1931 the 560 hp Mercury IVA was type tested and cleared for use. The modern fighter, for which the Mercury was mainly intended, needed such extra features as a hand or electric inertia starter, twin-gun interrupter gear, electric generator, oil centrifuge, engine-driven pump, and automatic boost and ignition control. This meant a redesigned rear cover, making the Mercury not interchangeable with the Jupiter in existing aircraft. Had it been, flight speed would have been increased. In 1930 a special short-stroke (5 in) Mercury, in a compact long-chord cowling, drove a Bullpup faster than a Jupiter had done, despite its being less powerful.

By 1931 Fedden had supervised many thousands of hours of running of both Mercury cylinders and complete engines, and of corresponding new cylinders of Jupiter size. Compared with the Jupiter these had roughly 50 per cent greater cooling-fin area, obtained by deeper and more closely spaced fins, so that the cylinder could dissipate more excess heat even when enclosed in one of the new cowlings. The disposition of the fins was altered to give better cooling in air currents of low velocity, and provision was made for attaching a new cowling. The crankshaft was redesigned with a larger-diameter crankpin and stiffer webs, and the connecting rods were of a different form and lengthened to reduce side force on the pistons. A new full-skirted piston was designed, twin induction pipes increased the volumetric efficiency at reduced charge temperature, and a very obvious change was that the redesigned overhead-valve rocker gear, and the push-rods, were all totally enclosed. This improved both the lubrication and reliability, and also reduced installed drag. The supercharger and drive was improved, and the rear cover arranged so that any required type of supercharger could be fitted or removed without disturbing other parts of the engine. The reduction gear was likewise refined and greatly reduced in weight. The whole engine was improved in detail, lightened and cleaned-up, and fitted with the latest automatic control, starting and accessory systems.

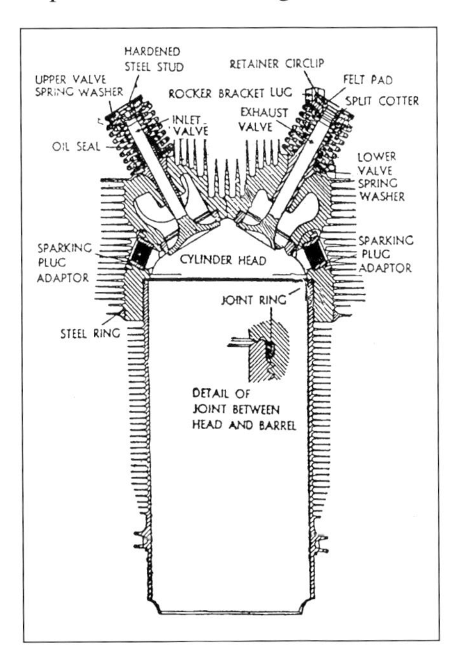

Cross-section through an early Pegasus cylinder; the joint ring was soft copper. (Author)

When all these improvements were incorporated in the Jupiter-size 1,753 cubic inch engine the result was such an advance it was given a new name: Pegasus. In 1932 Fedden launched the 7.5 in-stroke Pegasus as the replacement for the Jupiter, together with new versions of the 6.5 in-stroke Mercury for high-speed machines. They were winners from the start. One of the first customers for a Mercury was Vickers, whose Jockey fighter was described as "a winged projectile" by a national daily, the headline "240 MPH ABOVE THE CLOUDS" being quite something in 1931. In the same year a Mercury IV.S2 completed a type test which concluded with the 15 per cent overspeed which all Mercury and Pegasus engines were designed to sustain for five minutes without damage. At the over speed

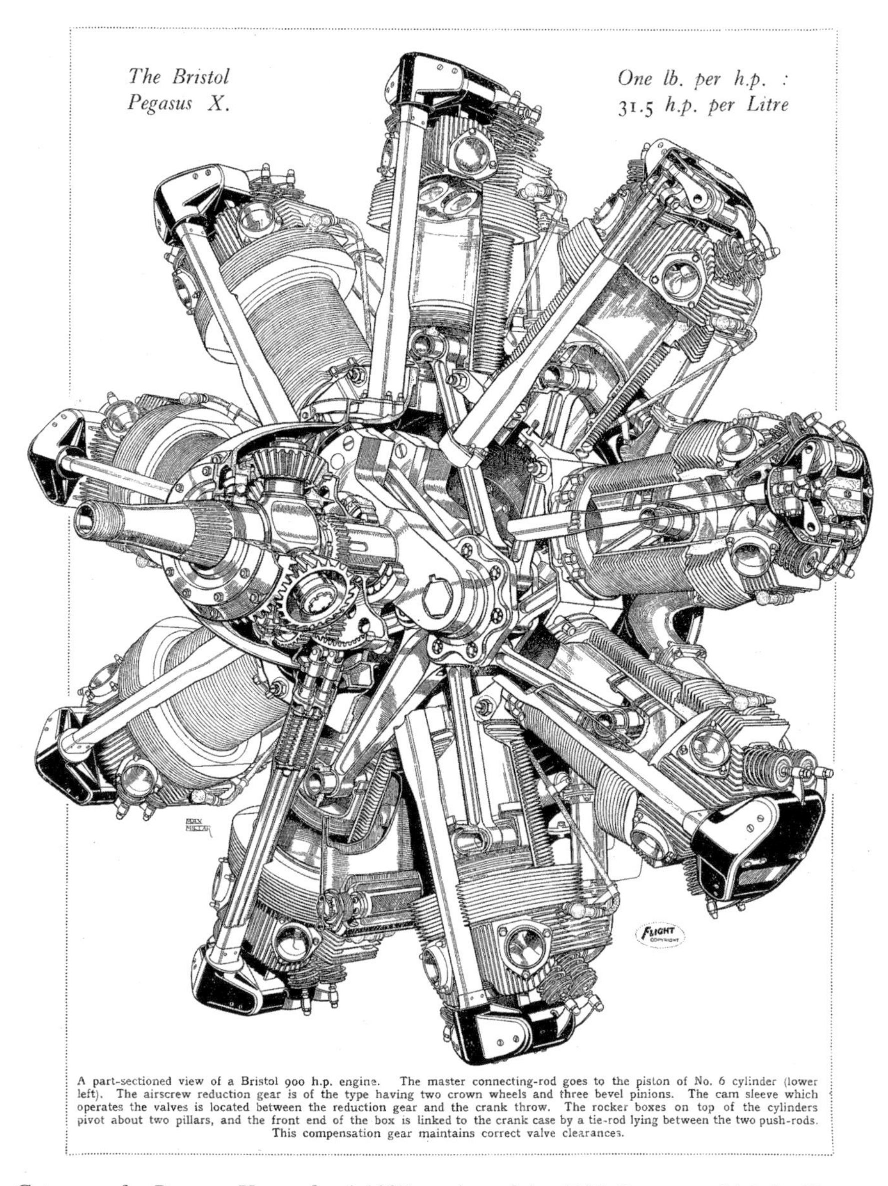

A part-sectioned view of a Bristol 900 h.p. engine. The master connecting-rod goes to the piston of No. 6 cylinder (lower left). The airscrew reduction gear is of the type having two crown wheels and three bevel pinions. The cam sleeve which operates the valves is located between the reduction gear and the crank throw. The rocker boxes on top of the cylinders pivot about two pillars, and the front end of the box is linked to the crank case by a tie-rod lying between the two push-rods. This compensation gear maintains correct valve clearances.

Cutaway of a Pegasus X, a refined 1937 version of the 1932 Pegasus, which itself was a development of the Jupiter (copyright bought from Flight by Bristol Aeroplane Co).
(Rolls-Royce plc)

of 2,600 rpm the Mercury developed no less than 893 hp using the old standard 77-octane fuel and mineral oil, and with commendably low cylinder temperatures. The pace of development, led by Fedden, was hotting up.

In addition to these extremely important new engines Fedden never stopped worrying about propellers. In the United States the wooden propeller was becoming obsolescent on high-power engines from 1931, having been superseded by units with steel hubs carrying two, three or four blades of light alloy or hollow steel. The metal propellers were more costly, and sometimes heavier, but they increased flight performance by five per cent or more and greatly reduced vibration and cost of maintenance. Moreover, they made a significant contribution to safety. In a belly landing, or in high-speed flight through large hailstones, wooden propellers were prone to shatter. Metal blades did not, and in a belly landing they tended to bend back to form a ski to enable the aircraft to ride over rough ground safely. In World War 2 tens of thousands of deformed blades were either melted to reuse the material or simply straightened out again. For the future the Americans were perfecting variable-pitch (v-p) propellers which could be set to a fine pitch for take-off, so that the engine could run at high speed for full power despite the low aircraft velocity, and then be adjusted to a coarse setting for high-speed cruising at an economical engine speed. Fedden had worked with Folland on flight trials of the Gloster/Hele-Shaw/Beacham v-p propeller on a Jupiter-powered Gamecock, but no British company showed any interest in making such propellers, or even metal fixed-pitch ones. So in 1927 Fedden started a programme to make metal propellers at Bristol, and by 1932 a range was in production with two, three or four blades of Elektron (magnesium alloy), held in two-part steel hubs. Meanwhile, he lobbied for a British v-p propeller, as he had no spare design capacity in his own department. Many were the aircraft designers and directors – especially at Bristol – who thought him at least an odd fellow, if not a positive nuisance, for constantly campaigning about things that need not have been his concern.

So totally immersed in his work was he that Mrs Fedden saw less and less of him. Though she could dominate him, in a way that would have been inconceivable to anyone else, they appear to have had little in common and – as was perhaps inevitable – drifted apart, though they dwelt under the same roof. It is not surprising that Mrs Fedden eventually found someone who would give her warmth and companionship, and the goings-on were soon fairly evident. Whether by accident or design, RF one day returned to Widegates at an unexpected time. The scene that followed resulted in the terrified lover jumping into his car, tearing off down the road and driving over the edge of Clifton Gorge to his death. A Clifton boy, who ought not to have been out of school, risked a flogging in racing to give the alarm. Though RF continued to do his best to help his stepson Tony Fedden, the young man's mother vanished from the scene. Henceforth the mistress of Widegates was Miss Cole, the housekeeper. Prim, with her hair in a tight bun, she was utterly efficient – and devoted to RF. Until it was blown to pieces in 1940 the pleasant house was run like clockwork. But one inevitably pauses to consider the deeper results of that disastrous first marriage.

During the 1930s Fedden began increasingly to meet his Norah again – in fact one suspects they never completely lost touch. The affection was as strong as ever on both sides, and it was soon clear that both realised that their first marriages had been tragic mistakes. The unbending air marshal was well aware of all this, but was implacably opposed to a divorce. Roy and Norah continued to seek each other's company – for lunch in London, on a fishing trip, or even at the Mill which, as related later, RF finally bought. There is no doubt that, though the situation was still sadly imperfect, Roy and Norah gave each other strength and comfort throughout what was a long and difficult period for both – though the outside world knew little of it.

What many did know – incorrectly – was that all really fast aircraft had to have in-line liquid-cooled engines. The prevalent jaundiced view of the air-cooled radial in Western Europe was accentuated by the fact that air-cooled engines were at that time never used in cars, except in the light and cheap kind of "cycle car" which was a distinctly inferior class. Later on, Fedden ceased to have to "sell" his engines at all; but in the early 1930s it was a different story. Sydney Camm, for example, professed to think it a shame that Sweden, and several very hot countries, should prefer the bluff Jupiter or Pegasus to the shapely Kestrel with which the original members of his prolific Hart family were equipped. In fact, the bluff Pegasus could pull a Hart as fast as any Kestrel, and also make it go further and climb faster.

Altitude was an area where Fedden's engines became supreme. In 1930 US Navy Lieut Apollo Soucek had beaten Neuenhofen's world record, but only by using a supercharged Wasp engine in a special aircraft fitted with a second, airframe-mounted supercharger to boost the one on the engine. Fedden calculated he could beat the American record using an ordinary Pegasus S.3, with no extra supercharger. An engine was taken from regular production, fitted in a Vickers Vespa two-seat biplane in place of a Jupiter VI (with which the absolute ceiling was 22,000 ft) and on 16th September 1932 it was flown by a specially kitted-up Cyril Uwins to 43,976 ft. The only non-standard features were small modifications to the impeller diameter and compression ratio, to the carburettor, and to the magnetos to prevent arcing across the safety gaps in the rarefied air.

This outstanding performance caught the attention of Col L V S Blacker, and Col Etherington of *The Times.* Blacker invited Fedden to the Royal Aero Club and asked how difficult it would be to fly over Mount Everest (about 29,140 ft) and what aircraft should be used. The result was the first

RF, Uwins and (holding the sealed barograph) Vickers Vespa chief designer, Rex Pierson.
(Rolls-Royce plc)

completely successful Mount Everest Expedition, financed by Lady Houston and *The Times* and led by Air Cdre P F M Fellowes. First and second pilots were, respectively, Lord Clydesdale (later the Duke of Hamilton) and F/Lt D F McIntyre (later managing director of Scottish Aviation). On 3rd April 1933 man looked down for the first time on the highest point on Earth. The aircraft chosen were a Westland Wallace two-seat army co-operation machine (developed from the Wapiti) and the generally similar Westland PV.3, both powered by the standard Pegasus S.3 fitted with small front exhaust rings and short-chord ring cowlings. Superb close-range photographs were taken, despite "the great wind allied with the immense overfall of air coming down over the crest" and the "ice rattling into the cockpit out of the great frozen plume of the mountain". Half an hour earlier Col Blacker, in the rear cockpit of the PV.3, had felt awe at the majesty of the immense Himalayas, with "straight to the front, over the leaping valve rockers of the great Pegasus, Mount Everest itself". It was no place for engine trouble, but the expedition made the four-month journey without breaking open their case of engine spares.

(Rolls-Royce plc)

For 1933 the Pegasus and Mercury were given stiffer crankshafts and even greater cooling-fin area. Detail improvements in cylinder and piston design increased the compression ratio to give greater power and economy even without improved fuel. The Jupiter was finally dropped from development, and production concentrated on the medium, low and unsupercharged Pegasus, and on the fully supercharged Mercury rated at 570 hp at 16,000 ft. All the new engines could be run in cowlings, and all could be overloaded. A Pegasus IIM, rated at 637 hp for five minutes, was run for 14 consecutive periods of 15 hours at 670-690 hp, followed by ten 10 hour periods at the same overload, with no parts-replacement save for a few small washers and split pins which did not affect reliability. Meanwhile extensive single-cylinder testing prepared the way for the issue in 1934 of DTD.230, the long-awaited 87-octane fuel for which Fedden alone had engines ready. This

With great courage, in a time of mass unemployment, Vickers pressed the Air Ministry to cancel the production contract for this biplane built to Specification G4/31 and instead buy their privately funded monoplane G.4/31, later named the Wellesley. The biplane was subsequently used to test the new long-chord Pegasus cowling with a front exhaust ring and rear cooling gills, as seen here. (Rolls-Royce plc)

fuel contained almost four millilitres of TEL in each gallon, and in certain adverse conditions could cause chemical corrosion or deposition inside the engine. Work went on at increased pressure to produce Mercury and Pegasus engines fully able to stand up to the new fuel, and to the resulting higher powers and stresses.

New cylinder barrels were designed with even more closely spaced cooling fins, with Whitehead's production problems compounded by the fact that they were now in chrome-molybdenum steel, with nitrogen-hardened bores. Valve gear was revised, and the exhaust valves sodium-cooled. Many other parts were strengthened and surface-hardened to resist wear. A standard long-chord cowl was designed, with an integral front exhaust manifold and, by 1936, adjustable rear cooling gills worked by a peripheral chain driving sprockets on irreversible screw-jacks that opened or closed the gills. The exhaust manifolds were enlarged, to give better gas expansion, flame-damping (important for military aircraft at night) and quieter running. The manifolds were assembled mainly from two fully tooled steel pressings which were riveted together, thus finally by-passing the weld problem. A new exhaust-system factory was built at Filton in 1937, taking over from the faithful Bill Lyons, and new pressings also flowed from 1,000-ton and 550-ton double-acting presses at the Austin factory at Longbridge. With these far-reaching refinements Fedden was working towards production engines that would stand up to conditions in the war he had been expecting ever since Adolf Hitler had come to power in 1933. Fedden probably knew the German scene better than any other British industrialist, and he sensed the changing outlook on his frequent trips there. In the 1920s he had worked to save his engine. In the 1930s he would increasingly work to save his country.

Though the main products could hardly be going better, he kept exploring alternatives. Exhaust turbos were never far from his mind, nor from that of Owner, who had been assigned to future projects; but, despite the encouraging results achieved with the Orion, the Air Ministry showed no interest. They did show some interest in direct injection and compression ignition, however, and Fedden obtained research contracts to explore both paths. As early as 1927 he had schemed a bold 11-cylinder diesel of 1,000 hp, and Harvey Mansell had done three years of single-cylinder running when it was decided, in 1931, to use smaller cylinders and build a diesel that would be installationally interchangeable with the Pegasus. This became the Phoenix, which was run as a complete engine in February 1932. Though superficially very like the Pegasus, the increased stresses and different operating conditions meant there were hardly any common parts. The Phoenix was cleared for flight in early 1933; flight trials in a Wapiti began in May, and in June the diesel's distinctive sound was heard at the RAF Pageant. By this time the engine had been converted to the supercharged

The Phoenix diesel (Rolls-Royce plc)

Phoenix II, rated at 485 hp. This ran on the bench with a remarkable absence of the clatter and vibration usually associated with compression ignition, and with the encouraging specific fuel consumption of 0.385 lb/hr/hp. The Phoenix II sustained its power at altitude unexpectedly well, cutting the Wallace's time to 15,000 ft by 15 per cent compared with the more powerful spark-ignition Pegasus originally fitted. So on 14th May 1934 Westland chief test pilot Harald Penrose did a ceiling climb, and his height of 27,453 ft remains unbeaten as the diesel altitude record. The diesel was investigated for economy and range, and there is no technical reason why it should not have gone into both military and civil use – with the side benefit of running on fuel oil which unquestionably posed a lower fire risk. But in 1934 the Air Ministry was frantically seeking higher powers, to which end high-octane fuels were making a major contribution, and the oil-burning diesel was starved of funds.

A second idea, for spark-ignition engines, was direct petrol injection into the cylinders in measured doses, instead of into the carburettor to form a combustible mixture with the incoming air. Direct injection demands a pump of extremely high and precise performance if the power and fuel consumption are to be competitive, and such a pump was unavailable. With the help of Lucas and CAV/Bosch the Bristol company developed such a pump in 1931, tested single-cylinder units, and in February 1932 ran the complete Draco engine, a direct-injection Pegasus. In 1933 flight trials took place in a Wapiti, but there was persistent bad fuel distribution, and flat spots when the throttle was opened. Hundreds of hours were flown, and Fedden became convinced that in the long term the direct-injection engine must prevail. But the Air Ministry judged the idea "heavy and complicated", and it did not fit in with their plan to build large numbers of traditional engines. By 1940 the fact that Germany had concentrated on fuel injection – emphatically reported by Fedden from January 1937 onwards – was abundantly clear to the Air Ministry. When a fuel-injection pump was stripped it looked complicated in comparison with a carburettor, but this was only one side of the picture. Direct injection offered such advantages as perfect running in all flight attitudes, immunity from icing and, eventually, higher performance all-round. In 1933 Fedden tried to fight the official disinterest, and brought pressure to bear on Lucas to keep working on the nine-plunger (5 and 4) pump, but eventually had to give up in 1934. Not until 1954 did Bristol go into production with a direct-injection engine, and this was the last type of piston engine the firm ever made, the Centaurus 373 for the RAF's Beverley freighter. Inability to appreciate the superiority of direct injection was one of the Air Ministry's bigger mistakes.

Fedden was incapable of being contented. Quite early in the 1920s he had begun to worry over the long-term need to make an engine much more

Two views of the direct-injection Draco. The rear view shows the five- and four-plunger pumps. (Rolls-Royce plc)

powerful than the Jupiter, even though the market for such an engine could not then be discerned. The Jupiter seemed likely to yield about 650 hp eventually (in fact the same-size Pegasus was ultimately developed beyond 1,000 hp, but this was largely due to new fuels becoming available which Fedden could not count upon). The answer he kept coming back to was to have more than nine cylinders, but these could not be accommodated in one radial row without increasing the frontal area. One could use two rows, as had been done in the First World War with rotary engines and the Jaguar. But Fedden used four valves in each cylinder, to improve "breathing", and the valve gear for a two-row engine with four-valve cylinders seemed likely to be a nightmare. In the early 1940s two Bristol licensees, Alfa-Romeo and Nakajima, did manage the feat, but only by making clumsy engines. So in 1930-31 a sustained effort was made on new-engine project studies, in parallel with a long-term effort on sleeve valves (the subject of the next chapter). No fewer than 28 possible future engines were examined in depth, having from 14 to 28 cylinders. By late 1931 the field had been narrowed to two. In 1932 the design scheme for a 20-cylinder engine with four radial rows of five was rejected: the winner was a 16-cylinder double-octagon. In the long term Fedden was already confident that the best answer of all would be the revolutionary sleeve valve, but this was such a stupendous task that the double-octagon seemed to be worth doing as an interim solution.

The new engine was named Hydra, because in a sense it was double-headed. The front and rear rows of cylinders were not staggered but arranged in line. Thus the adjacent cylinder heads were close together and could share a common valve drive. The Hydra cylinders were of only five inch bore and stroke, but the engine was designed to run at 3,000 rpm, almost half as fast again as the latest Jupiters. Valve problems were severe, but by June 1932 a vee-4 quarter-Hydra was running smoothly on the bench. Each pair of cylinders had twin overhead camshafts, like Fedden's Bugatti car. Direct-attack cams worked the inclined valves, and unlike previous Bristol engines the valve gear was totally enclosed. The quarter-Hydra was soon giving 190 hp at full rpm in a low wind speed of 75 mph without overheating. It sounded good, but there was excessive rocker wear and persistent oil leakage from the camshafts. Great effort was made to cure this, with electrically-driven rigs to flog the valve gear and supercharger drive. In January 1933 the first complete Hydra ran at up to 3,620 rpm, an unprecedented speed for a large non-racing engine, giving 870 hp. Despite mild oil leaks and ignition trouble it was flown in the Hawker Harrier biplane bomber used for many of the Bristol company's extended trials. Installationally the slim Hydra was superb, and its exhaust system a dream. But Fedden and Butler had made a fundamental mistake. With such a short stroke they thought they could get away without a centre bearing by making the crankshaft very stiff. They were wrong, and

The double-octagon Hydra (Rolls-Royce plc)

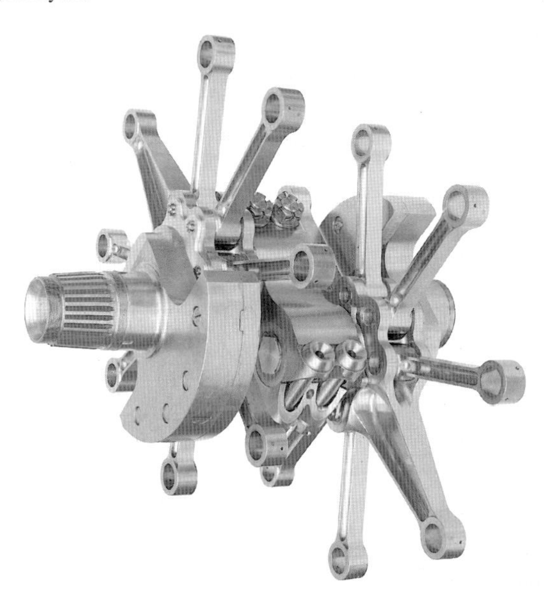

The Achilles heel of the Hydra was that the crankshaft, short and stiff though it was, lacked a centre bearing. (Author)

vibration at certain critical speeds made the fact plain. In any case, the power class of the Hydra could, by 1934, be readily reached by the Pegasus and Mercury using 87-octane fuel, which in 1931 could not be counted upon. So the Hydra was dropped, and the effort on sleeves redoubled.

The gigantic problem of perfecting the sleeve-valve engine was exactly the kind of challenge Fedden thrived on. Stories of his engineering meetings became famous. There was an occasion when, someone having the temerity actually to voice mild criticism, as he had just been invited to do, Fedden raised both hands to Heaven and roared "Can I get *no* co-operation?" Deep down he may have been laughing on this occasion – his closest colleagues could not tell – but when he was told he was difficult to get on with, and replied "Nonsense, I just prefer to have my own way … *and that's what I mean to get*", he was voicing nothing less than the truth. Early in the development of the Hydra, he said he wanted "more metal on the gudgeon pins" and Owner told him he could not have it! He looked positively

The Hydra installed in the Hawker Harrier, with a club propeller (not intended for flight). (Rolls-Royce plc)

shocked. "I most certainly can have it, and with knobs on if I wish" he shouted. Owner – one of the few who did not quail at such times – quietly replied "With the deepest regret, Euclid says you can have only one set of knobs in the same place at the same time". The blood rushed to his chief's face: he looked out of the window, fighting for control. Then he turned back to the drawing and raised a completely different problem.

Apart from sleeve valves, the most sustained development effort in the second decade concerned installations. The trusty Harrier flew hundreds of hours, with many engines and an even greater variety of cowling and exhaust systems, to verify in flight the results obtained in single-cylinder tests in which Mercury or Pegasus cylinders were run at higher and higher power in low-velocity cooling airflows until something just had to give. At first every engine save the Pegasus L (low supercharge) overheated. Gradually ways were found to increase power, reduce installed drag and yet obtain improved cooling. Best all-round results in 1934 were obtained with the polygonal (nine-sided) cowl developed by Boulton Paul, whose Pegasus-powered Overstrand and P.64 were respectively the fastest RAF multi-engined aircraft and the fastest British civil machine. By 1935 continued engine development had at last permitted use of the long NACA circular cowl with integral front exhaust ring which remained standard until near the end of the Second World War, when engines were redesigned for exhaust pipes bent round to discharge at the rear.

On 11th April 1934 Commendatore Renato Donati, an Italian First World War ace who had in 1927 beaten the world altitude record (with an Alfa-built Jupiter) by 56 metres, which was an insufficient margin to qualify, ensured his place in posterity by taking a Pegasus-powered Caproni 114 to a new world record of 47,680 ft. The fully supercharged engine was unmodified, and it drove a propeller with four fixed-pitch light-alloy blades. On landing, the aircraft taxied erratically for some time before coming to rest, and Donati was found in a state of collapse, having driven himself to the limit of his endurance to gain the record. Bert Newport, Fedden's man at Alfa's, was almost fired on the spot when Fedden saw the press announcement calling the Pegasus "Italian"; Fedden issued his own statement calling it "British", whereat Newport was almost sent home by the Italians.

Another satisfying event of 1934 was the opening of the Bristol Engine Apprentice School. Fedden had always been so concerned at the need to attract "the right type of boy" into the despised engineering profession that he was suspected by the Board of having a large bee in his bonnet about it. He badgered them incessantly to start a comprehensive training school to ensure a supply of future top engineers and technical managers. Graduates from engineering schools at British universities, especially Cambridge or Oxford, were not only ignorant of all save academic aspects of engineering

Donati's Ca 114 height-record aircraft. (Rolls-Royce plc)

but usually had an outlook deeply ill-adjusted to industrial management. Fedden's breakthrough, which at last won over the Board, was to get the Ministry of Education to put up half the cost of building and running such a school. It soon gained such a good name that its graduates were, like his original apprentices, being spirited away by the aircraft side of the firm and by other companies. Without this school there is no doubt the Bristol company would have been quite unable to expand swiftly to an engineering and management staff of 16,000 in the Second World War. In 1966 the Rolls-Royce board, naturally favouring their own school in Derby, sought to close the school – by then enlarged and with an enviable reputation – but reason prevailed and it remained one of the finest technical colleges in the world, under its new management, until closed in 1995.

In 1934 the first Mercury and Pegasus engines tailored to the new 87-octane fuel were in production, with ratings increased by about 15 per cent to 645 hp at 15,500 ft for the fully supercharged Mercury and 750 hp at low level for the Pegasus. The Mercury VIS was tested in a Bulldog all through the scorching summer of 1934, mainly at very high power, driving the Bulldog a full 45 mph faster than any of the Jupiter-powered ones in RAF fighter squadrons. All over Europe, and in many more distant countries, design teams in more than 60 companies were urgently trying to create new military aircraft – not for reasons of prestige but because the world scene was becoming more serious and menacing. The Mercury and Pegasus were the first choice for more than half these projects. These engines were of outstandingly advanced design, were the first in the world cleared for use on the new fuel, and in performance, reliability and price were unsurpassed even by the latest Wasp, Hornet and Cyclone engines from Pratt & Whitney and Wright in the United States. Several countries chose to buy the new engines from Bristol instead of extending their Jupiter licence to make their own, and in 1934 orders flowed into the Bristol Engine Department at a much higher rate than ever before.

This made Fedden an increasingly wealthy man. In addition to a handsome salary he received a 0.5 per cent royalty on each engine made to his design. In the early 1920s this had had the effect of providing him with a small bonus on top of his monthly pay. But the 10 years from 1923 to 1933 saw the weekly output at Bristol rise from less than one engine to several dozen, and the prospect was that it might soon be hundreds. This had not been envisaged when the original agreement was concluded, and as the 1930s progressed Sir Stanley White, in particular, was well aware that Fedden was making more money than any of the Board. He was often said to be the highest-paid engineer in Britain, and this was probably true. Not for an instant did anyone suggest that he was not worth it. Without him there would have been a stupendous sense of vacuum, and no other leader – not even several – could have sustained the pace at which he pulled his team along. At the same time there were many who would have felt relief.

From his earliest days Fedden had been imbued by a will to get on which had become more and more overpowering. This had nothing whatever to do with personal wealth or aggrandisement, but was the conclusion of an entirely reasonable thought-process which postulated that, if something was good to do, then it should be done with all one's might. If he had decided to build a weir – as he much later did – he would have placed concrete block on concrete block until the task was done. Physical tiredness would have been an unfortunate fact of life that would have reluctantly had to be accepted, but the ability of mind to triumph over mere matter was central to his philosophy, with which he had increasingly identified himself. Anything short of total dedication to the job would have been unthinkable. Fedden apparently daydreaming did sometimes exist, because there were times when distant forward vision was essential to create the right product. Fedden simply relaxing did not exist. He had little appreciation of how most humans "take a holiday". If he arranged a fishing or yachting trip it was so that he could talk shop intensely with the business associates or customers he brought with him. Fly fishing, the great lifelong pastime that he practised on the finest rivers all over the world, is thought of as perhaps the most supremely restful occupation there is. But even up to his thighs in a river, Fedden never relaxed. His reasoning was: fishing is for catching fish; it can require great

"Even fishing … RF never relaxed". (Author)

skill; it is a stern test, and every second counts; to win, you pit your wits against the fish; relaxing is out of the question. Thus, when he later took Sir George Dowty on a fishing trip to Scotland, Sir George, who was not a fisherman, found it rather amusing: "Roy would set off very early in the morning. He did not walk from pool to pool, he ran! During fishing he pursed his lips, making movements like those of a fish. We ate our sandwich lunch in a hut that stank of dead fish. After dinner our amusements were looking at books on fishing records, and studying tins of flies. No fishing is allowed on Sunday, so on that day he took me to see the lady who made the flies!"

Fedden sailing can be imagined. The objective was not to mess about in boats but to win. His first boats were all powered. The clinker-built dinghy *Dolphin* was built to his specification in 1932 and was frequently raced, especially in 100-mile contests in Poole harbour and for the Roy Fedden Trophy on the Avon in Bristol. With his boat-mechanic – who worked on a bench in the Bristol engine experimental shops – Fedden won more than half the power-boat races open to him in southern England in the early 1930s, and on at least two very rough occasions was the only competitor to finish (often another competitor was his stepson Tony). Later in the decade he graduated to big-time sailing, but in the early years it was a matter of fine tuning of the engine and getting his friend Arthur Gouge, chief designer at Short Brothers, to test the immersed parts in flying-boat towing tanks to reduce drag. Fedden summed up his way of relaxing as "rest in action". It was every bit as dedicated as his work.

His constant pressure to accomplish the maximum forced him to be exceptionally skilled. Not only was he one of the greatest of boat-racers with power and sail, but his early prowess on the motor race track never left him and each year he covered tens of thousands of miles in all parts of Europe in his various cars. He seldom used a chauffeur until long after his retirement. Few chauffeurs would have met his demands for safe travel at high speed, and it was a natural part of his life to cover great distances without a minute to spare. But nobody minded accompanying him. Being Fedden's passenger at 80 mph was likely to be more informal and friendly than the everyday atmosphere in the works – and less dangerous.

Many were the hard workers who cracked under the strain, or who for the good of their health decided they had to make a break. This was never easy.

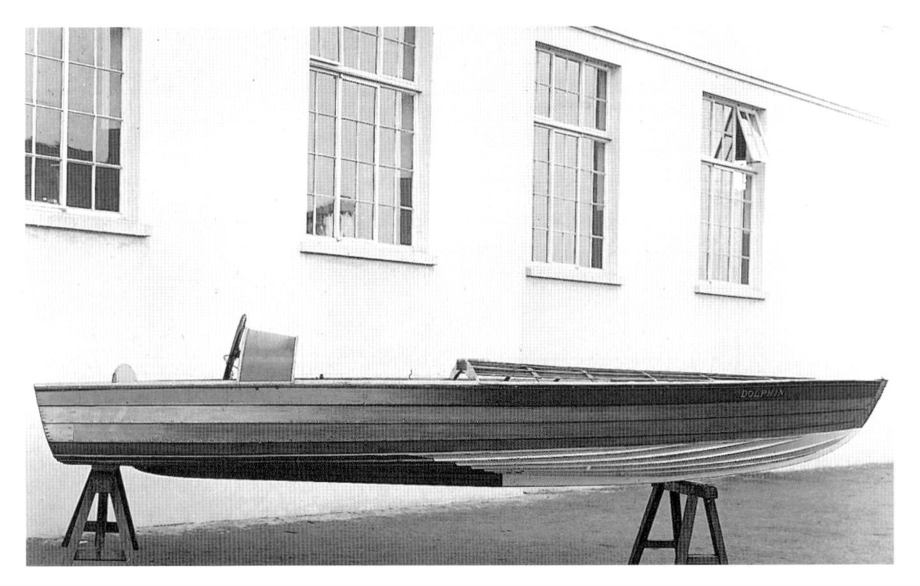

RF's Dolphin outside the head offices. (Rolls-Royce plc)

RF and mechanic racing Dolphin I (not the same boat as previous) at Framilode.
(Rolls-Royce plc)

RF didn't always win. (Rolls-Royce plc)

Working for Fedden was a real and valid job, where the products were world-beaters, and the rewards in every sense were considerable. To a great degree "it made a man of you". The problem was that you had to be a superman. Fedden at heart thought himself the kindest and gentlest of men, but to others he was quite frightening. He devoured people like a boa-constrictor, wrapping them up in his high-pressure world until they had ceased to be individuals with private lives of their own. From the start Fedden's stupendous energy and enthusiasm had made it inevitable that those near him should suffer crushing burdens, but increasing work loads on the Engine Department as a whole were not matched by the corresponding increases in engineering staff. In Stanley Mansell's recollection, "It was just about possible to cope if one never let up for an instant, if one had the innate capability not to tire or start making mistakes even at the end of perhaps 24 hours non-stop, and if one never ran into any kind of bad luck".

Gradually Fedden was forced into the habit of holding his main technical policy meetings quite outside regular working hours. By the 1930s it was the rule for key staff to be invited (commanded) to dine at Widegates on anything up to five nights in the week. Some were only needed on rare occasions, but RF himself came to hold a staff dinner every night that he was in Bristol. Staff would sometimes have time to go home first, and get smartened up, or see their families, but all had to be on parade at 8.30pm. Fedden would waste no time on idle chat but would at once get his guests seated round the great dining table. He would slice a pigeon or two, sent down from Fortnums, and play host at what was in other respects an excellent meal (though sparing on alcohol). Throughout, he would make efforts to unwind, to relax and to radiate outgoing *bonhomie* – efforts that obviously were an uphill and unnatural struggle for him. Then, before 10 o'clock, the table would be cleared, the cloth removed and replaced by engine drawings. Now Fedden no longer needed to put on an act; he could get to grips with one question after another, and the group would get through a vast amount of extremely hard work.

Potentially it might have been dangerous, because any engineer who believed in the dictum "find out what the boss wants and give him lots of it" would have taken the line of least resistance and agreed to all Fedden said. But RF always chose his associates well, and knew he needed men able to stand up to him. Rarely was there a night without a few heated words and often thunderous argument, with at least one of the team needing every ounce of character to hold his ground. After a long day's work it was no joke to go through all this, up to midnight or perhaps long after – especially as some unfortunates would leave Widegates instructed to prepare long reports ready for the 8.30 am start next day. Occasionally there were moments that made up for this, as when Harvey Mansell found he was charged with

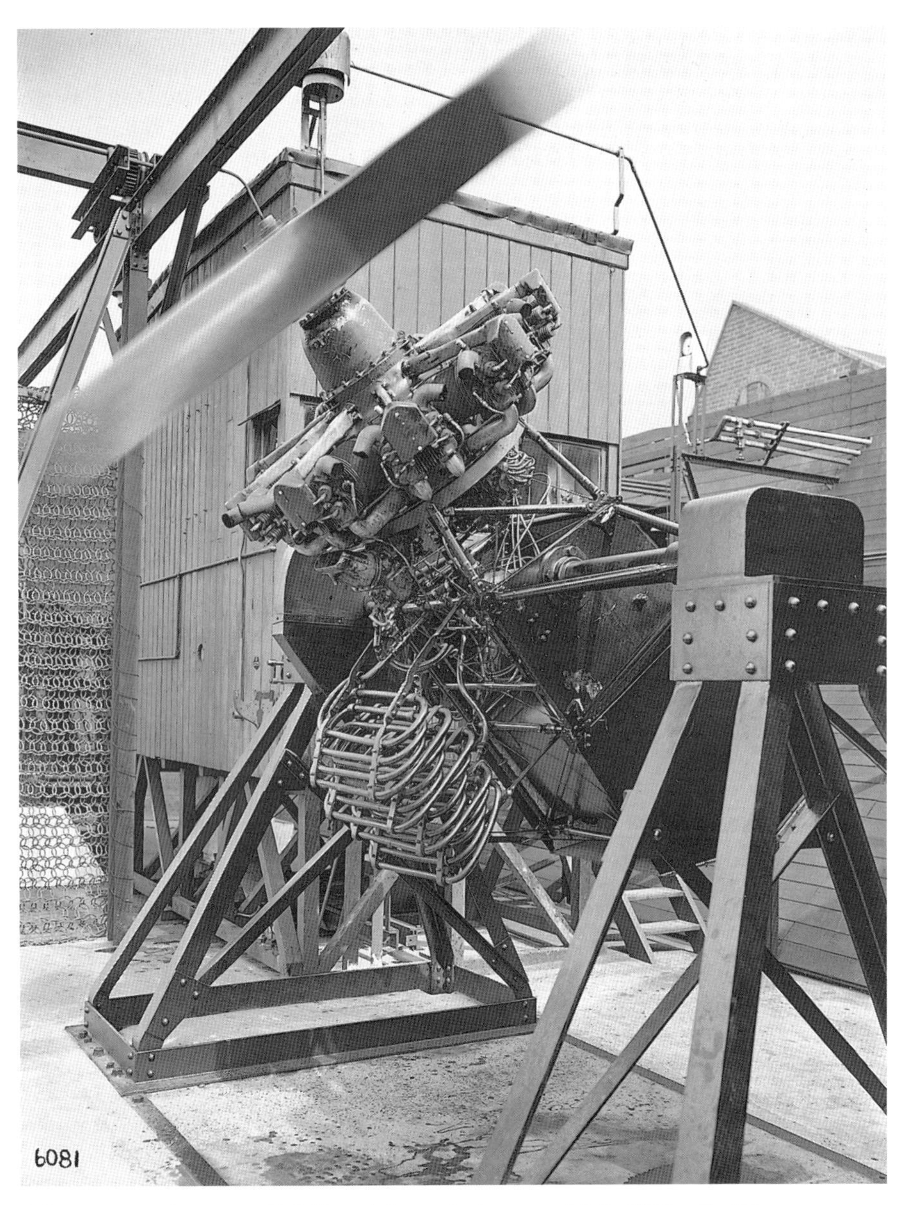

A Pegasus on what was called (though it was in the open air) the Tilting Test Hangar.
(Rolls-Royce plc)

accomplishing a physical impossibility. He timidly said “Sir, it won’t be possible to finish by the 25th”. Fedden, already on the next topic, said, “Of course you can, if you run 200 hours a week”. An even more timid voice said, “There are only 168 hours in a week”. Instead of an explosion, Fedden said, with tremendous enthusiasm, “Never mind, dear boy, run night and day!”

CHAPTER SEVEN

Sleeve valves

Fedden's greatest technical achievement was the sleeve-valve engine. He did not invent sleeve valves, but the inventors had failed to combine the resources and the steadfastness of purpose needed to make such an engine technically competitive, reliable and a proper mass-production job with interchangeable parts. Accomplishing this was a stupendous task, and far harder than Fedden had expected. So severe and prolonged were the troubles that not even his devoted staff were quite at one with him. From every quarter came experts predicting disaster, and some who suggested that, almost uniquely among engineering projects, the sleeve-valve engine seemed to have a curse on it. Yet the future of the Bristol company and even the British nation became increasingly committed to the sleeve-valve engine. During the second half of the 1930s it became frighteningly evident that a major European war was going to be hard to avoid, and Fedden – probably more than any other private individual in Europe – planned and prodded his own and other companies and government to be industrially ready for it. By 1935 he at last had a superb sleeve-valve engine; but each one had to be put together by hand, with the parts individually run together. Anything more useless for war purposes would be hard to imagine. The situation was critical, and Fedden knew that it could ruin his career, his company and, if war came soon, his country.

Many times even he was on the verge of throwing in the towel. There is a limit to how much work, worry and responsibility it is possible to stand. It does not help when there is hardly anyone to share the troubles. None of his team knew the entire picture, and it would not have helped to tell them. The Air Ministry faithfully supported him, and it would not do to have any doubts of final success where they were concerned. Likewise, the Bristol Board, though deeply concerned at the time about the amount of stockholders' money needed to perfect sleeve-valves, never wavered; in particular, they paid no heed to the barrage of critical observers who warned "watch that madman Fedden: he'll bring the whole Engine Department crashing down". The Board never came to see what the problems were, and preferred to learn how things were going from the Air Ministry. The important thing was that they trusted Fedden's judgement, and believed that eventually he would make good on his prediction that the new range of Bristol engines would be fundamentally superior to all rivals. It is important to note that not one member of the Board was in any position to judge such a technical matter.

Conventional spark-ignition engines use poppet valves in the form of discs carried on rod-like stems, like slender mushrooms. These discs can be seated on the open ends of the curved inlet or exhaust pipes so that all flow is shut off. Even under the great pressures inside the cylinder on the firing stroke each valve must remain a gas-tight fit against its seat. But a fraction of a second later the exhaust valve, and the inlet valve, will be pushed open by the valve gear driven by the engine. A cam pushes down the valve rod arranged parallel to the cylinder and the end of this rod then pushes the valve stem via a rocker on the cylinder head. The valve and gear are returned to the closed position by powerful coil springs. This means the mechanism is constantly oscillating and the head of the valve is continually slamming on to its seat. The valves get hot, because their heads are inside the combustion space in the cylinder. The exhaust valve gets very hot indeed, and by the 1930s had a hollow stem filled with sodium metal, which melts and circulates up and down carrying heat away from the head. Extremely hard Stellite alloy has to be deposited on the surfaces that come into violent contact as the valve closes.

Fedden could see big problems ahead. He used two inlet and two exhaust valves on each cylinder, to give better breathing, and studies convinced him that the valve gear for a two-row engine with four-valve cylinders would be a mechanical nightmare. But he had to design a bigger and more powerful engine, and so had to escape from the confines of the single row of nine cylinders. He also urgently wanted to overcome the problem of losing oil from the valve-gear, which was trivial in terms of actual loss – possibly a tablespoonful for a Pegasus on a long flight – but it was highly visible, and had begun to hurt his engines' saleability. Fedden was convinced the poppet valve might not prove the best solution in the long term, and as early as 1924 he looked at the alternatives.

One of the first sleeve-valve engines was patented by Charles Y Knight of Chicago at the beginning of the century. This used two steel sleeves, one inside the other, interposed between the piston and the cylinder. The sleeves oscillated straight up and down, and ports cut in them alternately uncovered the inlet and exhaust connections to the cylinder. Though complicated, and posing severe thermal problems because the waste heat had to be dissipated through three layers of metal, many of these Knight duo-sleeve engines were made in 1909-35 for all Daimler cars, and they ran so smoothly they were called Silent Knights. But in 1909 two engineers hit on a better scheme. Scotsman Peter Burt, of the Argyll Co, a leading British car manufacturer, and Canadian James McCollum independently patented the mono-sleeve in which a small crank oscillates a single sleeve in a simple cycloidal way with a rotary as well as an up-and-down motion. This greatly eased the problem of heat dissipation, reduced the number of parts, simplified the drive, opened the way to valve timing better than anything possible with poppet valves (because the shape of the ports could be designed to give any desired speed of opening or closing) and also admitted the combustible mixture with rapid swirling. The swirling improved the subsequent combustion, and later, when such things became important, enabled engines to run with higher compression ratio, and thus greater power and economy, for any chosen grade of fuel.

Burt and McCollum reached an agreement, filed a joint patent, and saw the mono-sleeve used in the excellent 130 hp engine entered by Argyll in the 1913 Naval and Military Aeroplane Engine Competition. As reported earlier, Fedden was impressed when he examined this engine (it was judged the winner and discarded). In 1915 he visited the Royal Aircraft Factory to see the mono-sleeve conversion of a Factory-designed vee-12. In 1922 he bought a Barr & Stroud motor-cycle which used the Burt-McCollum sleeve, and in 1925 the American firm Continental Motors ran a 220 hp radial using the same patent. In Britain, one of the pioneers of the internal combustion engine, Harry Ricardo, had been investigating the mono-sleeve at his experimental works at Shoreham. He found things extremely difficult even with water cooling.

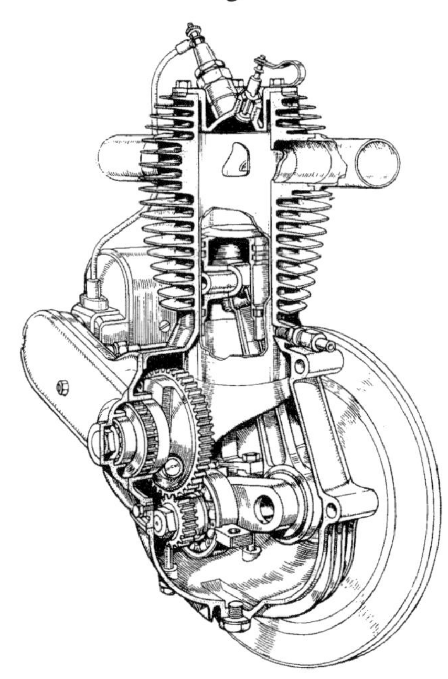

The 1921 Barr & Stroud motor-cycle engine. (Rolls-Royce plc)

Fedden decided to adopt the mono-sleeve in November 1926. The Burt-McCollum patent was just expiring, and the small use made of it seemed to be for reasons unconnected with the invention itself. After prolonged study, Fedden became convinced that, if the development problems could be overcome (and they did not seem likely to be formidable), the mono-sleeve ought to provide the perfect answer to all the strategic problems facing the Bristol Engine Department. He put up the scheme to the Board and to the Air Ministry, and eventually secured the approval of both. Money for development was voted by the Board and also by D R (later Sir David) Pye, the Ministry's Deputy Director of Scientific Development. Very importantly, Fedden sold the idea to the Ministry engine czar, Bulman, and made him almost excited, though he thought Fedden's development task would take a long time. Fedden was setting out with a handful of overworked engineers to bring about a fundamental revolution in engine design.

After extensive study Fedden and Butler decided to design an inverted vee engine, of low frontal area, with 12 air-cooled cylinders each 5.75 in by 6.00 in. By November 1927 Harvey Mansell had begun to run a single pair of cylinders which approximated to one-sixth of the proposed engine. The unit started and at first ran smoothly, achieving a brake mean effective pressure (bmep) of 135 lb/sq in at 2,000 rpm. But the nickel-cast-iron sleeves proved inadequate. The hot, high-pressure gas during the firing strokes heated and weakened the sleeves until they were bulging into the ports in the cylinder barrels, causing scoring, rapid wear and, eventually, seizure. Steel sleeves were tried, and these suffered from hot spots which again could not withstand the combustion stresses. In a sleeve-valve engine the sleeve forms the enclosure for the hot gas on the power stroke, and also provides the tube inside which the piston reciprocates. It has to be accurately made, and

The first inverted-vee two-cylinder sleeve-valve test engine. (Rolls-Royce plc)

withstand high stresses and temperatures, yet for good heat dissipation the sleeve wall must be as thin as possible. The ceaseless cycloidal motion of the sleeve, with the piston inside it, means it must have a hard abrasion-resistant surface. By no means least, its coefficient of expansion must not differ greatly from that of either the piston or the aluminium-alloy cylinder, because it must not jam when cold yet must stay a close fit at full power.

In the late 1920s extensive testing took place on numerous rigs which included inverted V-twin arrangements and also a six-in-line engine. The latter was to some degree regarded as representative of half the planned inverted V-12, though it was tested with the cylinders upright.

In 1930, after two years of utter discouragement, Mansell began running cylinders with improved sleeves forged in Kayser's KE965, a new austenitic Ni-Cr-W steel. Of the first sleeves made in this material, half were left soft and the rest nitrided to give a very hard surface. At the same time the cylinder and head were redesigned. In a sleeve-valve engine the end of the cylinder is closed by a "junkhead" with a central portion projecting down inside the sleeve with gas sealing rings like an inverted piston. It was difficult to cool

The six-inline test engine of August 1931. (Rolls-Royce plc)

Operation of the mono-sleeve valve. (Rolls-Royce plc)

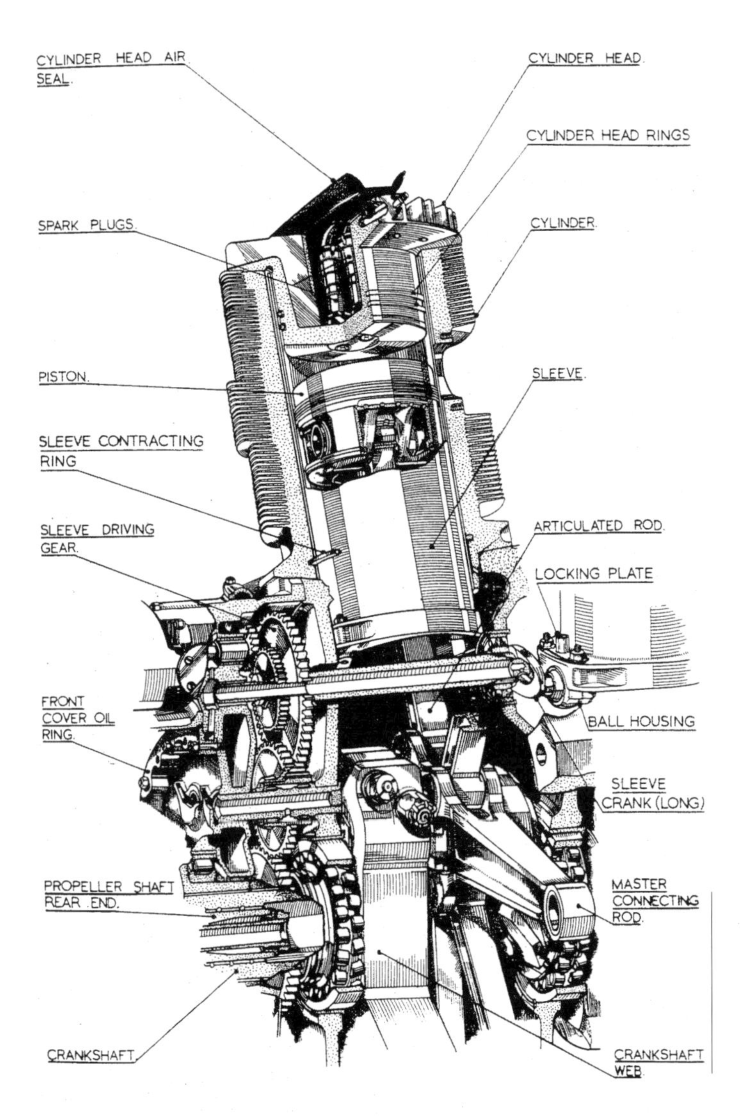

SECTION SHOWING CONNECTING ROD, SLEEVE DRIVE, PISTON AND CYLINDER ASSEMBLIES

Cutaway drawing of a wartime production cylinder (the ball housing etc, at right are for the adjacent cylinder in the rear row). (Rolls-Royce plc)

this kind of head, and the early examples rapidly overheated. But the 1930 cylinders had greater fin area, and a better aerodynamic design to duct cooling airflow down into the hot junkhead and out again. The result was a drop in head temperature of 50°C, despite an increase in bmep to 145 lb/sq in. Baffles were added to improve turbulent cooling round the two sparking plugs in the base of the head, and results improved almost daily. Every soft sleeve soon failed, but those with the nitrided surface gave results good enough for more rigs to be built.

In early 1931 Fedden abandoned the vee-12 configuration, coming to the conclusion that the radial would still be preferable, so the new rigs were single cylinders. One of the reasons for the change in configuration was that T B Barrington, who had come from the Sheffield Simplex Company and W O Bentley's team, and who later made his mark at Rolls-Royce, carried out a detailed study of sleeve-engine configurations and found that the best arrangements were single-row radials with odd numbers of cylinders, two-row radials with 14 or 18 (these were particularly good) or a 24 in the form

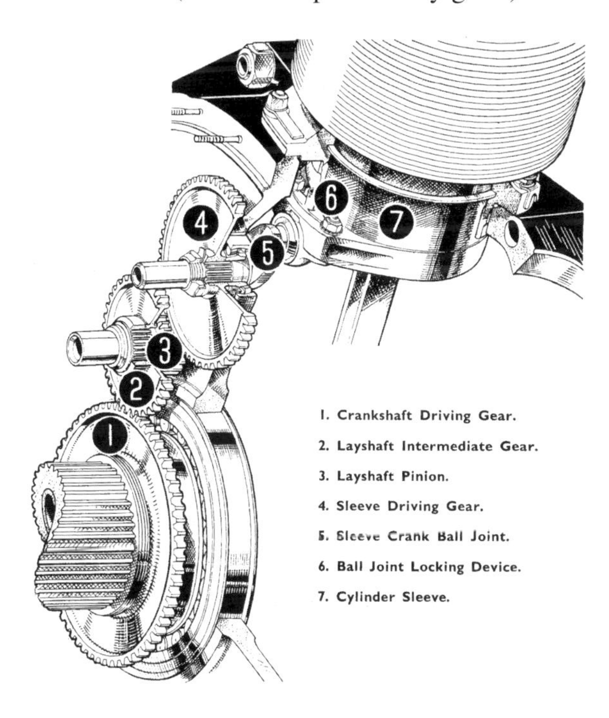

Sleeve drive mechanism. (Rolls-Royce plc)

of superimposed flat-12s, a configuration later made by Napier and Rolls-Royce. Properly designed, engines of these arrangements could have near-perfect balance with no need for counter-weights and with elegant sleeve drive gear. Most of the running in 1931 was on Mercury-size (5.75 in x 6.5 in) cylinders, but one rig had a vee of small cylinders of only 4.5 in bore and stroke. In March 1931 a single cylinder of the larger size was run at 2,000 rpm at a bmep higher than 120 lb/sq in for 100 hours, with no attention. This Fedden regarded as the turning point – though in fact it was only the first of several. From this time on, he felt he could say the high-power sleeve-valve was going to work. Though he called it "a hard row to hoe", it had been taken much further than ever before.

In late 1931 Fedden decided his first sleeve-valve engine would be a nine-cylinder radial using Mercury-size cylinders. It was named Perseus, and design went ahead rapidly. Gears from the crankshaft drove nine half-speed cranks, each of which oscillated its adjacent sleeve via a ball coupling. The sleeves had four ports near the top which intermittently lined up with triple inlet ports in the back of the cylinder barrel and two exhaust ports at the front. From the outside, the cylinder ports appeared to be about half-way down; in fact, they were near the top because the skirt lowered the bottom of

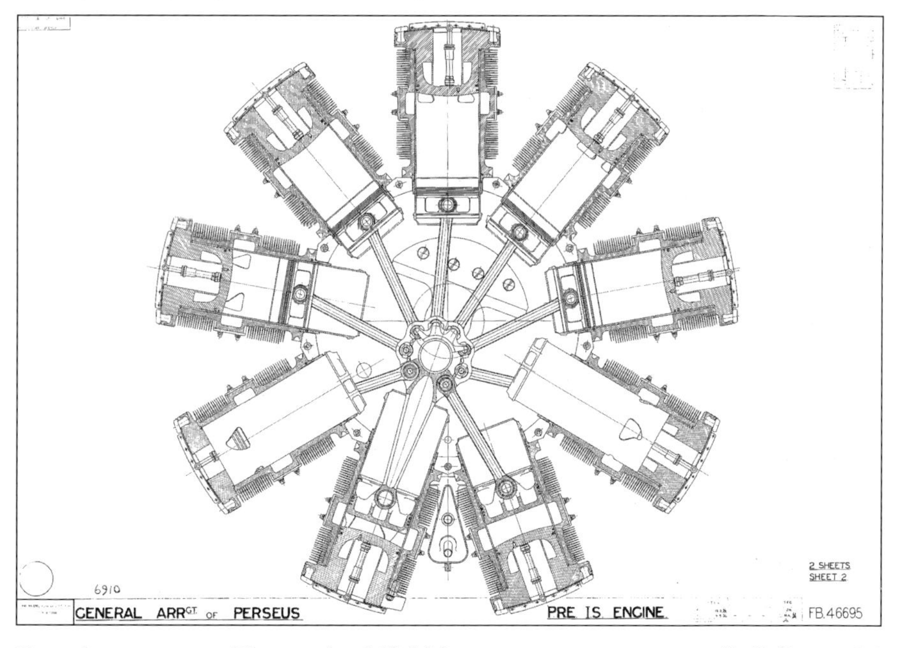

General arrangement of Perseus dated 18.5.36. (Rolls-Royce plc)

the cylinder inside the crankcase and the junkhead effectively lowered the top. At first Fedden had expected lubrication to pose several problems, but the combined rotary and sliding motion of the sleeves gave perfect wiping of the oil over the rubbing surfaces. Special refrigerator rigs showed that big sleeve-valve engines could be started in sub-zero weather, even though turning the engine necessitated shearing a considerable area of almost solidified oil. Wear on piston rings was so gradual as to be barely measurable. Mansell's rigs quickly adopted a deposit of gum on the inside of the junkhead, and carbon around the exhaust ports in the sleeve; but they looked exactly the same after a further 250 hours. During 1932 the first Perseus was built. Externally it was by far the "cleanest" and most elegant engine of its power ever made. Never before had anyone seen an engine so uncluttered or inherently simple. Moreover, it ran with unbelievable smoothness. Instead of having bouncing poppet valves, everything went round and round. Men who had lived with engines all their working lives just came and listened, entranced at the soft sound of the Perseus. Though it had the same size and number of cylinders as the Mercury, burning the same

One of the first experimental sleeve-valve cylinder barrels (left) compared with that of a Perseus I. (Rolls-Royce plc)

mixture of petrol and air, it did not make the familiar strident deafening noise, but emitted a deep, silky note unlike anything heard before. It did not sound as if it was working hard, but it was.

Fedden conducted the most painstaking comparative trials between the Perseus, and single Perseus cylinders, and counterparts with either four or two poppet valves. In 1933 Owner directed the design of a smaller 450-500 hp sleeve engine for the civil market: the Aquila, with 955 cubic inches from cylinders 5.00 in x 5.375 in. Then this size of cylinder was run and compared with an experimental 5.00 in x 5.00 in cylinder having two poppet valves driven by an overhead camshaft and specially tailored for running at high speed. Fedden was very much a "belt and braces" man. He wanted to go over wholeheartedly to sleeves, but had no intention of stopping development of the Pegasus and Mercury, nor of hitching his wagon only to the sleeve valve, until there remained no shadow of doubt of its superiority.

When the comparative trials were finished there was no shadow of doubt, at least on the score of performance. The Perseus cylinder was appreciably lighter than that of the Mercury, quite apart from the dramatic reduction in the number of parts, yet it had much greater cooling-fin area. The whole engine could run faster, up to a remarkable 3,200 rpm, yet it developed a somewhat higher bmep and gave more than 15 per cent higher power. On

Aquila III (Rolls-Royce plc)

100-octane fuel, then becoming experimentally available, the margin was much greater and the Perseus cylinder reached the outstanding bmep of 220 lb/sq in. As for the small Aquila against the high-speed two-valve poppet cylinder, this was almost "no contest", for the difference was enormous. Tests were also run with one of the latest American two-valve cylinders, which, though considerably bigger than the Bristol types (6.125 in x 6.875 in), gave useful information. The big US "pot" (from the Twin Wasp) did extremely well, but again the Perseus cylinder demonstrated its clear superiority. To round off these comparative fact-finding trials, Fedden tried to discover the ultimate power limit of the Perseus cylinder at that early state of development. Harvey Mansell was thwarted by the inability of the external supercharger plant to supply enough air; but the results were impressive, and surpassed anything that could have been achieved with any other known type of cylinder. (During the Second World War an old and much misused Taurus cylinder was put on a rig where the normal 15 lb/sq in air supply was supercharged by the blower from a 4¼-litre Bentley car. At a boost pressure of 32 lb/sq in the bmep reached the frightening value of 340; then the junkhead blew off the barrel and disappeared through the roof).

During 1933 the Perseus developed well, and it was successfully type-tested in May. The rated power for this test was 515 hp, with a maximum for take-off of 638 hp, under conditions far less arduous than those explored in single-cylinder running. This 100 hour test was followed by a 50 hour weak-mixture test and then a 50 hour high-power run on the same engine. It was apparent to everyone that the Perseus not only ran beautifully but needed hardly any maintenance. All that had to be done was keep a visual check on such things as loose nuts and oil leaks, which were extremely rare, and clean or change the oil filters. The engine stripped excellently. All who saw the sleeves commented on the glassy smoothness of the bores. They looked as if they could go on indefinitely without any further measurable wear, and in general the inside of the engine was cleaner than any ever seen before. In October 1933, the month in which the Aquila cylinder first ran, the first flight-cleared sleeve-valve engine in the world, the Perseus IA, with a nominal rating of 600 hp, was flown by Uwins in R-8, a company Bulldog IVA, using a long-chord cowl and wooden two-blade propeller. Another engine underwent overload testing at 710 hp followed by flight trials in which every effort was made (unsuccessfully) to induce sleeve seizure by soaking at extremes of temperature. All these early flight trials were made under severe ground-boosted conditions, with fuels of high lead content. In the summer of 1934 the Perseus-Bulldog reappeared with the new type of cowling in which the exhaust, instead of being collected in the traditional ring round the reduction gear, was ejected into a collector forming the leading edge of the cowl. From here it went through large muffs under the

Bulldog test bed for Perseus IA, here without cowlings. (Rolls-Royce plc)

belly to warm the cockpit. While Uwins dived and climbed the strangely quiet machine almost vertically at the 1934 SBAC show, work proceeded on five hand-built Perseus II engines.

In important ways the sleeve programme was marvellous. Fedden had begun it to find a way of overcoming basic limitations, but he found in the sleeve-valve engine major advantages he had not dared to predict. One was the smoothness that impressed everyone. Another was economy. He reported the early Perseus ground running as showing "a lower fuel and oil consumption than has ever been achieved before on a poppet-valve engine of similar layout." He also considered he could claim lower manufacturing cost, by less-skilled labour, using more easily obtainable materials, as well as lower maintenance cost and other advantages. Yet there was one obstacle that, if not overcome, would lead to the abandonment of the whole programme – with results for Bristol little short of catastrophic. The sleeves were just hollow cylinders, open at both ends, yet by 1934 nobody had been able to find a way to make them by mass-production methods in such a way that any combination of piston, sleeve and cylinder would fit together. Looking back, this seems remarkable; the modern production engineer might think this a simple task, but he would be wrong. It was a problem that transcended even Whitehead's prowess, because it was not amenable to attack by ordinary manufacturing techniques. It was simple to mass produce the sleeves, but they would not fit perfectly between the piston and cylinder

Assembly shop in late 1934 with Perseus beginning to appear among the poppet-valve engines. (Rolls-Royce plc)

because they could not be made truly round. If they did fit when cold they distorted out of shape because of the expansion of the hot cylinder. The two basic problems were inability of the production process to make circular sleeves, and the fact that the cylinder expanded when hot far more than did the sleeve. It was thus a problem of material selection from an almost infinite range of possibilities, in some ways resembling the exhaustive trial-and-error work of the pharmaceutical industry.

It took five long years to solve, and an expenditure of close to £2 million, which at the time was an astronomic sum. Eminent authorities warned the company Board that they were being ruined, and sometimes even Butler expressed his deep-seated fear that they were "chasing a shadow". Whole families of alloys for sleeves or cylinders were investigated, and many were used to make actual sleeves and cylinders which were then subjected to exhaustive tests on Harvey Mansell's rigs. And, though he was usually the first to know of each failure, Mansell was steadfastly unshakeable in his conviction that complete success would eventually be their reward.

While the immense search for the right materials was going on in the background, Bristol continued manufacturing the Perseus. The engine was

The Bristol stand at the 1935 Paris Salon, with two Pegasus, a Mercury and, for the first time, a Perseus and Aquila. (Rolls-Royce plc)

relatively simple to make, and the production time on cylinder heads and barrels was lower than for poppet-valve engines. Each sleeve was case-hardened and then carefully lapped to its own light-alloy cylinder. By this method of individual fitting it was possible to stabilise the very low oil consumption that was such a feature of the new engines, so that after hundreds of hours of running "all you need to clean the engine is a flick or two with a duster". The five handbuilt Perseus IIs made in 1934 were civil engines, yet were cleared to run on 87-octane fuel and develop high power. In October 1934 one was type-tested at 665 hp at 2,200 rpm and at a take-off rating of 760 hp at 2,525 rpm, which was the same general level of power as the bigger Pegasus. A cruise rating test at 420 hp at 2,150 rpm was then held for 250 hours, and the specific fuel consumption stayed at the excellent level of 0.435 lb/hr/hp. When stripped, the engine was found to be in marvellous condition; it did not suffer from the severe corrosion and deposition problems caused by tetra-ethyl lead on poppet-valve engines.

The problem was, what to do? The Perseus was potentially a world-beater. Fedden was itching to get cracking with more powerful two-row engines which would set a new standard of performance, neatness and cleanliness. The aircraft constructors were going to need them. But with each sleeve lapped into each cylinder, an engine could not be judged as anything but a handbuilt prototype. Major Bulman, though seldom enamoured of Fedden's strongly expressed schemes, did want to see sleeve-valve engines evaluated in Service aircraft. But Woods Humphrey, of Imperial Airways, used engines in only small numbers. He considered that each Perseus was already almost a "fit and forget" engine. After careful discussions he borrowed all five Perseus II prototypes, which belonged to the Air Ministry, and had them cleared for operational use with the remarkably long initial time between overhauls (TBO) of 300 hours. Two were fitted in the middle positions on Syrinx rated at a nominal 480 hp, and on 29th June 1935 this aircraft went into regular passenger service between London and Paris with very few of the passengers realising that they were the first in the world to be carried aloft by sleeve valves. The two Perseus ran like sewing machines: they were popular with everyone and at 317 hours were stripped at Filton and replaced by a second pair. It was not their fault *Syrinx* was almost wrecked by being blown upside down whilst taxiing in a gale. Two more Perseus were then fitted to the twin-engined Vellox freighter, and did so well the TBO was raised to 400 hours; it would then have been raised to 600 had not the speedy Vickers monoplane crashed one stormy night for reasons unconnected with the engines. The five engines had flown over 2,500 hours with virtually perfect results.

G-ACJK Short Syrinx, with two Pegasus and two ring-cowled Perseus. (Rolls-Royce plc)

As far as civil aviation was concerned the Perseus had arrived, and Imperial had such confidence they specified the engine for a later model of the Short C-class flying boat, as did de Havilland for the Flamingo landplane. New shops were obviously going to be needed for expanded engine production, and in mid-1935 ground was broken on the virgin grass on the opposite side of the Gloucester Road where the Engine Department's canteen had been built in 1930. The new production factory was designed for almost unlimited expansion, and contained a great deal of specialised tooling for sleeve-valve engines which Whitehead had convinced the British machine-tool industry would be vitally needed in the years to come. But the Perseus was still a hand-fitted product. So was the trim little Aquila, which was type-tested on 73-octane fuel at 500 hp at 2,600 rpm in October 1934, a bare month after the first run, and at the start of 1935 was offered to the civil market. This was the first of Fedden's new engines to be put on sale. It had seemed from the first to be attractive, and its flight development, beginning in May 1935 in Bullpup J9051 and being backed up the following year with the company's Bulldog G-ABBB, went very well indeed. Barnwell had prepared a three-view drawing of the Bristol 135 high-speed twin-engined monoplane as early as July 1933, before the Aquila had even been built, and this eventually crystallised as the Type 143 which was flown on 20th January 1936. By this time Fedden also had a military Aquila in the power range beyond 700 hp, one of which was used in the Vickers Venom fighter. The Venom, which was the first aircraft ever to fly with eight wing-mounted machine-guns, would probably have gone into production had not the Air Ministry rightly decided to go for larger fighters with more powerful engines. Likewise the Bristol 143 would probably have seen production had it not been for the British rearmament programme. As it was, the beautiful little Aquila found no takers.

The bigger Perseus, however, was practically dragooned into production, despite the crippling need to tailor each sleeve to its cylinder. Low-rate production under Air Ministry contract began in the main Filton works in October 1935, with delivery scheduled for January 1936. Some engines were designated Perseus IIIM, rated at 675 hp, and some were the Mk VIII type-tested at 810 hp at 5,250 feet. All were cleared on 87-octane fuel with the new de Havilland Hamilton controllable-pitch propeller. The 740 hp Perseus III flew with a long-chord cowl in a Bulldog and then completed a severe series of trials during two Canadian winters in a Hart, one of the main purposes of soaking at "30 below" being to see how well existing electric starters could crank the engine. In 1936 a Mk VIII deeply impressed the RAF by running 200 hours of operational service in a Vildebeeste torpedo bomber with no attention except to the magnetos, plugs and oil filters. Nothing like this had been known to the RAF, and to make the engine seem even more

R-7, a much-used test bed Bulldog, flew the Perseus III in this long-chord cowl with rear gills. The two small rings to the left of the propeller hub are the inlets to the ducted oil cooler. (Rolls-Royce plc)

Equipped with the Vildebeeste IV, RAF No 42 Sqn was the first sleeve-valve unit in the world. The propellers were the first made by Rotol. (Rolls-Royce plc)

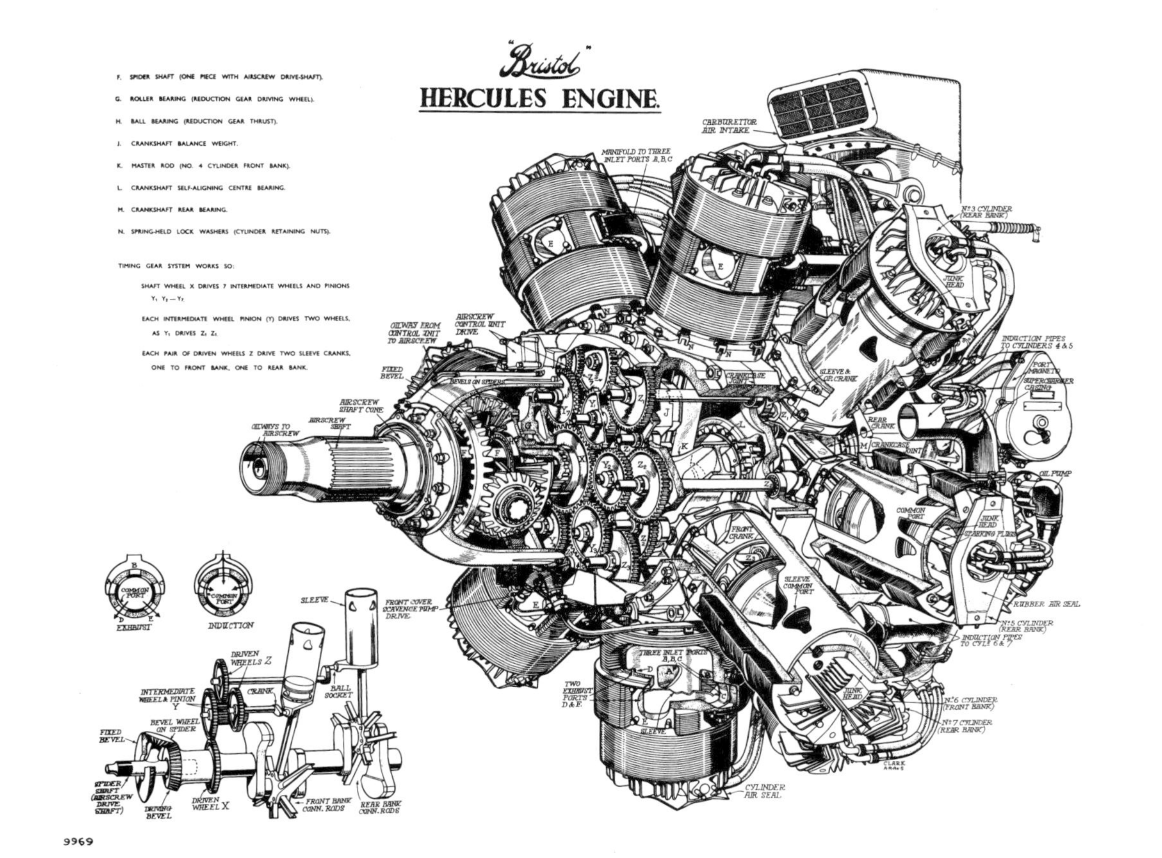

A cutaway drawing by J H Clark of The Aeroplane of a typical wartime production Hercules (rights purchased by Bristol Aeroplane Co).
(Rolls-Royce plc)

The Taurus had a diameter of only 46¼ in (1,175mm). (Rolls-Royce plc)

supernatural the oil consumption began low and then steadily decreased, a characteristic also noted by Imperial Airways. In 1937 a development contract was received for 50 Mk VIII engines, about half of which went to No 42 (Torpedo Bomber) Squadron to convert their Vildebeestes into Perseus-powered Mk IVs. The squadron, the first sleeve-valve unit in the world, went about its duties and soon learned that the Perseus could just be taken for granted. By the end of 1938 over 4,000 hours had been flown with outstanding success.

By this time Fedden had forced up the power of the Perseus to rival the best Mercury poppet-valve engines of identical capacity. After 18 months of testing, the Perseus XII was cleared for production at 890 hp at 15,250 feet at 2,750 rpm, and powers well over 900 hp were being obtained lower down. And, more important in the long term, much more powerful two-row engines had been designed. By 1935 – but not before – Fedden could see that the coming 100-octane fuel would enable the Pegasus to become a 1,000 hp engine, but future military and civil machines would need even higher power. He and Butler sat down in March 1935 to draw their second engine to bear the name Hercules, and it was to prove the most important Bristol engine of all time. It had 14 Perseus cylinders disposed in two staggered rows, with all the sleeves driven off one gear-train at the front. The crankshaft was in three parts, with front and rear balance weights secured by keyless maneton couplings to a centre portion carrying both crankpins, the

The Northop Gamma 2-L was registered in September 1937 with the first flight-cleared Hercules. (Rolls-Royce plc)

The first Taurus test bed was Fairey Battle K9331. (Rolls-Royce plc)

assembled shaft running in three generous roller bearings. The concept was a masterpiece.

The first Hercules, a fully supercharged engine, was completed in December 1935 and run in January 1936 with excellent results. Then priority switched to medium-supercharged versions, one of which was put through a 50 hour civil type test in November 1936. The Air Ministry allowed Fedden to exhibit this engine at the Paris Salon in the same month, and to disclose that the powers established in the test had ranged up to 1,375 hp. The Hercules was a centre of attraction at Paris, both for its simplicity and because it was easily the most powerful engine at the show. There is little doubt the Hercules was the most powerful type-tested engine in the world in 1936, and designers in seven or eight countries soon selected it for new military and civil projects. In 1937 work went ahead on new versions for 87- and 100-octane fuel, one of which had a two-speed supercharger – an enlarged version of that developed for the Pegasus XVIII – and Fedden was eager to begin flight trials. To his delight the company Board succumbed to Air Ministry pressure and agreed to buy a Northrop 2-L monoplane from the United States which was admirably suited to the task, and which incidentally evoked great interest among Barnwell's airframe team because of the quality and finish of its stressed-skin construction (which was partly why Air Ministry wanted it). The installation of the Hercules was outstandingly neat, and flight development went marvellously, starting in September 1937.

In November 1936 yet another new sleeve-valve engine was started on the test bed. This was the Taurus, an extremely slim two-row engine with fourteen 5 in-bore cylinders on which more than 6,000 hours had been run (but the stroke was slightly greater than the Aquila's, at 5.625 in). The Taurus was planned as a very compact engine in the 1,000 hp class to succeed the Mercury, and its diameter of just over 46 inches appeared to fit it admirably for high-speed aircraft. By 1938, when over 700 hours had been logged and the medium-supercharged Taurus II had run a 100-hour type test, a Mk II was installed for flight testing in a Bristol 148, a low-wing monoplane designed as an army co-operation machine and which the Board had actually hoped would test the Hercules. Bristol were permitted to state that the Taurus delivered over 1,000 hp, the actual figure for the Mk II being 1,050. Altogether Fedden now had the finest range of high-power engines in the world, and orders for all of them – poppet-valve and sleeve – were rising to levels which by previous standards appeared fantastic.

It was thus a matter of unspeakable relief that the long search for a way to make sleeve-valve engines with interchangeable parts finally came to a successful conclusion. The chief research programmes were not done at Bristol. One was at Slough, where Devereux had urged High Duty Alloys to ever greater efforts until they perfected a special light alloy, containing 12 per cent silicon, from which could be forged cylinders with a very low coefficient of expansion. The other was in Sheffield, where A E Thornton, chief physicist of Firth-Vickers, with the whole-hearted backing of his director Sir Arthur Grant, ploughed through detailed physical and metallographic investigations of 58 specially tailored alloys, involving more than 1,100 different heat treatments, before finally reaching complete success with a high-expansion steel from which the sleeves were made by centrifugal casting. To cap it all, Whitehead found a way to make the sleeves truly round. The answer was to grind each sleeve with a worn-out, undressed wheel incapable of cutting; the result was a perfectly cylindrical sleeve.

None of this showed on the outside of the engines, and the years of patient work were unknown to the public. In the vital last years of peace sleeve-valve engines flew thousands of hours, including one of the first crossings of the North Atlantic against the westerly wind, with every sleeve still individually lapped into its own cylinder. Not until late in 1938, when the vast RAF expansion scheme was well under way, with one-quarter of the RAF already committed to sleeve-valve power, did High Duty Alloys and Firth-Vickers find their breakthroughs and make the whole thing a certain success.

By 1938 the Bristol engine team, and Fedden above all, were so severely extended that they had virtually ceased to have any private life. Developing

The Centaurus crankshaft (in this case for a later production engine) was a beautiful example of precision engineering. (Author)

Centaurus IV crankshaft dismantled. Print dated 11.8.42. (Author)

Rod assembly for a Sea Fury engine (Centaurus 18). (Author)

the radical new family of engines was just one of the many giant burdens placed on this handful of men. The pressure never let up, but went on seven days a week.

Aero engines can give trouble in many ways, and for the next decade Bristol engines – though as good as or better than their competitors – were to cause seemingly endless trouble with high oil consumption, hydraulic lock, sleeve failure and in many other ways. Moreover, there was an incessant demand for greater power. Back in May 1937, partly because of fear of competition from the Rolls-Royce Vulture (a fear that was to prove unjustified), it had been decided that work should begin on an engine to give 2,000 hp. At that time nobody could predict that the Hercules would eventually be developed to give more than this power, and RF was authorised to work on a bigger engine. Barnwell suggested that "if Bristol made a flat (horizontally opposed) engine, only two-thirds as much horsepower would be required to give the same speed as a radial", but this doubtful belief was never put to the test. RF pointed out that, while the best solution would be an engine like the Hercules with 14 bigger cylinders, the quicker solution would be to use 18 Hercules cylinders.

In November 1937 Fedden and Butler began actual engineering design of the new engine. It was slightly larger than RF's initial concept, because their experience – reinforced by discussion with such aircraft designers as Camm of Hawker, Pierson of Vickers and Gouge of Short Brothers – suggested that there would always be a need for more and yet more power. Bigger, heavier and faster aircraft could reasonably be predicted as far ahead as one could see. The new engine, for which an Air Ministry development contract was obtained in February 1938, was named the Centaurus. It had 18 cylinders of the same familiar 5.75 in bore as all the other high-power engines but 0.5 in greater stroke (7 in), giving a capacity of 3,270 cubic inches. There was no doubt that the Centaurus would start life at over 2,000 hp, and by the end of 1938 it had been selected by the three designers previously named for projected fighters, bombers and flying boats. By working night and day the first Centaurus was running in July 1938, despite a seven-month wait for forgings for the crankshaft.

Thus, by the time war came, Fedden had succeeded in the colossal task of turning the sleeve-valve engine from an elusive dream into a superb new product-line, and of simultaneously breaking out of the confines of the single-row engine and leaping up to powers more than twice the 1,000 hp which had been his original distant goal. This achievement is enough for Fedden's name to be ranked with the very greatest in the history of engineering. But in fact in the second half of the 1930s the sleeve-valve engine was just one of his problems. An equally big problem was that war was coming. He could see this perhaps more clearly than anyone else, for the simple reason that he was in the most intimate contact with the Germans and had no diplomatic constraint to distort his view. His urgent wish was that his own country should, he said, "gird its loins and break out of its self-imposed lethargy". In the United States aircraft were pouring off production lines with flaps, neat retractable landing gear, and variable-pitch propellers, while in Britain in 1935 many of the new designs for the RAF and Fleet Air Arm were fabric-covered biplanes. Single-seat fighters still on the drawing board featured fabric covering and fixed-pitch wooden propellers, and there was a powerful school of thought – not only among the academics and senior staff officers but also in the fighter squadrons themselves – that it was a mistake for a fighter not to be a biplane with an open cockpit. Worse, there was still great reluctance to build a strong air force.

Much of Fedden's time from 1935 onwards was devoted to trying to awaken a sense of urgency in the British government to the approaching peril of the fast-growing Luftwaffe. He, more than any other Briton, had been taken to see the mighty industrial base on which the Luftwaffe was founded. The Germans chose Fedden because he was capable of accurately sizing up the capacity of a factory, and his word would be believed. But the King's Ministers and officials regarded this engine designer as altogether too outspoken. Some openly described him as "a dupe of the Germans", and to almost all officials his exhortations were judged tiresome. Some even thought he was grinding a personal axe to get more engines ordered. Nothing could have been further from the truth, but the British failed to make proper use of Fedden in their greatest hour of crisis. Had his advice been followed more fully and much sooner, the nation would have grown significantly stronger than it did during the last crucial years of peace.

CHAPTER EIGHT

Years of crisis

The 1930s were the pinnacle of Fedden's achievement at Bristol. In a decade he had almost singlehanded, and with a most imperfect relationship with the Board, driven the Bristol Aeroplane Company into the leading aero-engine position in the world. That the firm held this pre-eminent position was unquestionable, whether measured in terms of numbers of engines, numbers of customers, or income. But the imperfect relationship with the Board had many adverse effects, not least of which was the extreme difficulty Fedden had in hiring capable engineers at the time during the depression, prior to 1935, when plenty were available. Once Britain's belated rearmament programme got under way these men were all snapped up by others.

Extra men were desperately needed. The story of the Pegasus and Mercury sketched in Chapter Six, was one of engineering development on a large and intense scale, far surpassing anything attempted or necessary with the Jupiter. By the 1930s aircraft technology had begun sharply to go forward from where it had almost left off in 1918, and nowhere was this more evident than in engines and their installations. As the modern world knows well, there are exponential effects in man's progress which tend to demand ever-greater resources in men and money, and work which in 1927 one man might have done part-time was ten years later needing a team (each man working just as hard). Fedden could not get the men he needed, and it followed that – quite apart from Fedden's own consummate capacity for sustained effort – the burden placed on each member of his team became unreasonably large. By the 1940s this had sorely hurt both the men and the company.

After 1938 the demands on the Engine Department were so crushing, and so important to the nation, that nearly the whole staff worked special hours that involved day and night stints twice a week, as will be described. Until then the official hours were the normal ones for British industry, namely 0830-1700 Monday to Friday and 0900-1230 on Saturday. Overtime was essential. In the works the hourly paid employees could do well out of overtime, but the engineering staff received no benefit beyond the concession of free tea in the canteen. The higher one went, the harder and longer were the hours. Fedden himself somehow still found time to sail boats, to race and to fish, and to prepare and give long and significant lectures to professional organisations or customers at home and abroad. Preparing a major technical paper did not come easily. There was one occasion when an important draft was retyped twelve times, and six was average.

One evening in March 1934 Fedden took an evening off to give a more informal talk to the Bristol Yacht Club. His large audience at the Spa Hotel, Clifton, had come to hear "The Yachting Scene in the United States", which of course Fedden knew at first hand. For good measure he threw in some photographs of new multi-lane highways, aircraft plants, the Cadillac car factory and the Boeing 247D and Douglas DC-1, which were the very latest American civil transports. Fedden dwelt on the advanced design of these aircraft, and commented that nothing like them was available or even planned in Europe. He did not disclose that he had got Barnwell to lay out a streamlined small transport to be powered by two of the Aquila sleeve-valve engines. This project, the Type 135 mentioned earlier, was only a seven-seater but it promised to be if anything slightly faster than either of the American machines. On the other hand, no decision had yet been forthcoming from the Board, despite Fedden's goading that such a machine would be worth having, even if only as a modern high-speed engine test bed.

After the lecture Blos Lewis, Editor of the *Bristol Evening World,* stayed behind to ask whether the Bristol company could build a really fast modern transport rivalling the Americans. His boss, the formidable Lord Rothermere, had recently told his many editors he intended to buy "the fastest commercial aeroplane in Europe". Lewis had come to the lecture more to talk about this prospect than to hear about American yachting, because Rothermere had been intrigued by the mock-up of the Type 135 at the Paris air show. Fedden was intensely interested, and agreed to travel with Lewis on the breakfast train to London next morning. They had a long discussion with Rothermere and his aviation advisor, Brig-Gen Groves, as a result of which Fedden returned with the promise of an immediate order for the fastest transport Bristol could produce. Rothermere was one of the first customers for the class of aircraft that today is exemplified by the "executive jet". In addition to its obvious utilitarian use, the newspaper tycoon wanted to stimulate British industry to begin to make some direct use of aviation; and he also intended to give the most practical kind of lesson to the Air Ministry, because it looked as if the transport aeroplane he was buying would be about 20 or 30 mph faster than the latest RAF fighters.

Fedden reported to the Board and found them not exactly enthusiastic. Though they appreciated the prestige such a product might bring, it looked as if it might offend the Air Ministry, which was their only major customer. Barnwell, instead of being excited, appeared morose and could see only a succession of difficulties; Fedden thought he was affronted at his colleague's odd interest in aeroplanes, and at his nerve at again preparing the way for a new Bristol aeroplane. Gradually, however, the difficulties were ironed out, and work began on the Type 142, a development of the 135 with a smaller body and Mercury engines which Barnwell considered could exceed 250 mph, the speed Rothermere wanted. A week or two after work had begun in earnest General Groves visited Bristol to study the design, and two days later made what Fedden called "the most appalling criticism of it" in the *Daily Mail* (the main Rothermere paper). The Board were extremely concerned, and Sir Stanley White said to Fedden "As you are responsible for all this, you will go to London and retrieve the situation". This Fedden did, and his great ally Freddie Mayer, head of installations, volunteered to come too. The meeting started somewhat icily, but gradually became better, and before long the most uncomfortable participant was the aviation adviser. Rothermere assured the men from Bristol the order stood, and urged the utmost haste, because he wanted the Bristol 142 for the MacRobertson race to Melbourne – and Fedden had to explain that this was much too soon, because it was a mere six months off. Pity, because it could very easily have won that race, had it been ordered in time.

Eventually the Type 142 flew on 12th April 1935. It was the most advanced aeroplane in Europe, with a cantilever monoplane layout, all-metal stressed-skin construction, retractable landing gear, flaps, variable-pitch propellers (fitted after the first seven weeks on wooden four-bladers) and several other modern features which were being neglected in Britain but had for five years been wholeheartedly adopted in the United States. The isolationist Editor of *The Aeroplane,* C G Grey, reflecting the traditional

The Bristol 142 could be described as the first modern British aircraft, though it was at first fitted with four-blade fixed-pitch propellers. (Rolls-Royce plc)

Soon the *Britain First* was fitted with more modern American propellers, three-blade two-pitch bracket-type from Hamilton Standard. (Rolls-Royce plc)

Thanks to Fedden, the Bulldog assembly line was immediately replaced by one for the Blenheim. (Rolls-Royce plc)

The first Blenheims had 840hp Mercury VIII engines driving de Havilland (Hamilton licence) propellers. The exhaust pipes can be seen entering the front collector ring. (Rolls-Royce plc)

view of British industry, poured scorn on such advances; but to Fedden they were inevitable. He was so often in America that he could not comprehend the insular outlook of British aircraft designers and commentators, to whom American progress was dismissed as being unreal, exaggerated or irrelevant. But the MacRobertson race took place in October 1934. KLM entered a DC-2, a regular production airliner, and it carried a full load of passengers and mail to Melbourne in the second fastest time, being beaten only by the specially built D.H. Comet racer flying without commercial load. Most people in British aviation were shocked. When one of the new American aeroplanes was actually parked on the starting line at Mildenhall it was more difficult to pretend it did not exist, and still more difficult when major European airlines began to purchase it. Had it not been for Fedden – not so much for landing the order for the 142 as for prodding the Board and the aircraft side into keeping going with it, instead of abandoning the project in its early months – there would have been nothing in the same class in Britain until years later.

The 142 was accepted by Lord Rothermere, named *Britain First* and very publicly "presented to the nation" as an Air Ministry test aircraft. Far from being offended, the Air Ministry had been remarkably enthusiastic from the start, and collaborated both on features of the 142 and on a possible military derivative. When *Britain First* reached Martlesham Heath for acceptance trials, in June 1935, it staggered everyone. Not only was it a delight to fly, and much nicer and obviously safer than many contemporary Service machines, but it could fly level at 307 mph, beating the fastest fighters not by the expected 20 or 30 mph but by 80 mph! It was a foregone conclusion that a bomber version should soon appear, and within a matter of weeks Bristol had an order for 150 of the Mercury-powered Type 142M named Blenheim. Until this time the aircraft side had been having a very thin time indeed, and the whole company had been carried by the Engine Department. Now Fedden had found work for the whole company.

Many of the new monoplane airliners and bombers used Fedden's engines. At least 119 types of aircraft were designed outside Britain to use the Mercury and Pegasus, and more than 95 older types were converted to take these engines. Several airlines used no engines but those of Fedden's design, and the world-wide prestige of his engines was a very real factor in airline marketing. Even operators in the United States used Jupiters made under licence by the Bliss Co, and these gained an enviable reputation. Their only shortcoming – and in practice it was a major one because it was visible – was the extremely fine spray of oil from the valve gear. This was intensely disliked by pilots of aircraft fitted with a nose engine, because it deposited an oil film on the windscreen. For this reason only, Douglas would not look at the Jupiter.

With the improved valve gear of the Pegasus this oil loss was imperceptible. By this time the DC-2 and DC-3 were solidly established with Wright and Pratt & Whitney engines, and Bliss was unable to make any dent in the giant US market, but the loyalty of some operators to Bristol engines did result in a few conversions elsewhere. The first was for LOT Polish Airlines, which had decided to standardise on the Pegasus and already operated its three-engined Ju 52/3m fleet on Pegasus engines licence-built in Poland. In 1934 LOT ordered two of the brand-new DC-2Bs to be powered by engines made at Bristol, the choice being the Pegasus VI medium-supercharged variant running on 87-octane fuel and driving Hamilton controllable-pitch metal propellers. The engines for the first Douglas were delivered to Santa Monica on 30th March 1935, and flight testing began on 3rd July. The results were outstanding. Not only the test pilots of Douglas and LOT but also the US Army at Wright Field, the chief pilot of Swissair, and the chief vibration and soundproofing engineer at Sperry, among others, all commented on the fact that this was the smoothest and quietest Douglas – which meant the smoothest and quietest aeroplane of any type – they had ever experienced. Compared with the regular Cyclone-powered DC-2, the Polish transport cruised 3 mph faster at 180 mph and burned only 28.8 gal/hr of fuel instead of 31.7. The Pegasus thus had much to offer, and Douglas openly considered it made the DC-2 "a superior product".

First of the Pegasus-engined DC-2B airliners for LOT. (Rolls-Royce plc)

In Britain Fedden's department was extended to the utmost in delivering Mercuries for fighters all over Europe, and Pegasus for bombers and transports. In the civil field the biggest development was the Short Empire flying boat. In 1934 Imperial Airways and the British government had decided to launch a great global Empire Air Mail scheme, carrying mail without surcharge, and based upon a large fleet of flying boats much more capable than any British transport aircraft seen previously. The result was the S.23 "Empire flying boat", for which a £1.75 million order for 28 was placed in 1935. The type was known by Imperial as the C-class, each boat having a name beginning with that letter. The first, *Canopus,* flew from the Medway on 3rd July 1936, and services began in October of that year. The S.23 was powered by four Pegasus Xc medium-supercharged engines rated at 910 hp for take-off and with a normal output of 740 hp at 3,500 ft. One of these engines was subjected in January 1936 to a severe 250-hour weak-mixture test, with 15-minute bursts at take-off power followed by nine hours at weak-mixture cruise at 510 hp. Further testing included simulation of a tropical rainstorm, which did not penetrate the new pattern of ignition harness. The S.23 fleet exceeded specifications in carrying up to 24 passengers and 1½ long tons of mail for 800 miles at 165 mph.

The Short S.23 "Empire" flying boat opened up a major market for Bristol engines. G-ADHM was the second, Caledonia, with fuel sufficient to reach New York via Newfoundland.
(Rolls-Royce plc)

At first the Empire routes stretched only to the south and south-east, but in February 1937 experimental flights were undertaken on the North Atlantic – previously unconquered by aeroplanes except for bold and often fatal pioneer ventures – by *Caledonia,* which had extra fuel tanks and operated at a weight increased by 4,500 lb to 45,000 lb. Between Foynes, in Ireland, and Botwood, Newfoundland, numerous crossings were made in each direction in times varying between 10½ and 15½ hours (representing, said Fedden, about two million revolutions of each crankshaft and 50 million of the bearing balls of the superchargers). Later, Imperial and Qantas bought additional long-range boats, and the final Empire boats were of the S.30 type with Perseus XIIc sleeve-valve engines which could take off at 46,000 lb and then flight-refuel to 53,000 lb, and had much more than double the original design range. The great Empire boats were overworked all their lives, and lasted until 1948 when they were finally replaced by American landplanes. There are still some elderly travellers who regard these ships of the air with great affection – tiny and slow as they may be by modern standards – and consider that all that has happened since is, by comparison, uncivilised.

The Pegasus Xc of the original Empire boats was one of the final family of poppet-valve engines known as "the lightened series" because they were not only more powerful but also lighter. All were designed to run on 87-octane fuel with controllable-pitch propellers, and they incorporated improved cylinder heads and barrels, pistons and rings, exhaust valves, superchargers, carburettors, mountings and accessories. To some degree the increased power and reduced weight was due not only to engineering design refinement but also to the use of new materials of greater strength and durability. Fedden took immense pains to avoid fatigue problems, and throughout the 1930s continued his campaign to cut out exotic materials and processes and establish the manufacture of his engines on such a basis that, if war were to appear imminent, output could be rapidly multiplied from UK resources. He insistently drew the attention of the Air Staff to the fact that a single bomb on any one of nine factories – six of them in Sheffield – would completely halt Bristol engine output indefinitely. It was the kind of thing he could have ignored as not his problem, but it worried him ceaselessly. What worried him most and impelled him to issue streams of needling memos and recommendations, was that the people specifically assigned to look after such matters did nothing.

In 1935 there were not a few Britons who considered Fedden, with his incessant propaganda for a stronger and more widely dispersed engine industry, to be an unmitigated bore. It was a national tradition that Britain should always "muddle through" at the last minute, and the general opinion of the public was certainly not inclined to favour expensive armaments. Unlike the public, Fedden had the habit of instantly extrapolating from the scene in 1935 to the probable situation that would exist in another five to ten years – this was his job after all – and it disturbed him greatly. He knew how complex and interwoven modern armaments, such as aero engines, had become. No decision to increase the national manufacturing capability could have any significant effect within two years, and full production at the increased level would probably not be possible until four years had gone by. With Hitler at the helm in Germany it appeared probable that a crisis might be precipitated overnight, so that production potentials ought to have been increased four years earlier. Hundreds of important Britons heard Fedden's arguments, but most thought them tiresome.

One of the few who agreed wholeheartedly was Air Marshal Sir Hugh Dowding, by this time Air Member for Research and Development. Not surprisingly, Fedden thought the world of him, though he scorned some other air marshals. One day in September 1935 Fedden was visiting Dowding to argue the case for a British supply of modern variable-pitch or constant-speed propellers, which for five years had been one of his pet hobby-horses. The talk ranged far and wide; then, suddenly, Dowding said (and these were his very words): "Look here Fedden, I think you will be relieved to learn that the Air Staff have come to the conclusion that we are going to have a war with Germany. Quite when it will come we cannot say; it may not be for ten years. But what we must do as soon as we can is precisely what you have been advocating, and that is to build up a vast increase in our production potential … What we have decided to do is to choose an established manufacturer and then try to create a replica of his production process elsewhere. We have called the technique 'Shadowing', because it aims to create a second image of the original … Of course there is no reason why the Shadow should not be much larger than the original, but at present we merely have authority to choose our manufacturer and open

One of the research programmes of the mid-1930s centred on this single-cylinder test unit for a two-stroke diesel. In 1927, RF's team had spent a lot of time working with a large (512.6 cu in) diesel cylinder with poppet valves, but the 1935 rig had a sleeve valve. (Rolls-Royce plc)

negotiations. We have chosen you. Bristol engines are essentially simple, and easily made by standard machine tools and equipment. What also counted very heavily with us was your great experience in licence agreements with many foreign firms. We are convinced that with Bristol engines of established types we are minimising the risk in launching this bold procedure".

Elements of the two-stroke compression-ignition test engine: the sleeve with a central ring of ports, and its drive, and the piston with its rings and gudgeon pin.
(Rolls-Royce plc)

The idea struck sparks from Fedden instantly. Within minutes he had assured Dowding of his wholehearted co-operation, and gone far towards ironing out some of the potential pitfalls. Dowding expected no other response. Fedden was known far and wide as the passionate champion of such a policy, but other champions were surprisingly hard to find. Fedden left Dowding's office empowered to inform his Board and summon a meeting of possible participants. The latter were to be drawn from the motor industry, most of which were firms located in the Coventry and Birmingham areas. The Shadow Industry was to be created by the Government building and equipping a large new factory for each participant. The facilities would remain Government property, but the occupier would be required to recruit and train the labour and to undertake the entire running of the factory. Initially the factories would be fully tooled to make Mercury or Pegasus engines, but only a token order for 50 engines would be placed. Each factory would make its own portions of the engine, and one of them would carry out assembly and test. As far as possible, measures would be taken to provide for duplicate sources of supply to minimise the effect of one factory being bombed. Throughout, the Air Ministry would maintain resident supervisors and inspectors to keep a close watching brief and help iron out problems. The relief felt by Fedden was profound.

Where strong personalities are involved people tend to 'take sides' and, perhaps unconsciously, rewrite history. The above was checked and approved by many reviewers prior to publication, but when he saw the original edition Maj G P Bulman, Director of Engine Development (and of Production also, in 1938-41) sent the author a long diatribe describing the launch of the Shadow scheme and concluding "Fedden took no part at all in this amazing effort of co-operation." In his view the entire scheme was created by the Air Ministry (with himself in the key position) and Treasury, with Norman Rowbotham playing the pivotal role at Bristol. The author, incidentally, failed to find a publisher for Maj Bulman's own autobiography, which gave a very different slant on much of the story of British aero engines between the wars.

Dowding had expected the Shadow scheme to begin to move in about six months. Fedden thought the timing could be much quicker, but after a few days he wondered if it would ever begin at all. For a start, the Board of his company were very averse to the whole idea, seeing nothing but difficulties and bad business. Possibly more serious was the cool reception Fedden had when he invited to Filton the heads of seven large motor car firms. They had plenty of work already, and knew nothing of aero engines. They were unimpressed with the scheme as a business venture, and showed no enthusiasm to take part. There was one outstanding exception, however, and he practically launched the scheme single-handed. This giant, in both senses of the word, was Billy (later Lord) Rootes. The son, with his brother Reginald, of a Canterbury garage owner, he had from modest resources built himself up into the very personification of a tycoon of the motor industry. He

Hercules in production at the Rootes Shadow factory in Coventry. (Rolls-Royce plc)

put his not inconsiderable weight right behind Fedden, and when the rival car firms realised the Shadow industry was actually going to happen they decided they had better be in on it.

In three weeks things were moving, but the big problems came later. In the United States in 1942 a similar situation occurred when the Ford Motor Co was charged with making the Pratt & Whitney Double Wasp. Edsel Ford and his production czar Charles Sorenson came with a large team to examine the Pratt & Whitney operation in the most minute detail for two weeks, and finally announced that Ford would have to duplicate it in every detail. But in Britain in 1935 Fedden found the British motor industry only too eager to show him the error of his ways. "Look, old man", they would say, "you simply can't expect us to use these ridiculous Reinicker gear shapers; we'll buy high-speed Pratt & Whitney grinders. And as for the idea of using expensive Genevoise jig borers just to drill holes in a production crankcase, we think you need your head examined". This kind of talk characterised every Shadow meeting in the early months of 1936, and Fedden did not have authority to insist on Bristol methods being duplicated to the letter. He explained the Reinicker rolling shapers, revolving on steel tapes, by the need for the vital supercharger gears to have a proper volute shape with a generous radius between the teeth. He did not mention his youthful preoccupation with gear design resulting from his having read, from cover to cover, a 1904 classic on the subject by the Brown & Sharpe machine-tool firm; but he did explain how Butler and Whitehead had tailored their supercharger gears to the Reinicker method. He also explained that the high-precision Genevoise machines were also part of the genius of Whitehead who had realised that they could pay for themselves with their speed and precision without the need for jigging. The car makers, however, knew better. Though some of them remembered that Fedden had begun in their own industry, he was in 1935 regarded as just another of the spendthrift aircraft industry engineers whose lavish resources blinded them to what an economy-minded production engineer could accomplish.

So the great car company which handled the supercharger section of the first Shadow engine, the Mercury VIII for the Blenheim I, set up an impressive line of Pratt & Whitney gear grinding machines. The Air Ministry had not stopped at 50 engines; by late 1938 orders ran into thousands. By the time the first sets of Shadow gears had run 10-15 hours a total of 400 had been delivered to Daimler for final assembly. It was then that the breakages began, dozens of them occurring in the air and not a few with fatal results. Bulman was very angry indeed, confirmed that no Shadow gear could be trusted beyond 10 hours, and ordered an immediate switch to Fedden's Reinicker method. (Bulman himself disputes the above; he says Bristol used Swiss MAAG gear grinders while Rootes substituted cheaper

Orcutt grinders, and that none of the faulty engines got into service). After this, criticism of the ridiculous aircraft industry was conspicuously absent. The proven methods, so painstakingly established over 20 years at Fishponds and at Filton, were never again departed from in the slightest degree without careful consultation. In December 1938, when most of the Mercuries in the RAF's Blenheim squadrons were Shadow-built, one of these engines and a duplicate made at Bristol were stripped, shuffled together and re-assembled. The results were fully satisfactory. By this time the Shadow factories had not been closed down and held in reserve, as had been expected, but were themselves being hard-pressed to provide the huge output needed by the RAF's belated but wholehearted expansion scheme. Before war began Fedden had passed the plans for the eventual establishment of a much bigger Shadow scheme to build the Hercules sleeve-valve engine. This time there were no experts who knew better, and the Bristol sleeve procedures were followed exactly.

The astronomic increase in output schedules for Bristol engines called for enormous quantities of advanced machine tools, not only for the new Shadow plants but also for the parent company, whose works had been constantly extended since 1934, especially on the east side of the Gloucester Road. In 1936 Fred Whitehead had set up a small office in the United States, at Hartford, Connecticut. This proved to be another of his brainwaves. Not only did it greatly facilitate the ordering and quick delivery of standard US machine tools but it also actually designed a number of special-purpose tools and other plant which American firms produced in short order. The British machine-tool industry was quite incapable of fulfilling such orders, and was in any case grossly over-extended by the nationwide rearmament programme. Fedden estimated that Whitehead's office in America reduced the time taken to get the Shadow industry into production by more than six months. As finally constituted the original Shadow engine industry was operated by Bristol, Daimler, Rootes, Austin, Rover and Standard. The Shadow work-force at the outbreak of war in 1939 was 51,850, and growing. Shadow Controller at Air Ministry was W A (Bill) Sales.

One of the fastest-growing sections of the Bristol company from 1935 was concerned with engine installations. Fedden, through the versatile Mayer, paid ceaseless attention to how his engines were installed, and continual improvement enabled drag to be reduced, cylinder head temperatures to be kept down despite much greater output and closer cowling, and maintenance to be made easier. An example of the gains in performance was afforded by flight trials of a Mercury-Hart in 1936. With the original Townend-ring cowl it took 9 min 30 sec to climb to 17,000 ft, with a head temperature of 200°C, and could reach a speed of 196 mph. With the new Bristol long-chord cowl completely enclosing the same engine, apart from the open front and variable

From 1936, many test beds were needed to support the expansion in engine development. This Hawker Hart was fitted with skis for testing the Pegasus in the Canadian Arctic.
(Rolls-Royce plc)

exit slit under the adjustable gills, the time to 17,000 feet was cut to 7 min 23 sec, with a head temperature of 185°C, and maximum level speed with gills closed rose to 209 mph. To ease engine-changes Fedden planned each new mark of engine as a self-contained unit, with a four-point anti-vibration mount and all the pipes and electric cables grouped into neat quick-disconnect couplings. One of the first of these engine-change units was designed for the Polish DC-2s, and these also incorporated the complete oil system and tank. Several aircraft, including the Aquila-powered Venom fighter, featured the swing-open installation first used on the Brandon and Taxiplane of 1924.

One important area where Fedden was not his own master was in the propellers his engines drove. From the First World War onwards he had carried on a missionary campaign for variable-pitch propellers, and he fretted at the woefully slow progress Gloster Aircraft was making with the only promising British v-p propeller, the Hele-Shaw Beacham. One of these had performed well in flight trials in 1931 on a Gamecock, but Fedden then kept badgering Harry Folland, Gloster chief designer, because nothing more seemed to be happening. Bristol themselves then picked around the edges of the problem. The Engine Department made simple propellers with fixed-pitch blades of magnesium and, from 1935, of "densified" wood, with multiple laminations bonded under heat and high pressure to form an extremely strong blade much tougher than the traditional wooden type. Unfortunately, Fedden had no resources to spare for the complex engineering of a new v-p mechanism. In September 1933, on one of his visits to the Bliss company at Brooklyn, he paid a call on the Hamilton Standard Propeller Co. This firm had patented and perfected a simple v-p hub with two or three blades balanced by bracket-type counterweights at the roots and capable of operating either in a fine pitch, for take-off and landing, or in a fully coarse pitch for cruising. This was the only v-p propeller that had ever been fully approved, or put into production. Fedden thought the Hamilton terms a bit steep, as regards both licence fee and royalty, but he decided to take out an option for the British market to break the stumbling block that was hurting both his engines and, increasingly, British aircraft.

The Bristol Board turned the idea down flat – partly, Fedden was convinced, because they considered their employee had no business to keep involving himself in such peripheral affairs. Fedden became exasperated trying to persuade them of the size of the market, and of the way in which fixed-pitch propellers were rapidly becoming outmoded everywhere that the Hamilton had penetrated. Fedden, with Frank Nixon, interested de Havilland in the American propeller, and dropped his own option. He then unburdened himself to the sympathetic Dowding. The air marshal welcomed the introduction to Britain of the proven Hamilton propeller, but he also expressed his faith in the Hele-Shaw Beacham design and asked Fedden if he would supply the Air Ministry with two propellers to this design. Fedden agreed at once, because he too believed in the British hub and was impatient at the way it was hanging fire. Gloster Aircraft were not in the least offended at Fedden taking the order, and Hugh Burroughes and Folland collaborated with him in setting up a propeller design office at Bristol and in tracking down the original Hele-Shaw designer, Milner. Though Fedden could not have set up a team to develop a propeller from scratch, he welcomed the chance to perfect this existing design.

His new propeller group quickly discovered that the faulty operation of the British hub had been due to distortion of the casing, which allowed oil to leak and reduced the pressure available to swivel the blades. The obvious answer was a stiffer hub, and within weeks a casing had been machined from a solid forging like the banjo of a truck back-axle. There followed a most successful ground test, the first ever with a British v-p propeller, and then a 100-hour flight programme with a Mercury-powered Gauntlet fighter. But by this time, in 1935, de Havilland Aircraft had followed Fedden's advice, picked up the Hamilton licence, and was tooling-up for quantity production. From the summer of 1934 Fedden had added an oil control valve for the

Taken on 27 March 1935, this shows the Hamilton propeller about to fly on Mercury-Bulldog R-8. This was entirely on RF's initiative. (Rolls-Royce plc)

Hamilton propeller to all his latest production Mercury and Pegasus engines, and in fact roughly nine out of every ten of these engines sold throughout Europe up to 1939 were fitted with Hamilton three-blade propellers (to the chagrin of the Bristol Board). Another propeller rival was Rolls-Royce, which had also been given an order for two Hele-Shaw propellers by Dowding and had been developing it along different lines. Bristol's hub used a cylinder with radial pins sliding inside the forged steel hub, while the Rolls design used a fixed inner piston carrying an external sliding cylinder driving the blades by push-pull rods. Fedden was not anxious to see two versions of the Hele-Shaw; his passion was for mass-production of the best standardised article. And what really depressed him beyond measure was that the Bristol Board still wanted to have nothing to do with propellers. This time the main excuse was that such a venture would not be worth the candle as de Havilland was taking all the business with the Hamilton propeller!

Fedden once again decided to do something he called "rather unconstitutional". He invited two of the top Rolls men, Arthur (later Sir Arthur) Sidgreaves and E W (later Lord) Hives, to lunch at the Royal Thames Yacht Club in London – Fedden's favourite club, and suitable neutral territory for a chat with his greatest rivals. He expressed his concern at the failure of the Bristol Board to authorise production of his propeller, and emphasised that the development problems were solved. He stressed that "In the national interest we must set up a unified modern propeller production programme for Britain". He suggested the two great rivals should get together on propellers, produce an agreed design and set up a jointly-owned company to make it. Before they got up from lunch the broad agreement had been reached. There now only remained the hesitant Bristol Board, but to Fedden's delight they accepted the idea. Fedden picked one of his original Fishponds team, Bill Stammers, to be general manager of the new company, and Stammers coined its name, Rotol, by merging the names of its two parents. Sidgreaves was appointed chairman, Sir Stanley White deputy chairman, and Fedden and Hives were made directors. To get things going, an office and small factory were rented at Llanthony Road, Gloucester, where the design was completed and small-scale production started in the winter of 1936-7. Meanwhile Fedden searched with Haldenby of Rolls-Royce for a permanent site, nearly finding one at Shrewsbury, and finally went with Whitehead and Stammers to see a site midway between Gloucester and Cheltenham. It was perfect, and they straight away pegged out the grass from the plan of the great factory they had prepared. By mid-1937 the Rotol works was taking shape, and production began by the end of that year.

In late 1935 William E Prytherch, of the National Physical Laboratory, was invited by Fedden to a meeting at the Air Ministry. He recalls, "I was astonished that such a boyish man should wield so much influence. The gist of the gloomy meeting was Fedden's insistence that the forthcoming British monoplane fighters would be too slow to catch the new Messerschmitt, and said that an extra 12 mph would be needed. He said the Merlin engine gave adequate power, but that the Watts or Jablo fixed-pitch wooden propellers could not translate this power into thrust at maximum speed. He turned to me and asked 'Can you make large forgings in magnesium alloy?' I replied that I saw no reason why this should not be possible.

"On leaving the meeting a hand fell on my shoulder. It belonged to W C Devereux of High Duty Alloys, who astonished me by saying not only that the whole of his organisation was at my disposal but that he would give me £250 if I produced a satisfactory forging. I was not used to doing things for money, and to avoid difficulties I joined HDA. Fedden was unbelievably exacting. Making small test forgings that met his specifications was one thing, but achieving all his figures, in every part of a large forging, tested in every direction, took 18 months of often heartbreaking slogging.

"At last we produced forgings that met Fedden's requirements. The Ministry ordered 27 of them, to be made into three-blade propellers. Three of these propellers were fitted to specially prepared Vickers Wellesley bombers. The advertised objective was to break the world long-distance record, but the real and secret objective was to test the endurance of the magnesium-alloy blades." As described later, the long-range flight also tested Pegasus engines in a new cowling, running on 100-octane fuel. The new Rotol propellers performed flawlessly.

Prytherch continues, "Following this, the Ministry ordered HDA magnesium-alloy blades by the thousand. When they were fitted to Spitfires and Hurricanes the maximum speed was increased by 20 to 27 mph, coupled with better take-off and faster diving speeds. I doubt if this would have been achieved in time for the Battle of Britain without Fedden's drive and determination, so in my view he made a big contribution to our victory in that battle."

Rotol Airscrews Ltd had two strings to its bow. The main product was the all-British hydraulic propeller, which at first had blades of magnesium alloy but by 1939 was switching to densified wood. The second product was an American propeller of completely different form, the Curtiss Electric. This had been designed as a fully variable answer to the newly developed constant-speed version of the Hamilton, and as it was completely developed and qualified Rotol bought the licence as an insurance. Both propellers went into mass production. After 1942 the hydraulic type was continued alone, and it remains in production to this day in much refined forms, together with many other products, in what became Dowty Rotol, and is now Dowty Aerospace.

The Rotol electric propeller was tested on the Northrop 2L, here fitted with an experimental Hercules. This aircraft was thoughtlessly scrapped during World War 2. (Rolls-Royce plc)

During the 1930s Fedden reached the pinnacle of his power. He was never made a director of the Bristol Aeroplane Co, however, and antipathy grew between the aircraft side and engine side which neither "side" sought to overcome. Thus, when Frank Owner was appointed to a steering committee after the war and sat down to coffee with such exalted aircraft men as Frise and Russell, someone asked "Who's this? An engine man? Heave half a brick at him!" And it was not said entirely in jest. This perpetual state of loggerheads, which was continually manifest in very real ways that were sand in the works of the whole company, was displeasing to Fedden who worshipped at the shrine of progress, efficiency and the most unimpeded forward drive possible.

He was utterly intolerant of delay, from whatever cause. He therefore never overcame the suspicion with which he had been viewed in 1920, when the canny Grieg had come to inspect his books by night. His integrity and honesty were always beyond question, but his overwhelming drive was altogether too much for the Board, who considered him quite capable of selling the whole works if that seemed in the national interest. The Board in the mid-1930s remained completely under the control of the White family and had yet to include any outsider. There was no special wish to keep the Board within the family but the Whites, the White Smiths and the Verdon Smiths were all extremely sound businessmen. They were certainly not timid reactionaries, nor did they fail to understand the vital importance of Bristol engines and Fedden's fantastic accomplishments. But he was altogether too big, too unpredictable, and too much for them. They could just about manage the situation if they kept him at a distance in a subordinate position. It was a strange love-hate relationship, in which Fedden was impossible yet indispensable.

It was a love-hate relationship with his own staff. Stanley Mansell considers him "One of the original greats … he always tried to be sociable and charming, but it was hard work for him. It conflicted with his wish to get on with the job." D. E. Collett recalls "He was like a tin god; if a message went out that RF was coming through the shops there was a sudden breeze through the place and it became like an Army parade. He knew everyone's Christian name, but never used it; and nothing ever escaped his eagle eye. Everything was deadly serious; even his boat racing became a matter of endless research and testing to improve performance and reliability. It seemed un-English, because the English are meant to lose graciously, yet at

The test hangars for production engines in November 1936. (Rolls-Royce plc)

heart he was the most English of men." According to Eric Turner, "Serving him was the most wonderful training ground in the world. Exposure to such intense pressure had a strange kind of reward in itself."

Cyril Luby's first contact with him came when the Jupiter was first given a forged head. Luby, who retired in 1973 as managing director of the Rolls-Royce Bristol Engine Division, was then the young foreman on the cylinder-head section. When Whitehead brought the first completed forged head to Fedden the response was "slice it up". Luby had toiled devotedly to make it, and refused point-blank. Fedden sent for the young rebel. He then quietly explained why it was necessary to slice the head up to ensure that it contained no hidden imperfection – "and, my boy", he said, "we'll have to slice one or two more in early production to make sure our quality is repeatable". Luby had expected an explosive row and to be fired; instead he left the great man's office completely won over. But Rex Goldby recalls "You tried never to go into his office at all. It was a sanctum. He was the unapproachable; you spoke his name with bated breath. The red light on his

RF's office in the 1930s: "You entered literally at your peril ..." (Author)

door was usually on, and you entered literally at your peril." Odd, because Fedden considered himself the personification of reasonableness and goodwill.

He had a somewhat ascetic way of living. He adhered to an impeccable standard of behaviour. He was never known, even in his frequent and much feared outbursts of anger, to utter any word that was in the slightest degree obscene. He believed rigidly in never doing anything to excess except working and playing. He drank very sparingly, had come to abhor smoking and, though his working days were separated by periods of sleep seldom exceeding five hours, he took care on any foreign trip to be in bed before 11 pm. He never went "out on the tiles". Bert Newport, who for many years was his representative in Italy, recalls a visit paid by Fedden to Milan, in company with Devereux. After instructing Newport to "Get Dev some long spaghetti" Fedden retired to bed. Devereux winked at Newport and in a few minutes both were hitting the night spots, where they remained most of the night. Newport returned first and hastily tucked himself between the sheets. Next morning at breakfast Fedden told him "Wonderful man, Dev. I just met him coming into the hotel in a pullover. He told me he'd got up early and been for a jog-trot round the park". It would never occur to Fedden to doubt it.

By the 1930s Dev's policy of setting up High Duty Alloys offspring to support the manufacture of Bristol engines throughout Europe was largely complete, but he often went with Fedden on Continental visits. After 1934 they both noticed a sharp change in Germany. That great country under the Nazis had acquired a sense of national urgency and purpose, and to some degree of arrogance and superiority, which had not previously been noticeable. Fedden still got on well with individual Germans, but it was disquieting to find himself "back in 1913" to the extent that the German factories were becoming far bigger and busier than those in Britain (his own Bristol, for example, had virtually nothing in the works on the aircraft side until 1936). In 1936 he did not visit Germany, but he was himself visited by a group of the most senior German aviation men, led by Generals Milch and Udet. Erhard Milch was State Secretary at the new Air Ministry, and, under Goering, the main architect of the Luftwaffe; Ernst Udet was the chief of the *Luftfahrtministerium* technical department and thus in charge of Luftwaffe procurement policy. They were allowed to see the Bristol works and spent much longer looking at engines than at aircraft despite the fact that the prototype Blenheim had been completed. Their chief object of interest seemed to be Fedden himself.

What Fedden did not know was that the Nazi government was looking for individuals in Britain, France and the United States to whom they could show off their newly created military and industrial might. Nowhere was this more impressive than in the German aircraft industry, which by 1936 had swiftly overhauled those of all other countries to become, in terms of output, No 1 in the world. Disclosing its true strength was not a security oversight. On the contrary, the Germans hoped that, by demonstrating to potential enemies that there was no hope of Germany being defeated by force, those nations might be persuaded to stand peacefully aside and not interfere with Germany's (or, rather, Hitler's) plan for the future, which involved taking over almost all of Europe. The kind of man Milch and Udet were looking for had to be technically highly competent, extremely quick to notice details, skilled at assessing industrial potential, psychologically "switched on" so that he would make full use of every opportunity, and possessed of such stature that his opinion would be wholly credible. The first name on their list of candidates was Fedden, and he was their final choice.

As a polite return invitation to their visit to Bristol, General Milch invited Fedden to Germany in June 1937. He went with Ken Bartlett, who was by then Bristol's continental sales manager, and was accompanied by the company's German agent Baron de Ropp. At every turn it was clear that no foreigner would normally be permitted to make such a tour, but that, once the German Air Ministry had emphasised the "special nature" of this visit, every door was opened. It was exactly the reverse of normal procedure. Usually, and especially in the crisis-torn Europe of the late 1930s, nations shielded their latest technical and industrial developments from foreign eyes, particularly when the subjects were military. Previously the Germans had been doubly anxious to hide their construction of an air force, because it defied the Versailles Treaty. But here was the most highly qualified Englishman being shown the complete picture of the German aircraft industry!

Before he left for Berlin on Monday, 7th June 1937, Fedden told both his Board and the Air Ministry, but received no comment or instructions from either. There was the same apparent absence of interest on his second "official" visit between 2nd-12th September 1937, when he was accompanied by Baron de Ropp and Bill Evans, head of his experimental department. [In fact Sir William Verdon Smith shared Fedden's concern and later read his German reports with intense interest, but Fedden remained unaware of this.]

He characteristically wrote reports on the two visits extending to 110 densely packed pages. They are important historical documents. The mere itinerary is impressive. For example: "Thursday 10th June. All day at the Junkers aircraft and engine factories at Dessau and Kürton. By diesel-engined Ju 86 to Dessau and by car to Kürton, with Herr Helmut Sachse, General Director of Engine Development of the German Air Ministry; Herr Koppenberg, General Director of Junkers; Dr Mader, Chief Director of

Junkers Motorenwerke; and other officials." That visit alone generated nearly 20,000 words. On the tour in September he was taken to a wide range of vast shadow factories which had been completely unknown in Britain. The big report goes into the greatest detail. From Krupps at Essen to an underground magnesium plant deep in the Hartz mountains, Fedden wrote in his little blue notebooks all the figures he was told, checking them against what he could see and looking for discrepancies, and asking countless questions about plant, methods and policies. Nothing was held back. Everything was told truthfully, because the Germans knew Fedden would detect a falsehood. They knew their accomplishments were formidable, and needed no exaggeration.

Fedden appreciated what the game was: Germany feared no other nation in Europe, and wanted to stay friends with Britain and, as Fedden later put it, "keep us in a Munich frame of mind, so that we could be relied upon to stand aside while they became Top Dog". But he considered it his duty to find out everything he could, and report to the British Secretary of State for Air in the fullest detail. This might be playing into the Germans' hands, but it was obviously a case of forewarned is forearmed. Hence the 110 pages, which time and again show Fedden's ability to notice trivial details and to ask the right questions. The basic scene was impressive in itself. Nowhere else in his experience could one visit a succession of factories each about a mile long and specially built within the previous two years for producing modern airframes or engines. Security was tight, and everywhere there were careful, yet quick, identity checks by armed guards with Alsatian dogs. The inside of each plant was like a dream. Everything was on a huge scale, spotless, lavish and working fast yet effortlessly on a single shift. The workers were fanatically devoted to their nation, and relieved that, after years of depression, they now had a government that brought security and prosperity. To most of them the creed of Nazism meant little, but a strong and vibrant Germany meant everything.

In his report Fedden commented on the declared policy of HM Government, in launching the first RAF Expansion Scheme on 22nd May 1935, of bringing the RAF to "a state of parity with any potential aggressor". He also noted that such a state of parity was to be achieved "within two years". Later, when this prediction was demonstrably incapable of fulfilment, it was replaced by the declaration of achieving "parity with Germany by April 1939". All such hopes, said Fedden bluntly, were "quite out of the question." He estimated the output of large military aero engines for the calendar years 1937 and 1938 to be 4,500 and 6,500 in Britain and 8,500 and 9,000+ in Germany; his figures for aircraft were 700 and 2,000 for Britain and 2,500 and 3,000+ for Germany. But behind the figures lay Fedden's desperate anxiety that Britain had small and inefficient plants, a basically wrong "production mentality", and no hope of coming anywhere near the German output without a drastic rethink. He pointed out "In common fairness to the British industry, it must be appreciated that the conception and expansion of the German Air Force has been on far broader lines than anything visualised in this country. The Germans started with a clean sheet, a clear-cut policy, and unlimited money. They commenced on their raw-material suppliers and machine-tool industry, neither of which has received consideration in our Expansion Scheme. In the event of an emergency arising, the position is even more serious, inasmuch as the majority of British raw material, engine, and aircraft plants are already working two shifts and at almost maximum capacity, and therefore have no reserve to draw upon."

Fedden must have known he would anger the Air Staff when he wrote "It is felt that there is tendency to consider too many types of aircraft in this country for the Royal Air Force, instead of cutting down the number and paying more attention to simplification of design and increased production facilities, rather than striving for the last mile an hour." And he hardly pleased the Civil Servants with "The administrative organisations, both in the German government and in their industry, are developed on a more thorough basis, in addition to which we have to reckon with the tremendous seriousness and enthusiasm of everybody connected with this industry in Germany." He called for "fearless and drastic action ... every day of delay makes the task more difficult." His concluding sentence was "These reports may appear to strike an alarmist note, but the writer is profoundly concerned at the situation, and is confident that a true representation of the case has been made.' This was exactly how Fedden put things; "fearless and drastic action" was his battle-cry throughout his long life.

The Cabinet found 110 pages too much to digest, or even to look at. Eventually, almost a year later, after some pressure from the Air Staff – which saw no reason to disbelieve Fedden – the new Air Minister, Sir Kingsley Wood, spoke to Fedden on 3rd August 1938, and asked for "a short précis". But much earlier in October 1937, the government decided they could not ignore Fedden completely. A new post had been created, Minister for the Co-ordination of Defence; Winston Churchill failed to get it, and the portfolio went to Sir Thomas Inskip, later Lord Chief Justice and the first Lord Caldecote. He invited Fedden to suggest a plan for reorganisation of the British aircraft rearmament scheme to increase efficiency and output. It is typical of Fedden that, within ten days of the request in October 1937 he had prepared a formidable document setting forth a wide range of changes which though "the minimum that should be made to accomplish the desired results", were in effect a revolution in procedures and organisational structure.

Predictably, his recommendation was for a more clearly defined structure under a government Aircraft Controller, a permanent appointment for "at least 5 to 7 years and preferably longer", responsible only to the Air Minister and charged with carrying out the defined policy of the Air Council. The policy itself had to be far-reaching, not overambitious, backed by sufficient finance and "above all, when once settled, it must not be changed." Under the Controller Fedden would have appointed nine section controllers, each assigned a division such as Aircraft, Armament, Accessories, and Finance, with supreme responsibility for research, development and production. He made many further suggestions, and then turned to the drastic rationalisation of aircraft types, recommending that the Second Expansion Scheme, to run from early 1940 until 1943, should involve only four basic types: a 420 mph twin-engined fighter, a 300 mph general-purpose and reconnaissance, a four-engined medium bomber cruising at 280 mph and a four-engined heavy cruising at 250 mph. He elaborated on a plan to make the maximum use of Canadian industry, building completely fresh plants with experienced British management and with the fullest consultation with the US government, to concentrate on building four-engined aircraft and their engines for delivery by air to Europe. After many other general and detailed proposals he signed off with "The Aircraft Controller … would have to be fearless and selfless, and would have to have the courage and pertinancity to liquidate the army of 'spanner throwers' who, at the present time, seriously believe they are doing useful work, but in actual fact are continually sapping the vitals of the whole organisation".

There followed a number of discussions with Inskip, at which the Minister found himself cast in the difficult role of trying to fend off this champion of change by pointing out as many difficulties as it was possible to imagine. Some of Fedden's ideas were simply "too drastic" while others "could not be afforded", and the situation was to some degree the irresistible force meeting the immovable object. Inskip was a loyal servant of the Crown but apparently unable to appreciate that most of what Fedden was proposing might actually be sound and desirable; if he had come to realise that a war was coming, he hid the fact very well. A long correspondence ensued, which became increasingly strained as Fedden pointed out how many months were being wasted. At one point Inskip retorted that the concept of an absolute czar of aircraft production "is quite impossible having regard to our Parliamentary system … Our system is irksome and to some extent dilatory in its effect, but unfortunately we have to put up with it." Indeed he later went so far as "There are a great many things done in Germany which I should like to see done here if our Constitution, public opinion and our financial resources permitted". And he came to close quarters with "My criticism, if I may respectfully say so, of your document is that you assume an absence of action with regard to many of them, but your assumption is really not well founded … criticism based on want of knowledge is really just as mistaken as complacency".

There could hardly have been two more dissimilar English gentlemen than Fedden and Inskip. Both were deeply concerned to do their patriotic duty, but Fedden felt that vital time was being frittered away by inactivity and the foolish efforts of an army of people whose sole objective appeared to be to block any action. He was probably less in "want of knowledge" than anyone else in Britain. He instantly replied to Inskip, commenting, "After the most careful and detailed perusal of the various answers given by the government … I am quite appalled at what I believe to be the inaccuracies and misleading statements made … If this information was given with the direct intention of confusing the enemy, then I am, of course, willing to accept it, but if it is done purely to defeat political enemies and to impress the British public, then I think a grave wrong is being done".

Fedden waded in with numerous ideas and proposals, all prompted by his thorough knowledge of the desperately dangerous position of his country. Rationalisation of aircraft types, the training of engineers and national policy on aeronautical research all came in for vehement comment, and Fedden was especially concerned with Shadowing, which Inskip had suggested Fedden did not "fully appreciate" (!). Shadowing, said Fedden, "must go right back to the point at which adequate supplies or stored reserves are available … your remark 'the outlay would be formidable, and the return in peacetime negligible' applies most forcibly to the entire Shadow industry. A successful air raid on Sheffield would definitely bring the output of engines to a standstill for many months … it is essential to have an additional steel melting plant some distance from Sheffield, either in South Wales or Cumberland … " He turned to armament – Inskip rather asked for it, by remarking that Fedden had barely mentioned this topic previously – and related how impressed he had been with the 20mm Hispano cannon being fitted to some Bristol aircraft for export. "Having met the designer, I arranged for him to come over and stay with me, and I took him to a conference at the Air Ministry … At the end of an hour I was thanked for having brought my friend along, and told that nothing further could be done in the matter. My friend was absolutely staggered at our reception, and could not believe that the unenlightened views expressed were those of the Technical Heads of our Air Ministry responsible for our armament". Fedden also knew the 20mm Oerlikon when it was "a secret new gun … I took this report to the Air Ministry and described what I had seen. No real interest was taken, and I was told that it would be better if I really did not worry myself with armaments, but kept to my own job. I was very intrigued when I went to Germany last year to see this particular gun fitted to the latest German equipment, and to hear that about 2,000 were at present in service in the German Air Force". Fedden went on to comment on a debate in the House of Lords where soothing syrup had been poured on the question of RAF machine guns. The weapon in question was clearly the American Browning, and Fedden commented, "The technical position of these guns is by no means clear, the deliveries are not satisfactory, and most of the aircraft firms which I know of have nothing more than a wooden model of a gun".

Inevitably, Inskip eventually wrote, "I think it would be better not to continue the correspondence". Later in 1938 Fedden again saw the Air Minister, Sir Kingsley Wood, and got him to agree that there ought to be "a big hard core of highly qualified engineers and administrators". Fedden genuinely, and somewhat naïvely, thought that such exhortation might accomplish real results. It was at about this time that Inskip, having been told that Allen's of Bedford had discovered some of the tooling used to make the 140 hp Le Rhône rotary in 1916, had ordered that it should all be sent to Fedden "as I was sure it would prove useful". He was not being sarcastic.

In May 1938 Fedden was invited to a meeting with Inskip and Sir Warren Fisher, in the course of which he suggested Arthur (later Sir Arthur) Gouge of Short Brothers as a man who could run a master plan for airframe production. They then had a meeting with Gouge and other notable figures from the industry, before Fedden sailed on SS Bremen for New York. On the voyage he again wrote to Inskip, having promised to do so, "if the spirit moved me". He regretted "the inadequate and amateur organisation which is at present at the helm". He again set out the structure of a more effective government and industry system for trying to secure air supremacy for Britain – a structure which at that moment was being worked out for him in great detail by A P Young of the BTH company, who shared Fedden's feeling of helpless desperation. Ocean voyages gave Fedden the time to prepare mountains of words, and on his return from this trip he dictated major reports on RAF training, on how to compete with the United States in civil aviation, and on several other topics including a monumental review of the nation's supplies of material for engine production and what ought to be done to safeguard them in the event of war. If one ignored the clichés, the whole series of documents stood up as valid and helpful, but Fedden could discover no machinery in government for taking any action.

Between 11th and 14th October 1938 he made his last and most significant visit to Germany under the Nazis. He read a classic paper on the sleeve-valve engine, was an official delegate to the Lilienthal Gesellschaft conference (where he received the signal honour of the Lilienthal Ring) and also attended as President of the Royal Aeronautical Society, the great professional body of British aircraft engineers which played an increasingly central role in his life. On this visit he was no longer surprised at further expansions to the giant factories he had come to know well, and at the sinister feeling of a master plan that was to engulf the world. What bothered him unexpectedly was that at the impressive ceremonial dinner at the Neue Palais at Potsdam, at which he received the Ring from Hitler and presented the RAeS Gold Medal to Zeppelin commander Dr Eckener, there were other non-Germans present and they appeared to be completely overshadowed. At the centre table there was a gorgeous riot of colour from the Nazi uniforms. The only guests in evening dress were Sir Arthur Henderson, British Ambassador; Col Charles Lindbergh, representing the USA; and Fedden. Lindbergh appeared mesmerised by the scene, saying "We can't think of having a war … we aren't capable of fighting them, we must temporise – you British must continue to treat with them". This was precisely what Prime Minister Chamberlain had done two weeks earlier at Munich, and it was what Fedden had always predicted would inevitably happen, and go on happening, so long as one negotiated from a position of relative weakness. What disturbed Fedden was the speed with which the Nazis had overtaken their rivals in armaments.

It was at that dinner that Group Captain Vatchell, Henderson's air attaché in Berlin, confided to Fedden (to whom he was related) that he was required by the British government to send back, "encouraging reports"; he murmured "My dispatches must always make it clear that the tanks in their parades are made of cardboard". He also confirmed that, while the Air Staff regarded Fedden as of enormous value in providing abundant detailed intelligence on German aviation, he was extremely unpopular in the Government for his "dangerous scare-mongering". Even his German hosts were cool towards Fedden at one point on this visit. He had always truthfully professed to understand little German, yet at the dinner he delivered a fluent speech in that language. Lavrillé, head of his licence drawing office, had coached him with it, guttural noises and all, until he was word-perfect. It never occurred to him the Germans would think he was – as he put it – "a dirty dog".

Perhaps the most important moment of that trip was his encounter with Bruno Bruckmann, Technical Director of the great BMW engine firm, whom he had known for years. With disarming frankness the German engineer told Fedden "We have decided we do not need to acquire a licence for your Hercules motor. Not only do we hope to rival it with our own engines but we are developing a new type of engine for aircraft, a gas turbine". Fedden at once reported the fact to the Air Ministry, yet the emergence of a German jet engine towards the end of World War Two is supposed to have come as a surprise. He was never able subsequently to find out if any action had been taken as a result of this startling item of intelligence in October 1938.

When one recalls the British politicians of the 1930s it is difficult to come to any other conclusion than that these classically trained little men, with pin-stripe trousers and stiff wing collars, simply did not want to face the facts of the real world. They were, in fact, incapable of being "used" in the way the Nazi leaders had intended they should be used, with Fedden as the messenger; but this was for the worst possible reasons. When Milch chose to show the whole works to Fedden he was being Germanic and logical. Fedden would understand everything he saw and would report correctly; and, of course, he would be believed. The only agonising question that must have been running through Milch's mind was, "Suppose Fedden's reports, instead of making the British give up trying to compete, spur them into frantic rearmament?" Never for a moment did the Germanic mind guess that the actual reaction of the British government would be, "These reports are unwelcome and so we will either ignore them or pretend they are untrue and brand Fedden as a scaremonger". It was because Fedden had the logical

Installation of the Pegasus PE6S in the Bristol 138A, showing the ducting through the intercooler. On the right are the 70-gal main fuel tank topped by a 12-gal gravity tank, with the 10-gal oil tank immediately in front. (Rolls-Royce plc)

Germanic kind of mind that he judged that Britain ought to take notice of the Nazi menace, instead of burying its head in the sand. There were many other examples at the time of this almost incomprehensible attitude of the British Government, which appeared to be based on a vague belief that the menace of the German dictator would somehow go away. Fedden knew better.

By 1938 the British industry was at last working flat out, though it was still relatively puny in size. The number of Mercury and Pegasus engines built was much more than doubled between 1936 and 1938, and production of the Perseus also got into its stride. Three times the Pegasus made world headlines. In 1934 the Air Ministry ordered a special high-altitude research aircraft, the Bristol 138A monoplane, powered by a Pegasus with an M-ratio blower and with a separate airframe-mounted supercharger driven by a flexible shaft clutched in by the pilot at the normal rated altitude. The auxiliary blower boosted the main supercharger via an intercooler, and increased the rated altitude to 42,000 feet! On 28th September 1937 Sqn Ldr F R D Swain flew the 138A, using a special Shell fuel, to a world record height of 49,967 ft. On 30th June 1938 Flt Lt M J Adam took off from Farnborough after the 138A had been given a larger blower and finer-pitch propeller, and set a new mark at 53,937 feet. This was the sixth time Fedden's engines had taken the world altitude record in nine years. The third headlines came in November 1938. The RAF had formed a Long-Range Flight equipped with the Vickers Wellesley, the efficient monoplane bomber designed by B N (later Sir Barnes) Wallis to use geodetic basketwork construction. The Flight's aircraft had Pegasus XXII engines with non-standard long-chord cowlings and gills, running on 100-octane fuel and driving the new Rotol variable-pitch propeller with three magnesium blades. At 03.55 on 5th November the three aircraft, led by Sqn Ldr R Kellett, took off at the greatly overladen weight of 19,000 lb from Ismailia, Egypt, and flew non-stop towards Australia. One aircraft had to land at Koepang, but the other two reached Darwin to set a world distance record of 7,162 miles flown in 48 hr 5 min.

The Wellesley was one of 28 new types of aircraft for the RAF or Fleet Air Arm that used Fedden's engines. From 1937 the emphasis was strongly on sleeve-valve engines, the Perseus, Hercules and Taurus all being immediately accepted throughout the airframe industry for all classes of aircraft. The crushing burden of being responsible in a uniquely personal way for the engines that provided 52 per cent of the horsepower of the RAF and Fleet Air Arm had not changed Fedden in the least; it suited him perfectly. He was constantly serious, constantly preoccupied in intense thought, and constantly concerned to reduce the vulnerability of his operations. What would happen if the Engine Department was badly bombed? He drew up a plan for dispersal. The first move was to disperse the

Assisting Swain from the cockpit. On Adam's flight, an altimeter was mounted above the coaming in the 'gunsight position'. (Rolls-Royce plc)

Superficially resembling one of the special long-range Vickers-Armstrongs Wellesleys, K7772 was actually a test bed for the Hercules. (Rolls-Royce plc)

The biggest single application of Fedden's engines was the Vickers-Armstrongs Wellington, which took over 30,000. This version with Pegasus XVIII engines was a Mk VIII, with ASV (air to surface vessel) radar and a retractable Leigh light under the fuselage. (Rolls-Royce plc)

design and project staff, and he leased Tockington Manor, a fine house north of Bristol owned by Major Salmon, and installed Nixon and 12 project engineers there in August 1939. A second string to his bow was found at Fry's chocolate works on the other side of the city at Somerdale, whither the main design office was transferred. But he was unable to find a bomb-proof production factory, nor overcome his dangerous dependence on plants in Sheffield.

The most enduring of all his finds was the old mill on the Usk in Breconshire which had been in his thoughts since 1895. It was partly the splendid salmon fishing that attracted him, but mainly it was the feeling of peace and serenity. Buckland Old Mill offered him a bolt hole where he could briefly escape from the unrelenting tensions of his life. Soon after war broke out he bought the mill for £6,000 from Col Monty Llewellyn. He got a mile of fishing on both sides of the river. He and Llewellyn could not agree whether £250 or £500 was a fair price for the cottage where lived the keeper, a wonderful Scotsman named Law; they tossed and Fedden won. At first Fedden had only a living room and tiny kitchen, but gradually he extended the mill and created a dwelling place of extraordinary character that people who knew Fedden only at work might not have expected. The Mill endured throughout the rest of his life. So too did another property. It was in early 1939 that the Royal Aeronautical Society, seeking new premises larger than 7 Albemarle Street, found the superb house at No 4 Hamilton Place, available for £14,000. Secretary J Laurence Pritchard told Fedden and Devereux the money had to be found within an hour. The money was found, Dev. saying, "Let's have a go; Fedden and I will stand surety." It has been the Society's home ever since – and its value today runs far into seven figures.

In the summer of 1939 Fedden went to Norway on holiday. Like so many of his holidays it was really just an excuse to collect a lot of friends and customers and talk shop, but in the course of it Fedden drafted a long letter. He had for many years considered that his company was in need of reorganisation. To him it seemed incongruous that the Bristol Aeroplane Company should in 1939 have a structure almost identical to the one it had in July 1920. The family Board still presided in exactly the same way over a company which officially made aeroplanes. As an off-shoot it had an "engine department", which was very much a subsidiary with no representation on the Board. Yet by 1939 Fedden's 31 men had become 16,000. The number of engines delivered exceeded 26,200, with a value several times as great as that of all the Bristol company's aeroplanes. Fedden considered the company should be reconstituted either as two divisions of equal status or as two companies. He put this into his letter, together with many other suggestions concerning the long-term running of the company. He then put it into an envelope, addressed it to the company's managing director and posted it.

The following photographs show a selection of foreign aircraft powered by Pegasus and Mercury engines:

Letov S328 (Czechoslovakia, Walter Pegasus) (Rolls-Royce plc)

Junkers Ju 52/3m of LOT (Germany, PZL Pegasus) (Rolls-Royce plc)

Junkers Ju 86K-13 (built by Saab of Sweden with Pegasus from Nohab and PZL)
(Rolls-Royce plc)

Breda 46 (Italy, Alfa-Romeo Pegasus) (Rolls-Royce plc)

Savoia-Marchetti S.73 of SABENA (Italy, Alfa-Romeo Pegasus) (Rolls-Royce plc)

Savoia-Marchetti S.79 in Istres-Damascus race (Italy, Alfa-Romeo Pegasus) (Rolls-Royce plc)

Fokker D.21 (Netherlands, Bristol Mercury) (Rolls-Royce plc)

Fokker T.5 (Netherlands, Bristol Pegasus) (Rolls-Royce plc)

Fokker G.1 (Netherlands, Bristol Mercury) (Philip Jarrett)

PZL 37 L0s (Poland, PZL Pegasus) (Rolls-Royce plc)

Saab (Heinkel derived) S5c (Sweden, Nohab Pegasus) (Philip Jarrett)

CHAPTER NINE

The break

Young Marjorie was pleased to have landed the job of secretary to Frank Nixon. It meant that she would be helping to produce the Bristol engines on which so much of the Allied war effort depended. She had met Mr Nixon and liked him. The only thing that worried her was the ogre called Fedden. Everyone in Bristol knew that he was the head of the Engine Department, and his reputation was unique. She was terrified of meeting him, though she discounted much of the Fedden aura as mere embellishment. Surely nobody could be so inhuman, so forceful, so frightening? Hopefully she would never know. But the hope was a pious one. After she had been at work for about an hour on her first morning the door opened and a man appeared. He seemed to overwhelm the little office. Looking straight at her boss the monster said, "We agreed to meet in three minutes Nixon, it is now nearly four minutes". When she opened her eyes again both men had gone.

Just after the outbreak of war, RF (right) was visited by the Air Minister, Sir Kingsley Wood. On the left is Whitehead, with the head of Butler just visible behind him. (Rolls-Royce plc)

She did not at the time realise that she was herself unique. Until she came Fedden had refused to have a woman anywhere near the engine works. Clerks, stenographers, secretaries, tea ladies, charwomen, typists – all were men. It was popularly felt that Fedden would have been uneasy in female company, but the truth of the matter was that he considered they could not be driven as hard as men. Men would not be likely to burst into tears – though where Fedden was concerned even this was occasionally the case. Women were strictly taboo – until the Second World War made it essential to have them in their thousands. Then, eventually, Fedden even took on a lady secretary. And, far from regarding her boss as an ogre, she passionately idolised him. Fedden's apparent failure to notice this only served to exacerbate the situation; as far as he was concerned she was a machine, and a machine that worked well.

From 1930 Fedden's personal assistant team comprised three carefully selected young men of exceptional ability. Bill Evans was his assistant on technical matters and Arnold Clinton assistant on administration and company organisation. His private secretary was Harry Maddocks. Fedden's intense desire to help such gifted young men soon became submerged under sheer pressure of work, and the workload quickly grew to the point where four more young men were taken on as shorthand-typists. One of these, Eric Turner, understudied Maddocks, and in 1936 took over from him as private secretary.

Having someone so directly under his thumb as Maddocks caused Fedden to behave almost like a variety turn. The explosions were frequent, and every few days one of them would end with the unfortunate secretary being instantly fired. Early the next morning Fedden would stride in and call out to the little adjoining office "Good morning, Maddocks". He would have been shocked if Maddocks had not been there to reply.

Later Fedden collected four further personal technical assistants, all gifted engineers. First came Ian Duncan, a kindly and dedicated man. Adrian Squire was the son of the man who gave his name to the Straker Squire. Alex Moulton came from the Spencer Moulton family of rubber engineers whose buffer plates had been made by the company that became Brazil Straker. Peter Ware was the son of the carburettor expert with whom Fedden had lived before the First World War. All were picked out not because of their family background but because of their obvious great potential. At Bristol they acted as extensions to Fedden's eyes and ears, as highly technical secretaries, and ultimately as his ambassadors in dealing with customers and officials.

They were instrumental in maintaining excellent communications throughout Fedden's empire. But the link with the Bristol Board, which should have been the best of all, became steadily worse. In the United States, where Fedden could from 1925 have had any aero-engine job he chose (but was far too patriotic to think of such a thing), companies judge solely by results. Personalities do not enter into the picture at all. This was by no means the case at Bristol. In Fedden's view, the Board suffered from the vast superiority complex that until the Second World War characterised British aristocracy, and which the sufferer never knew existed. Fedden always remained an employee, and in his case the Board could see his complex only too clearly. It was a totally different one. Enigma he might be, but he was a man of destiny, and almost everything in his world was subordinate to his great mission. His mission was to make better engines for Allied air power, and nothing could deter him. If he could be contained within his own department he could be tolerated; but it seemed this was too small a compass for his giant mind. The letter he had sent Sir Stanley White in August 1939 had been regarded as a mighty danger signal. The Board never sent an acknowledgement, and did not for a moment consider the suggestions put forward. It realised the company ought perhaps to be restructured, but Fedden's detailed suggestions merely ensured that nothing would be done – yet.

As Fedden had never had any close contact with any of the Board he had no idea how sharply his suggested long-range master plan for the Bristol company had deteriorated their relationship. In any case he was far too busy to give it much thought. Under the redoubled pressures of war he had reluctantly been forced to relax some of his standards, on materials, on procedures and in many other ways, but as time went by it was eventually found possible to make many concessions on new engines and even more on repairs. This was despite the fact that the powerful Taurus and Hercules were far from out of the wood. Though the Hercules was earmarked for bigger production than any other Bristol engine, by an enlarged Shadow organisation with a vast assembly plant at Accrington, it suffered from many snags. In some aircraft, cooling troubles were severe. Sleeve drive cranks failed in fatigue after quite short periods, despite endless care to avoid fatigue in their design and manufacture. Supercharger gears acted as centrifuges and separated out surprising quantities of the insoluble lead salts which in the sleeve engines were passing into the engine oil from the high-octane fuel. Sleeves were being overstressed by thick oil forcing shut the spring-loaded ball vent valves in the cylinder heads. Bad trouble was met with both crankshaft and supercharger bearings. The double main bearing of the Hercules crankshaft was Swedish, and could not be duplicated by any company in Britain. Fedden had been assured that arrangements had been made for production in Britain, but war came before the British plant had got going. Bearings were henceforth shipped from Sweden to both Britain and Germany. Those sent to Bristol were sometimes smuggled by sea, but by

Three generations of Hercules: a display exhibit of 1937, a Hercules X SM of 1942 and a 2,000hp Hercules 230. (Rolls-Royce plc)

1943 speedy BOAC Mosquitoes were bringing over not only cargoes of bearings but also key Swedish engineers who eventually managed to produce acceptable bearings from the great Skefco (SKF) works built at Luton.

These difficulties increased the pressure on Fedden's team, and Eric Turner recalls those days clearly. In his office was a new Telecord machine which on wax discs recorded meetings held in Fedden's office around a table with a microphone. A meeting on cylinder trouble with the Taurus went on all day. At 4 pm a Beaufort crashed on the hill behind Filton, killing test pilot Chris Washer. The cause was swiftly shown to be the same hydraulic-locking problem. The dismal meeting continued until after 10 pm. Turner was busy typing from the Telecord discs and doing a first-order editing job to distil the substance of the discussion. After a drink at *The Plough* inn at Patchway he went on to 02.00 next day. He went by car to Frank Owner's house and, as Owner edited each page, re-typed a perfect copy for Fedden. He was finished by 0630. After lying on top of his bed at home for an hour he returned to the works. The crash report and minutes had to go to the Minister of Aircraft Production, Col Moore-Brabazon (later Lord Brabazon). After Fedden had read everything carefully a great deal was re-edited once or even twice, taking until nightfall. Then Turner took the report to London arriving at Paddington Station in the small hours. He got a taxi to Albert Hall Mansions, saw the housekeeper, told her he had to give the big envelope to the Minister personally and found him reading reports in bed, having previously had a late debate at Westminster. Brab looked over the tops of his half-lenses and boomed, "Thank you, that is all". Turner found a train that got him back to Bristol by about 8 next morning. He was 20 minutes late in the office, and was reprimanded by an irate Fedden who complained, "You were not here when I buzzed".

This little episode typifies Fedden at work. Was it necessary? Did the Minister instantly read the report, leap out of bed and call on the machinery of government? Would he have noticed if he had received no report at all? Did other leaders of industry make such efforts to keep him in the picture? Most of these questions are rhetorical, and Fedden would not have wasted time considering them. To him it was second nature to thrash out all the problems to the nth degree non-stop not only because men's lives were at stake – and, when nothing more could be done to report and recommend, second nature to spend what others might think an unreasonably long time in dotting the i's and crossing the t's of the resulting document, which might well approach in bulk a local telephone directory. It probably never occurred to Fedden that the Empire would not fall if he then merely sent the report through the post; immediate delivery by hand was taken for granted. But central to the whole task was how it was regarded by Fedden's lieutenants.

Turner recalls that particular panic with nostalgia, and neither at the time nor today feels any sense of rebellion or futility. Indeed, most of Fedden's old colleagues feel a stupendous debt of gratitude for what they increasingly regarded as a privilege, and the world's best training ground. Frank Nixon insists "We enjoyed the long hours, knowing that we were contributing something. Indeed I look back on my years at Bristol as some of my happiest, despite gossip to the contrary. There was a far better spirit of camaraderie than in many another firm, and a generally more relaxed attitude."

When people reminisce it is often difficult to determine what actually happened perhaps 50 years before. Alan W Bruce vividly recalls repeated failures of Perseus engines in the Fleet Air Arm. "I had been working on Hercules and Centaurus centre bearings, and also fitted the two high-power Hercules HE.6SM test engines with torquemeters built into their reduction gears. After the Battle of the River Plate failures of the Perseus engines in aircraft carried by the British cruisers [not so, the only Fleet Air Arm Perseus-engined aircraft were the Blackburn Skua and Roc, never catapulted from cruisers, BG] led to a panic search for the cause. Two engines were recovered and rushed to Patchway. I established at once that the sleeve cranks in the lower cylinders had failed because of hydraulicing (hydraulic lock caused by trapped oil) as soon as high power was reached on take-off. That was easy, but very exhaustive investigation, starting with the design calculations and ending with testing of surviving cranks, and careful reading of the Bristol service instructions, failed to reveal the cause. Not until later was it discovered that the Fleet Air Arm's own operating manual for the Perseus completely omitted the vital instruction to open the oil drain cocks in the junkheads of the lower cylinders before hand-turning the engine prior to firing the Coffman cartridge starter." Even more astonishing, Bruce is convinced that this was known all along. He insists "The investigation on which I had been put was nothing more than a 'blind'. I expressed my opinion forcibly, for which I was put on the mat by one of Fedden's personal assistants".

On top of the giant task of making the big sleeve-valve engines wholly reliable, despite the need to wring from them more and more power, the mighty Centaurus was in urgent need of development. Though it had first been type-tested in October 1939 at a power of 2,000 hp, subsequent development languished as the war effort demanded absolute priority on development and mass production of proven engines. Applications of the Centaurus were severely and tragically delayed. The Vickers Warwick bomber, which should have been in production before the War, did not even fly with the Centaurus until April 1940, and continued to be held up until it was technically superseded by four-engined heavies. Camm's Tornado fighter could have flown with a Centaurus in 1940 also, but the development of a good British fighter with a radial engine was – in Fedden's view – deliberately prevented by official bias, centered around Air Marshal (later Air Chief Marshal Sir) Wilfred Freeman. Freeman disliked Fedden as intensely as he liked Hives and his team at Rolls-Royce. The antipathy was quite open, and whereas Major Bulman's problems with Fedden never appeared to warp his judgement, Freeman never tried to exercise any judgement on Bristol engines save to reject them. When the Tornado ground to a halt through failure of the Rolls-Royce Vulture engine, the Centaurus could have been fitted to a specially tailored airframe within two or three months (Fedden sent Camm an engine in November 1940). In fact, to the disgust of Freeman, Camm did contrive to build a Centaurus-Tornado, and when he flew it in October 1941 it turned out to be the fastest fighter ever built in Britain up to that time. In its original form it reached 402 mph, but with a redesigned engine installation and four-blade propeller it reached 412 and then 421 mph. Later in the war with a Centaurus IV in a further redesigned installation, it reached 429 mph. Camm became enthusiastic, and managed to get a Centaurus fitted to one of his new thin-wing Tempests,

Three generations of Hawker fighters with Centaurus engines:

HG641, the Centaurus-Tornado (Rolls-Royce plc)

LA602, the prototype Tempest II (still with Typhoon tail) (Rolls-Royce plc)

Production Fury for Pakistan (Rolls-Royce plc)

which then (August 1942) was called the Typhoon II. Freeman was furious, and had the engine taken out again. In return Fedden said he wondered whether he could get Freeman impeached for seriously undermining the war effort. The Centaurus fighter was not allowed to fly until June 1943, by which time the excellence of the German Focke-Wulf 190 and American P-47 Thunderbolt had made it difficult for Freeman to insist that a radial-engined fighter must be inferior.

The above is one of the passages the author was less than happy with. He accepted it because Fedden virtually dictated it, but he was astonished that none of the text reviewers required it to be modified. To obtain a contrary view, Bulman writes "The implications that Freeman was a spiteful little man trying to harm the war effort in order to hurt Fedden, and that he was anti-Fedden and pro-Hives, would be ludicrous if they were not so libellous. Wilfred was appointed Air Member for Research and Development in 1936, replacing Dowding who went to Fighter Command. He was the most powerful Chief I ever had. His immense personality, his instant powers of decision and perception were an abiding tonic..." It was surely unfortunate that there was such a clash of characters between him and Fedden, which unquestionably did harm the war effort.

In any case, personal antipathy between Fedden and Freeman played little if any part in holding back the development of the Centaurus. The underlying reason why this otherwise outstanding engine played no part in the war effort until 1943 was simply that it was not ready for production. This was primarily because Fedden's development engineers were still too few in number, and they were seriously overstretched. Even when, in late 1942, the basic Centaurus was beginning to come "out of the wood", installed engines still suffered from imperfect cooling. As related later, overcoming this problem appears to have been assisted by Fedden's study of the enemy's BMW 801 installations. Through the darkest days of the War the tiny team assigned to ready the Centaurus for production succeeded only in assembling a succession of essentially handbuilt development engines. Some of these powered different marks of B.1/35 Warwick, but until the very end of the War all production Warwicks had the imported Double Wasp. Bristol's own applications, starting with the Buckingham, did not fly until well into 1943 (through no fault of the engine). Moreover, for fighters the Centaurus needed either a two-stage supercharger or an added turbosupercharger, and Fedden had nobody to spare for such effort.

Indeed, even the Hercules suffered seriously from the inadequate number of engineers. Quite apart from basic matters, such as the desperate need to produce satisfactory crankshaft main bearings in Britain instead of relying on Swedish products, the engine itself still suffered what by 1941 were recognised as design faults. Of these, the most fundamental was that the traditional snail-type entry to the supercharger was aerodynamically poor and was acting as a barrier to further increase in power, especially at altitude. Fedden was aware of this as early as August 1940, but other demands on his team were judged to have priority. Fortunately the RAE at Farnborough, notably Hayne Constant, studied the problem and suggested a direct axial (so-called "turbine") entry. This was developed in Bristol's Research Department by Neville Quinn. It enabled mass flow to be significantly increased. Another major advance was a redesigned cylinder junkhead, made partly of copper for conductivity, created by "Geordie" Lee, a Cambridge graduate seconded from Shell. This was an elegant solution to the problems of temperature reduction and ignition advance, but Fedden was unable to get it adopted; indeed, long after his departure, the Board minutes of 9.02.43 record that Rowbotham "abandoned Sir RF's scheme for copper inserts". Only much later were these improvements introduced for the Hercules and Centaurus, immediately bringing the former into the 2,000 hp class.

In the early months of 1940 it was obvious that, even with all the Shadow factories in full production, it would be impossible to deliver engines in the numbers needed. In particular, though there was as yet no production application, in due course the Centaurus would emerge as possibly the most important British aero engine and there was nowhere where it could be made in quantity. In April 1940 discussions began between the Board, the Air Ministry and the Canadian government to see whether a large factory could be built in Canada to make the Centaurus. Arguments revolved over whether the factory should be managed by Bristol, or by the Canadians (if so whom, RF emphasising that nobody in Canada had any experience of any precision manufacture) or by an American company. Whoever managed it, the factory would require American support (in particular machine tools), as well as a large number of Bristol staff (to RF's amazement, Rowbotham suggested "Whitehead and two assistants").

Finally, on 9th May 1940 Fedden and Frank Nixon sailed from Liverpool, hearing the following day of the end of the phoney war and the start of the *blitzkrieg* through the Low Countries. C D Howe, the Canadian Defence Minister, and leaders of Canadian industry were soon convinced of the importance of the scheme, which would have given an assured bombproof supply of the most powerful engine the Allies possessed. Alfred P Sloan, the famed head of General Motors, wanted the factory located in the United States, but he and his production wizard William Knudsen, Director of what later became the War Production Board, finally agreed to help all they could with experienced managers, tools and equipment. The company was to be formed jointly by Bristol Aeroplane of Canada, Vickers and Alcan, and it was to be a very big undertaking. One snag was the US embargo on export of machine tools, but Sir Henry Self, head of the British Purchasing

Commission in Washington, and Arthur Blaikie Purvis, a brilliant British millionaire who was a director of Du Pont, managed to obtain a waiver of this rule from President Roosevelt so that the big Bristol project could go ahead.

Fedden never suggested as much, but it is possible that his enemies in Britain – who did not exist only in his imagination – may have sabotaged this plan, because it never came to fruition. Just as the last major obstacle seemed to be cleared, the phone rang beside Fedden's bed in a New York hotel in the middle of the night. It was the British Minister of Aircraft Production, a post just created by the new Churchill government (and precisely what Fedden had urgently campaigned for three years previously, and been told was quite impossible). Lord Beaverbrook, rightly called "The Beaver", told Fedden brusquely to drop everything and come home at once. "And, could you bring with you as many magnetoes as possible, we're desperately short of them". Before Fedden could ask him the number of cylinders the magnetos were to serve, the Minister had rung off. Fedden guessed (correctly) that nine-cylinder magnetos were needed, and he managed to get 1,000 packed into two crates. His ship, the *Britannic,* was sunk by a U-boat on the return trip, on the day France fell. Fedden lost most of his baggage, but the vital cargo for The Beaver was unscathed. When he eventually arrived at Liverpool Fedden found a man with a Ministry car waiting to whisk him to The Beaver's presence.

"The Beaver" saw it as his duty to do everything in his power to make aircraft pour from the factories. He didn't care what aircraft, so long as there were more of them. In this he was unconsciously emulating an outlook common in Nazi Germany and even in the Soviet Union. New designs, which might win a long war but which were not already in production – such as something at de Havilland called the Mosquito – were instantly cancelled. As soon as he heard about the proposal to make the Centaurus in Canada he said "I'm not interested, I want Fedden recalled".

As soon as they met, Beaverbrook wrung Fedden's hand and said, "Did you bring those carburettors I wanted?" Fedden had no trouble sorting this out, but the next question stumped him. It was, "Fedden, how long will it take you to pack up at Bristol and join me?" It was almost 20 years since Fedden had been asked this kind of question, because the thought of his leaving Bristol was known to be ridiculous. He asked the Minister what he had in mind, to be told, "You are to be my chief liaison official with the United States. Everyone tells me you know America better than anyone else. You will be invaluable to us; there are countless things you can get cracking on right away". Beaverbrook was amazed and incredulous when Fedden said he could not leave his three great sleeve-valve engines, and when he actually said he thought he was doing a better job at Bristol the Beaver snapped,

"What rot, don't you understand I need you … Go away and think about it". Fedden still refused. Sir Stanley White said he was grateful for Fedden's loyalty.

This loyalty was tested even more keenly just a year later. Fedden found himself trying to kill an hour before having an evening meeting in blacked-out London. He actually went to the cinema, naturally leaving word at the Royal Thames Yacht Club where he could be found. During the film a message was flashed on the screen for him to call at the box office. There he was requested to proceed at once to the new Citadel building at the Admiralty. He went, sent in his name, and at once was greeted by Brendan Bracken, MP, the Chief Parliamentary Secretary to the formidable Prime Minister. "Terribly sorry to trouble you, but Mr Churchill wants to see you. I'm afraid we can't disturb him at present, there's a big naval engagement going on". The *Bismarck* was being hunted down in the Atlantic, and Churchill was following the operations continuously.

Fedden had come to know Churchill well in the 1930s. Both had shared a deep common interest in watching Hitler and trying to prevent Germany from gaining an unassailable military lead. They had met frequently. Churchill several times came to meet Fedden at the Bristol Yacht Club and spent hours listening in great detail to all he had seen and heard in Nazi Germany, and he had come to regard Fedden as the leading figure in the whole of British industry. Once, after a stormy meeting with what could fairly be called "little men" at the Air Ministry, Fedden in exasperation said he was going to report to Churchill. So shaken was the meeting that for days afterwards Fedden was dogged, and the telephone rang wherever he was to ask his whereabouts. So in May 1941 Fedden had no cause to fear the imminent meeting. But when he was ushered in at 3 am next day, to find the Prime Minister in a dressing gown, smoking a cigar and in direct radio contact with the fleet at sea, he soon wished he was far out in the Atlantic himself. Churchill said, rather formally, "Mr Fedden … I want you to give up your job at Bristol and come and take over the whole of our engine production for us". Fedden began, "Sir, I am honoured that you should ask me to do this, but … " Churchill interrupted with, "WHAT? I demand that you should do it!" Fedden had no doubt in his own mind that he ought to refuse – and to make him doubly sure, the man who held the post that was offered happened to be a close personal friend. But Churchill was not unlike Fedden in many ways. The refusal shocked and angered him, and he not only never forgave Fedden but never contacted him again.

Fedden also ran foul of Beaverbrook in a more trivial way. Yet perhaps it was not so trivial. The Beaver, visiting Bristol, asked Fedden how it was that nobody was smoking, and was told "It is not permitted". "Of course it can be permitted", said Beaverbrook rather testily. Fedden began to argue. "Look,

Sir, you could not allow a man on a precision grinder in the toolroom, working to a tenth of a thou, to have a fag in his mouth …" But Sir Stanley White snapped, "Shut up, Fedden, you're living in the past". And this was in a way perfectly true. Fedden increasingly longed for the "good old days" when everyone worked and worked and worked. The outbreak of the Second World War was the final spur to changes which resulted in what Fedden came to regard as the unfortunate modern world where nobody needed to work at all. He was very far from being the tyrannical employer of the Victorian era; indeed, he forever protested "I was always champion of the underdog. This caused many eyebrows to be raised, but my early life had taught me to understand the lives and problems of others". What he abhorred was the thought of able-bodied men giving less than their all. To him the Welfare State, characterised by government management of one's life, by subsidies, by excessive smoking, by free hand-outs, and above all by sapping the rewards of hard work, could only lead to ultimate disaster. To him there was nothing on Earth so richly rewarding as hard creative work, or even merely hard work as a cog in a big and worthwhile machine. In his early days in industry this attitude was universally taken for granted, but he gradually discovered an extraordinary new outlook which decreed – in deeds rather than words – that one should do as little as possible for as much as possible. This freedom to smoke at work was, he thought, just one more step along the road to ruin.

Much earlier Fedden had smoked himself. He had preferred a pipe, but one day he decided that smoking was a pointless and undesirable habit. He immediately threw all his pipes away, and never gave the subject another thought. It was part of his religion of mind over matter. He never seemed to think about food and drink either, though to be knowledgeable about such matters was naturally essential in order properly to entertain others. Serving the grosser needs of the flesh – in any way – was an inferior preoccupation, and took time which could more profitably be devoted to important things.

One of these important things was constantly to lay the most careful strategic plans for the future for as far ahead as could be seen. From the mid-1930s he had ceaselessly worked to rationalise and strengthen not only his Engine Department but the broadest possible spread of British industry. With the collaboration of Bowyer and Goodinge of the SBAC, he worked his way through the entire spread of topics where design or material could be standardised: sparking plugs, pipes and fittings, circlips and other small parts, accessory drives and mounting pads, mechanical control runs, propeller shafts, and numerous families of steels, light alloys and other metals. After looking carefully at the concept of a separate APU (auxiliary power unit) to drive accessories, he concluded that the main engines were a preferable source of shaft-power and got Rotol – under D R Pobjoy, who had earlier produced engines under his own name – to design and develop standardised accessory gearboxes mounted on the airframe to drive all aircraft accessories. The package was undisturbed by an engine change, and indeed could be driven *in situ* by different types of engine.

Going beyond this, Fedden had been concerned to discover in 1936 that the Germans were one jump ahead of him. The *Reichsluftfahrtministerium* had directed the development of engines in the form of complete "power eggs" which could be removed from the airframe and replaced swiftly. As engines in similar power classes were made to be installationally interchangeable, it would in theory be possible to swap engines of quite different types in the same aircraft, or change the whole Luftwaffe engine programme without affecting the airframes. This was a powerful advantage to German aircraft programmes. Fedden at once talked to Hives to see how far this would be possible in England. Though at first the products of the two companies seemed to be utterly dissimilar, genuine unstinted collaboration under pressure of war gradually made it possible to emulate the Germans. Unfortunately, the further the work went, the more it was held back by Ministry red tape and real or imagined industrial jealousies, and it reached fruition only towards the end of the War. Fedden could see no reason why it should not have been standard practice in 1939.

Even more heretic than making different engines interchangeable was Fedden's ardent belief that for the War there should be fewer types of engine. He suggested concentration on Bristol and Rolls-Royce. In fact this would have favoured Rolls commercially, because at the start of the war Bristol had the lion's share of the market, but most observers – especially those who knew Fedden – instantly thought this a plot to expand his own empire. The company hardest hit would have been Napier, whose Sabre engine took years to get right – at one point Freeman reluctantly asked Fedden whether Whitehead could briefly be lent to Napier to help, and he soon cut the rival's oil consumption by half – and eventually the harsh force of business competition brought about even greater rationalisation than Fedden sought to gain as a matter of wartime expediency. But, at the time, his advocacy of such a policy was consistently misunderstood and suspected.

One way in which his farsightedness was thwarted was in what he considered the most vital long-term matter of all: the constant supply of good young engineers. When he had discussed the matter with Hives in 1932 the Rolls man had gone back to Derby and at once laid the groundwork for a large apprentice school which stood the company in good stead in its subsequent huge expansion. Fedden not only had to fight his Board, who gave in only when the Education Minister was persuaded by Fedden to pay half the capital cost, but he also was restricted in the allowed size of the school – many of whose graduates were then promptly re-assigned to the aircraft side of the firm. The result was that the Engine Department, at that time the biggest aircraft engine centre on Earth, continued to be a poor relation that was desperately short of properly trained technical staff. The work load was thus beyond human endurance, and some of Fedden's closest associates – including Butler, Harvey Mansell, and Harry Higgins, who managed the Experimental Shop – gave up their lives long before their time in testimony to the fact. Shortage of staff was also the dominant reason why the department was increasingly unable to keep abreast of its technical problems, let alone ahead of them. From 1937 onwards the whole department had been, for all practical purposes, on a war footing; and by 1939 there were whole programmes that were beginning to slip, despite an average working week by the entire technical staff of about 75 hours. (D E Collett recalls that a typical week would be: Monday 08.30-17.00, plus 2½ hours overtime to 19.30; Tuesday 24 hours non-stop, from 08.30 to 08.30 Wednesday; the rest of Wednesday free; Thursday, 35½ hours non-stop from 8.30 Thursday until 19.30 on Friday; Saturday, 08.30 to 13.00. For this he would take home about £4.75. The thing that mattered was getting the job done).

Despite such toil, there were more and bigger jobs to do, and the company inevitably began to slip a little behind Rolls-Royce, which had by this time approximately twice as many qualified engineers. One example of the

This Vickers-Armstrongs Wellington V was powered by the Hercules VIII with two-stage mechanical superchargers. (Rolls-Royce plc)

slippage was the great Centaurus, which was in any case – with incredible ministerial shortsightedness, one might judge – never allowed to occupy the time of more than a very small staff. Indeed many of the strategic decisions of the period 1939-42 completely ignored the needs of a long war calling for new and more advanced aircraft. Another was the development of the Hercules for high-altitude flight. In 1938 Fedden, then ceaselessly looking for new developments, had schemed a very advanced compound engine. The basis was a Hercules, but all it drove was a large two-stage mechanical blower; an exhaust-driven gas-turbine was geared to the propeller. The arrangement was in some ways similar to the Nomad engine later attempted by Napier in the 1950s. Rig testing showed great promise, Butler prepared detailed drawings for the complete engine, and an especially important finding was that the sleeves could work happily with the high exhaust back-pressures. With the outbreak of war the project was dropped, the Ministry view being that it was "of a long-term nature" and thus not needed. But work continued on the high-altitude Hercules VIII for the pressurised Wellington V, one family having a two-stage mechanical supercharger and intercooler and the other having the American GE turbocharger. Neither ever saw

Mock-up of the Hercules HE15 with GE turbosupercharger. (Rolls-Royce plc)

production. Fedden said he felt this keenly, and took "full responsibility for these failures", but in fact the Ministry and the airframe contractors could have achieved success had they co-operated. As it was, it was policy to leave high-altitude flight to the Americans.

Fedden's empire was beginning to show tiny cracks. One which was so gradual he did not particularly notice was that Norman Rowbotham, who had returned from Gnome-Rhône to become engine works manager, was a very active political animal. Rowbotham was quite unlike Fedden; he was a charmer, and he soon got on good terms with the Board. He gradually assumed control of the entire production side of the department, and by 1940 Fedden began to realise he was losing personal control of this side of the department. Rowbotham, the Shadow industry tycoons and the Ministry – as personified by Freeman – appeared to be campaigning against him and trying to sap at his authority.

Fedden's standing with the Board had in any case taken a major turn for the worse after his unsolicited long-term master plan of August 1939. He had no personal contact with the Board from then until Christmas 1939, when he was abruptly sent for by the Chairman, Sir William Verdon Smith, who was a great and tactful man. "Ah, Fedden ... I want to talk to you about the matter of your commission, paid to you on engines sold to your design. As you know it was to be in the amount of one-half per cent up to a total of £200,000 and at one-quarter per cent thereafter. In 1920 we were thinking in terms of Jupiter engines priced at about £1,000, sold in twos and threes. Now we are selling engines priced at many thousands of pounds, and we are selling them by the thousand ... ." Fedden broke in at this, and protested, "What you say is perfectly true, but our production is increasingly of sleeve-valve engines, and I have never had a penny royalty on any of them ... In fact, I consider I am being harshly treated on these engines, which are entirely my brainchild." The Chairman expected this and quietly commented, "When your 1920 agreement was drawn up we had no thought that it would involve such sums. The amount of your commission has reached a very high figure, and we are having difficulty with the authorities. I am afraid that we cannot go on under the present arrangement." He had had similar interviews with other Bristol designers, who had offered no argument.

Fedden considered briefly, and then offered to take a much reduced commission, and moreover to make it retroactive to the extent that he voluntarily handed back a sum in excess of £200,000. In the United States such a situation would have been unbelievable. Fedden was being penalised for being too successful, to the extent that the Board, pressured by the Government, were treating him like a spoilt child and refusing to honour a carefully drawn up legal contract. It was fundamental to Fedden that he did not, like most men, have to work to earn a living. The job itself, principles, honour, these he thought much more important things. For many years he had done almost all his business entertaining at Widegates, apart from that done afloat or wading in trout streams. By the end of 1939 this had cost him at least £3,000 – then a vast sum – but he had never thought of sending in an expense account to the Board. He gradually came to believe that this lavish entertainment out of his own pocket, which would otherwise have had to be paid for by the company, was in fact a cause of smouldering jealousy. It was one more thing that his growing band of enemies disliked. They imagined Fedden not only lived like a lord but made a good income with inflated expense accounts.

Sir William Verdon Smith knew this was not so. When Fedden made his generous gesture on the matter of royalties, he said, "I'm glad, Fedden. I think this clears the air. I can offer to extend your present six-year agreement to 1945, after which we propose to offer you a pension and consultancy." But Fedden replied, "I'm sorry, Sir, but you have not referred to my constructive suggestions on company reorganisation. I do not feel I can enter into any new arrangement with a company which appears unwilling to support my suggestions ..." Sir William more quietly replied, "I'm sorry that you have raised this matter. I am saying nothing whatever about the worth of your suggestions, which do not enter into the argument. But I must tell you that the Board took exception to your letter. It would really have been better had you not written it."

The rather strained interview ended by Fedden saying, "I am sad that our relationship should not be better. But in this time of national crisis I hope you will agree I should stay at my post. I will agree to serve the company for the duration of the War and for six months afterwards." The Chairman accepted this gentlemen's agreement, but nothing was put into writing.

One of the changes increasingly levelled against Fedden was that he was reluctant to move into the secret new field of gas turbines. This was precisely true. Frank Whittle had come to see him in March 1931, and Frank Owner had sent a report to his boss affirming that "Flying Officer Whittle's gas turbine proposals are entirely sound in principle and will certainly come to pass ...". But Owner doubted that this would be for another ten years, which was a shrewd guess. Privately he told Fedden "A centrifugal blower of the highest efficiency known, driven by a turbine running at a temperature we consider it could withstand, wouldn't pull the skin off a rice pudding". In later years Fedden often quoted this last remark (which is also attributed to Hives, at Rolls-Royce); he undoubtedly felt defensive where gas turbines were concerned.

In fact this reluctance was based on common sense. Other British firms were doing all the gas turbine work that appeared to be needed or that industry could handle. The great sleeve-valve engines were vitally needed

Luftwaffe map showing the Bristol Aeroplane Company at left and the Engine Department at upper centre. (Ken Wakefield)

An inverted enlargement of the preceding photograph showing the main engine works (1), Rodney Works (2), the old West Works (4) and the runway (6). (Ken Wakefield)

Mr Butler 19 FEB 1931

Have you any Comments. A.H.R.F.

~~No 2 FLYING TRAINING SCHOOL,~~
ROYAL AIR FORCE,
~~DIGBY,~~ Felixstowe
~~LINCOLNSHIRE.~~
16.2.31.

Mr A.H.R. Fedden
Chief Engineer
The Bristol Aeroplane Company.

Dear Sir,

I enclose the first instalment of a brief summary of my work and opinions, I'm sorry that it is not yet complete but the field covered is rather large. I will send on the remainder as soon as it is complete.

You may be interested to hear that I have received a letter from Kearton, a well known authority on turbines and turbo compressors, in reply to one from me. He confirms one of my major arguments, and confirms my method of working generally, in that he gives two worked examples using exactly similar methods.

I may have some difficulty, after all in getting over on Friday, but I shall know definitely tomorrow when the C.O. returns. I will wire if I cannot come. I hope I am not inconveniencing you, but I hope you will understand.

Yours faithfully
F Whittle.

18 FEB Recd

Whittle's letter to Fedden (Rolls-Royce plc))

war-winners upon which must be lavished every ounce of development energy. The Engine Department team were grossly overworked, and to launch forth into the completely new arena of gas turbines would probably prove disastrous. And how could anyone be sure gas turbines would make any contribution to the war effort? Later Fedden derived great comfort from discussing the matter with his close friends at Wright and Pratt & Whitney, the leading American aircraft engine firms. They too had decided the war must be won on piston engines. Others, such as GE and Westinghouse, former steam-turbine companies previously outside the aviation industry, could look after the revolutionary new jets. But the pressure from Freeman and Bulman on Sir Stanley White was incessant – "You really must get Fedden to snap out of it; piston engines will soon be obsolete and you won't have an Engine Department left". Gradually the cry was taken up by some of Fedden's own staff, but it was a superficial and unfortunate view.

On 25th September 1940 removal of the Engine Department was attempted more abruptly by the Luftwaffe. In that week the enemy's attacks suddenly switched to the aircraft industry, and it was Bristol's turn on the

Memorial to those killed on 25 September 1940 (female staff Christian names in full).
(Rolls-Royce plc)

Wednesday. A large force of Heinkels, completely unmolested, came in from the Bristol Channel and accurately bombed the works, the worst damage being sustained by the Engine Department's enormous new plant at Patchway. One large bomb hit a personnel shelter, killing 25, and the total killed outright numbered 99. One was Tom Copley, a renowned aerodynamicist who had left Fedden's staff at the outbreak of war but had come back to visit his former colleagues. Another was Fedden's personal assistant on the Centaurus programme, Adrian Squire (young Moulton was summoned to take his place). That evening, as a glorious sunset filled the sky beyond the Welsh hills, Fedden – who had been at Air Ministry that day – chatted with a solitary works policeman on the main gate at Patchway. When he got home to Widegates, after midnight, he found that, though it was almost five miles from Filton, a stray bomb had demolished the house completely.

On the Friday the Luftwaffe came again. They did not know that a squadron of Hurricanes had been detached to Filton on the previous day ready for such an attempt. When the sirens sounded thousands of workers

RF at the wedding of his niece, Mrs Elizabeth Thomas, in the garden of the recently bombed "Widegates". (Mrs Elizabeth Thomas)

streamed out of the works, across the Gloucester Road and into the surrounding fields. They saw the Hurricanes rout the big enemy formations, shooting several Heinkels down; not one bomb hit the works. Fedden, however, was to experience further personal loss at the hands of the Luftwaffe. He was a wealthy man, and could always buy another house; but there were two properties he could not replace. One was a marvellous collection of Bristol glass, which he had built up from before the First World War, and hardly a single piece escaped destruction at Widegates. The other possession that meant much to him was his enormous collection of trophies, nearly all of them for sailing or power-boat racing. Most of these were salvageable, and he carefully collected them from the ruins and took them to a silversmith in Bristol who spent weeks restoring them to something close to perfection. One day around Christmas 1940 the job was done; Fedden was told by telephone, and he said "Oh good, I'll collect them tomorrow". Early next morning he drove into the city centre, finding the way blocked by firemen's hoses and heaps of rubble. The premises of the silversmith had received a direct hit. This time there was nothing worth salvaging.

Fedden gathered together what possessions he had left, and moved into a suite at Tockington Manor. More of the staff were dispersed to temporary project and design offices. One was at Leny House, Clifton, and another at the Pavilion at Clifton Zoo. The team at Somerdale was enlarged, and work began on what Fedden had finally concluded must be started at the earliest possible date: a new engine much more powerful than the Centaurus. Under the revived name Orion, a study was made for an 18-cylinder radial with a bore of 6¼ in and capacity of 4,140 cubic inches. It incorporated several features planned for future models of the Hercules and Centaurus. One was an exhaust system with the pipes discharging straight to the rear from aft-facing ports. Another was a new design of head consisting of a close-finned copper base, with nickel-plated flame face, shrunk into a steel body. The Orion was drawn in detail by Butler in early 1941, and promised to be a superb engine rated at an initial power of about 4,000 hp. Several airframe constructors welcomed it, and Arthur Gouge (Short Brothers) and Rex Pierson (Vickers) began projects for large bombers and flying boats using four or even six. Such very big machines appeared certain to be needed – in peace, if not during the War – and the one thing Fedden wanted to avoid was having to couple together groups of smaller engines.

With the Centaurus he had what appeared to be the most powerful aero engine in the world. With the Orion added at the top end of his family he considered the Bristol company would be able to offer an unbeatable range of engines, not only to win the War – which he said in 1941 would probably last until 1946 – but also to win the fierce commercial battles of the ensuing peace. Fedden was frankly and totally committed to the sleeve-valve piston

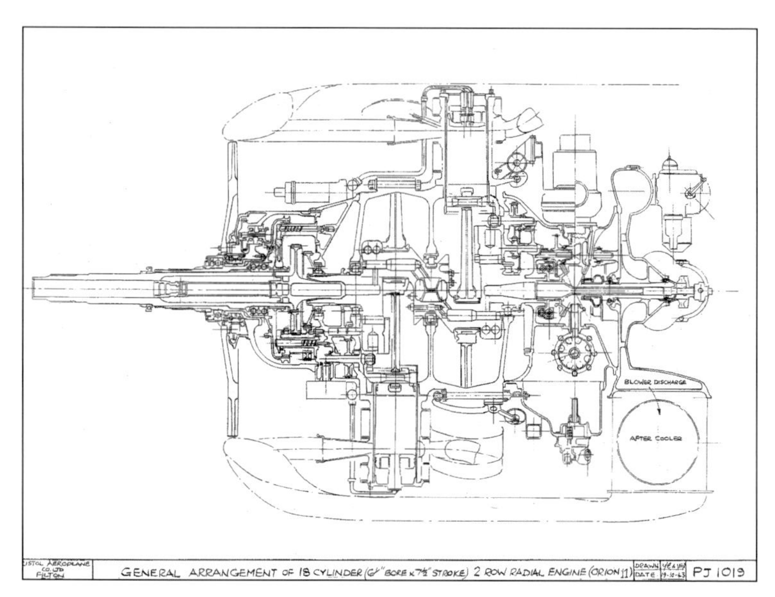

18-cylinder Orion (traced from original by Dave Gardiner)

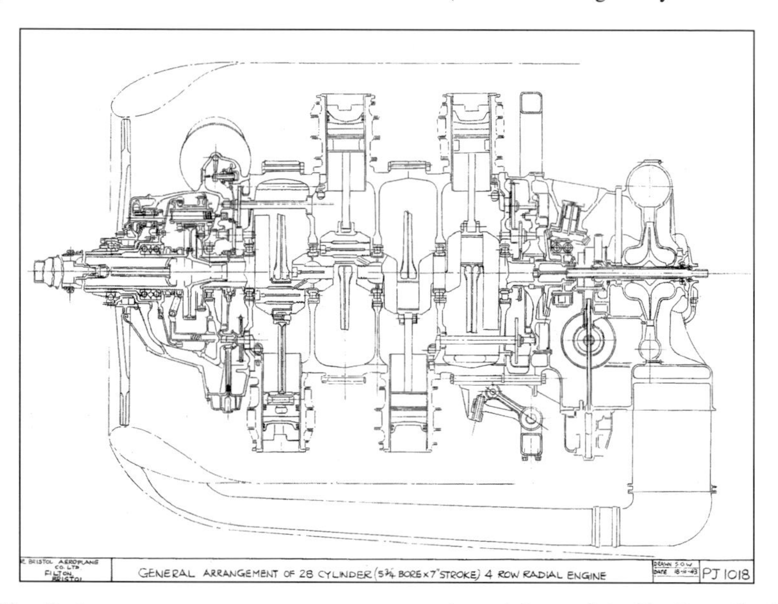

The 28-cylinder (traced from original by Dave Gardiner)

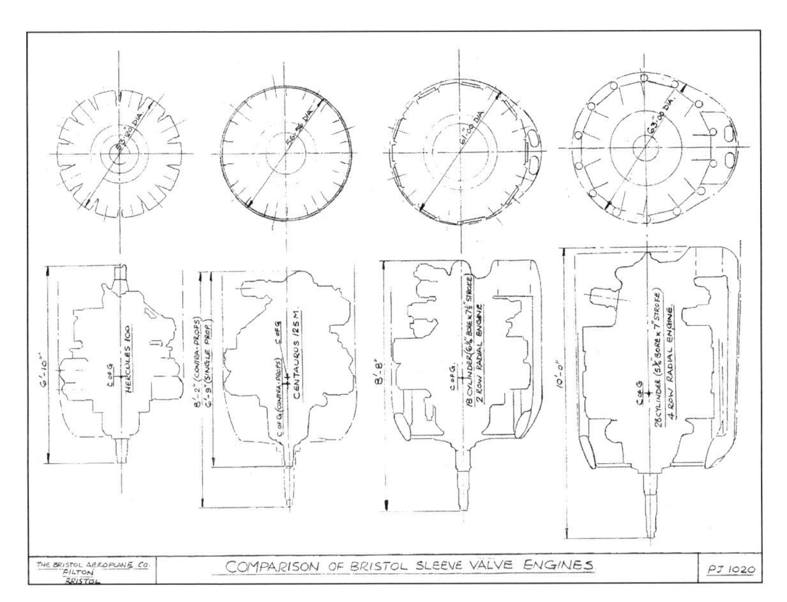

Comparison with Hercules and Centaurus (traced from original by Dave Gardiner)

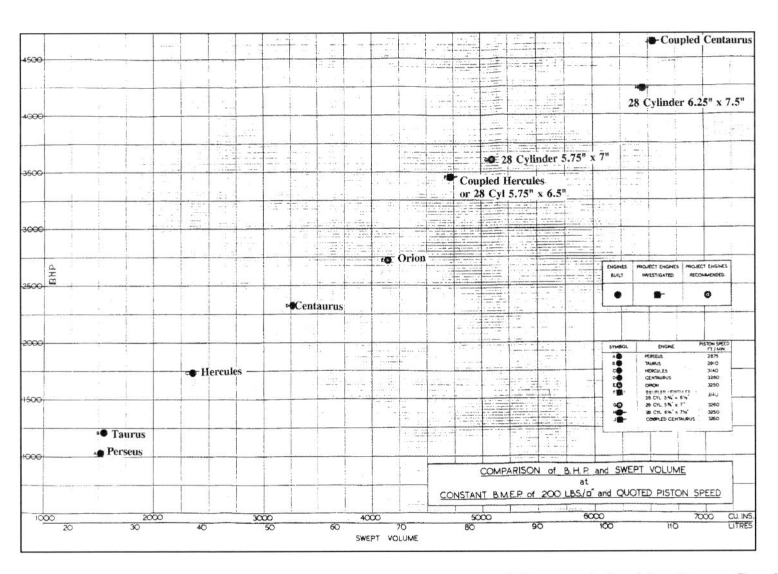

Predicted power output (traced from original by Dave Gardiner)

engine, which he was certain would be needed up to at least 1955 and probably later. He had no doubt his company could – if it had the strategic judgement and motivation – be the world leader in piston aero engines during the whole of this period, providing the foundation for a world-beating series of British aircraft. It is characteristic of Fedden that, in early 1941, in the grimmest period of the War and long before the formation of any Brabazon Committee to study the problem, he was deeply engaged in considering the design of the aircraft for the post-war period. It was partly because of this that he appreciated the importance of the Orion.

Despite this, he kept studying gas turbines. Though these were officially judged less important for the country's immediate needs than established engines, he had by the end of 1940 come to believe that they would soon develop beyond the "skin of a rice pudding" stage, and he noticed that no company was paying much attention to gas turbines other than plain turbojets for short-range combat aircraft. By February 1941 he had decided to start a project for a quite different kind of engine: a turboprop, with a specific fuel consumption no higher than an equivalent piston engine at a speed of 300 mph at 20,000 ft. The relatively low speed was because he intended it for large, long-range transport (and possibly bomber) aircraft of

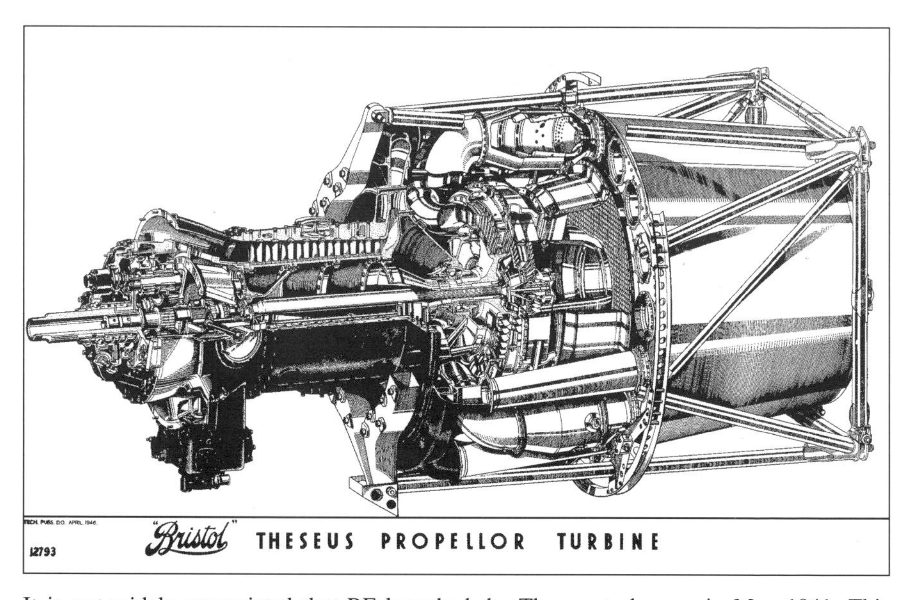

It is not widely appreciated that RF launched the Theseus turboprop in May 1941. This drawing, dated April 1946, shows the heat exchanger on the right.
(Note incorrect spelling of propeller!) (Rolls-Royce plc)

the post-war period. He considered it should be a direct rival to the Orion, and asked Owner to study an engine sized to give 4,000-5,000 horse-power. But, by the time drawings began to take shape at Tockington it had been halved in size, to speed development and avoid, as Fedden said "biting off more than we can chew". It was named Theseus. One of its unusual features was that it had a mechanically independent turbine to drive the propeller. Another was that it was schemed with an optional heat exchanger to reduce fuel consumption.

Though the Ministry of Aircraft Production were extremely slow to contract for any Theseus hardware, Owner's turboprop project staff grew as the work of designing the engine increased, and by the end of 1941 the basic design was completed. So too was that of the Orion, but again Fedden could obtain no authority from the Ministry or the Board to go ahead; and in this case he was deeply troubled, because the timescale was much closer. Even the existing piston engines were not driving ahead in the way he wished, largely because the Engine Department had grown an entirely separate production organisation under Rowbotham and Roger Ninnes, backed by the Board. This was cut off from Fedden's control. Rowbotham became ever more smooth, gentle and agreeable, especially where the Board was concerned. His management of the huge Shadow factory at Accrington was exemplary, and he not only gained the confidence of the Board but was recognised as a possible man to replace Fedden – which was exactly what he had in mind. Like Fedden, he had been bombed-out in September 1940. It may have been significant that Sir Stanley White invited Rowbotham to come and live with him. Eventually Fedden believed that his colleague was missing no opportunity to tell Sir Stanley of Fedden's adversities or supposed shortcomings. This campaign supercharged the highly political atmosphere, until – whether they wished to or not – the senior staff in the Engine Department found that they were being drawn into the tangled web. Each man had to decide if he was for Fedden or against him. Most tried to stay non-committal, but it seemed obvious that matters would have to come to a head. Indeed the Board were soon openly discussing the possibility of replacing Fedden by Rowbotham. All they lacked was an acceptable reason.

On Monday, 1st January 1942 Fedden went by train to London for a Ministry meeting. Settled in his first class compartment he opened *The Times* and found, in the New Year Honours List, under the heading Knights Bachelor, his own name. He had been told the news by Lord Brabazon a week earlier, and it gave him a great thrill. The following day he called the senior staff together in the main drawing office and told them the news, pointing out that the honour was really to his entire team. He was merely the figurehead. To his amazement and distress he found that what he had come to regard as "Rowbotham's clique" were indignant, even answering him back and saying they disagreed with the honour. For years Fedden had considered that he was the victim of jealousy; suddenly this had become open and intense. He fully appreciated there might be mixed feelings up at Filton House, but he never expected anyone to be against him in his own team.

Daily he waited for comment from the Board. On the Wednesday Butler organised a quiet and sincere cocktail party, but not a word came from the Board – though a day or two later he received a very brief telegram of congratulations from Sir Stanley, sent from his home. What had happened was that the Board regarded Fedden's knighthood as very much the last straw – and a stupendous shock. Previously he had been merely a handful; in future he would be impossible. Sir Roy! They could not bring themselves to accept it. In Fedden's view, "They deprecated this dreadful turn of events as if it was wicked. Within three weeks it was obvious they were out for my blood. I was ignored, passed over in taking decisions … they made things so impossible

A group at New Filton House on the occasion of the visit of the Minister of Aircraft Production in July 1941. Front row, from the left: N Rowbotham, G S M White, H S Thomas (Assistant MD), Sir Stanley White Bt (MD), Rt Hon J T C Moore-Brabazon (the Minister), Sir W G Verdon Smith (Chairman), J Eaton, J Eaton Griffiths and RF. Rear: C O Worth, Capt Cyril Uwins, L G Frise, Maj G H Abell, W A Fernie, Capt K J G Bartlett and H S Pollard. (Rolls-Royce plc)

for me it broke my heart." Fedden never outwardly showed any emotion, but from the start of 1942 it was painfully clear that his life at Bristol was never going to be right. He determined merely to hang on, work as hard as he could, and leave as soon as the War was won.

But on 6th February 1942 he received a brief letter from the chairman giving him six months' notice. On requesting an explanation he was told the Board were dissatisfied with his handling of the executive side of his department, "but", said Sir William, "I do not wish you to leave; we merely desire to change your terms of employment in the form of a new agreement". The proposed arrangement ignored the unwritten gentlemen's agreement of December 1939; it curtailed Fedden's authority as chief engineer, gave the company the right to dispose of his services at six months' notice, and appeared to Fedden to be "incompatible with my ability and established position within the company and in the country". He stated that he intended to abide by the gentlemen's agreement for the period of the War.

Time dragged on, the Board refusing to make the slightest compromise or meet Fedden half-way. He got on with his work as well as he could, in circumstances of extreme tension. The great Centaurus was beginning to move at last, partly because of the shock inflicted by the arrival in Britain of Luftwaffe aircraft powered by the BMW 801. The first to be examined was the Do 217E bomber, examples of which were used over England by KG2 from the last weeks of 1941.

Ken Lemoir recalls how, early in 1942, one of the Dornier bomber's BMW 801A engines was sent to Rex Goldby's office, with its bent propeller blades the only evident damage. Mounted upright, it was divested of cowling, and Fedden came to see it the moment it was free. Lemoir "will never forget the reaction of the great man on viewing this amazingly compact assembly 'Now that's what I call an installation masterpiece! How on earth do they cool the pots? Mr Goldby, get your men to do a stage-by-stage breakdown of this conglomeration, and let me know when each stage is ready for viewing'". Lemoir remembers that, though the axial cooling fan, colour-coded baffles and peripheral oil cooler were all impressive, Sir Roy's attention was focused on the rear-swept exhaust pipes. "He was aware of the existence of something of this nature because of the small frontal area of the installation in the Fw190 fighter, but this was the first time he'd seen it in the flesh … The idea was introduced on the Centaurus shortly afterwards. Likewise was the addition of an induction fan to the rear of the spinner … I've appreciated more and more in my mature years the fact that Sir Roy could openly admire the engineering genius … of an enemy in time of war".

On 23 June 1942 an Fw190A-3 landed by mistake in South Wales. After inspecting it Fedden said "It was an engine installation far superior to anything we have achieved in this country". Though true, this hardly went

The BMW 801A, studied at Bristol in early 1942. (Rolls-Royce plc)

down well with Sydney Camm, but the Hawker designer appreciated the urgency with which Fedden's installation engineers worked on the proposed Centaurus-powered Typhoon II. They improved the whole front end of the aircraft, sweeping the exhaust pipes to the rear and arranging for them to discharge in neat groups on each side recessed into the front fuselage. All excrescences, such as the oil cooler and carburettor air intake, were submerged, reducing the frontal area from 23 sq ft to 18.6 sq ft. On 8th July 1942 Fedden told T O M Sopwith of the Hawker company of "a most successful type test at 2,280 horsepower" of the CE.4 engine; very soon this power was raised to 2,375 and then to 2,520 hp in the production engine, designated Centaurus V. The engine was installed as a "power egg" for easy removal, and Hawker's calculations confirmed what Fedden had preached for nearly 25 years: that an air-cooled radial could have less drag than any other piston engine and make a fighter go faster. Ultimately the Typhoon II was renamed Tempest II, and it went into production as one of Britain's fastest fighters in 1944.

Centaurus engines were used in many other types of aircraft. In RF's opinion, Bristol themselves were "barking up the wrong tree" with the Buckingham (he was right), but he had high hopes of the proposed Super Beaufighter, though Frise and his team could see nothing but problems and in the end gave up on this promising aircraft. Another "vastly improved aircraft" which came to nothing was the Centaurus-engine B.8/41 Super Stirling, but that still left a growing demand for this engine in the 2,500 hp class. To build them Fedden, after campaigning for seven years, at last got his bombproof factory. It was a token realisation of his pre-war exhortation that vital industry should go underground, and to bring it about there had to be interminable meetings and endless paperwork before the last obstacle was surmounted. Corsham, about 20 miles east of Bristol, was a disused stone mine. After trucking out thousands of tons of "gob", the interior was swept clean and the long galleries filled with machine tools and other equipment to make the Centaurus. Bungalows were built for workers, men were transferred from Bristol or recruited locally (not easy because no skilled men, or even fit men, were left) and any woman who would come was welcomed. It took time for conditions to settle – at first, on a bright spring day, there would always be a waist-high fog inside – but eventually, after a lot of staff and management changes, the unique plant got into its stride. Ultimately it was popular, the apparently germ-free atmosphere resulting in an extraordinary absence of colds. The man who finally got the plant humming, Fedden's former apprentice Cyril Luby, built up an impregnable resource with 800 personnel on development and 3,200 on production. This was what Fedden had longed for in the pre-war years.

While Fedden's personal situation dragged on in a steadily deteriorating way, he did his best to run design and development, while Rowbotham – by now openly the Board's protégé – managed production. During 1942 Fedden introduced injection-type carburettors for both the Hercules and Centaurus, the first types being imported from the US Bendix company but later switching to a Hobson product designed at the RAE. He also got an Orion single-cylinder rig running, with remarkably fine results. Meanwhile, he brought in a firm of engineering consultants as efficiency experts, and succeeded in making many of the staff very cross. Today no experienced manager would do such a thing without fully briefing the whole staff, but Fedden was far too busy. It never crossed his mind that any difficulties would ensue, yet it was the general – but wholly erroneous – view that the objective was to produce an independent report recommending that Fedden be given control of all technical work throughout the Bristol company. When Sir Stanley heard about the proposal to have outside experts study the company's procedures he said "Right, they can begin with the Engine Department". Fedden was, as always, merely seeking a solution best for the company, but Bill Evans, chief experimental engineer, emerged from

Two generations of Centaurus: a Mk XVIII (later written Mk 18) for a Sea Fury, with magnetos on the rear cover; and a Centaurus 661 installed in an Ambassador with Hobson direct injection, LT generator at the rear and HT distributor at the front. (Rolls-Royce plc)

Fedden's office one day shaking with anger, saying "He's had the consummate gall to put these bastards in over Butler" (who was universally adored). Even Owner, having been refused his requested title of chief designer and then seen three months of his planning torn up by one of Fedden's reshuffles, eventually was driven to hand in his notice to Sir Stanley – Fedden having, as always, said "Never mind, dear boy, come back in the morning and tell me you feel better".

In the midst of the drama and tension something happened to bring a moment of light relief. Alex Moulton, a singularly tall and good-looking young man, had occasion to enter RF's inner sanctum at Tockington Manor to collect a document from the lady secretary. A few moments later he came to Peter Ware's office, visibly shaken, and the following conversation ensued:

"Peter! Do you know what I've just seen? I had to go and see Miss ... – and I found her flouncing about on the bed, stark naked!"

"Good God! You mean she's making a play for you?"

"Heavens, no – it's RF ... the poor chap was there, and he didn't know quite what to do. One moment he would tell her to get dressed, and the next he would turn away and look out of the window. He was extremely embarrassed."

It was all the result of the previous months of strain. Peter and Alex told nobody, the secretary recovered her composure, and nothing of the kind happened again (she stayed). But RF was the last man on Earth to get mixed up with what he would have called "that sort of thing"!

In July 1942 Fedden had consulted Col Llewellyn, the new Minister of Aircraft Production, who had agreed to back him on a written proposal that he should be retained as chief engineer during the War, with "complete

The Bristol sleeve-valve cylinders: from the right, Taurus, Perseus/Hercules, Centaurus and Orion. (Rolls-Royce plc)

freedom of action in all matters concerning design, quality, testing and installation of aero-engines". He thought he was being overgenerous in surrendering production, but when the Board saw the phrase "complete freedom of action" they laughed aloud and said, in effect, "over our dead body". There followed weeks of delicate negotiations between the Minister, the Board and Fedden (never all round a table together). Eventually the Minister considered he had won for Fedden a three-year contract with the title of technical controller, and asked Fedden to collaborate. Fedden agreed, with grave inner doubts based on the fact that the supposed agreement was full of ambiguities. He had written to the chairman asking for "a restoration of confidence and getting together", but received no reply. Fedden had been advised to go on an extended tour of the rest of the industry; he then returned to Bristol. He found the situation, if anything, worse. He was asked to sign a document which gave him greater responsibility yet tied his hands completely. He advised the Board and Minister the document was unworkable.

By the middle of September 1942 the situation appeared hopeless. Though the Minister did his best to achieve compromise, and requested that no drastic action be taken, the Board were intransigent. On 1st October Fedden received a brief letter from the Chairman forbidding him to carry on with any

de Havilland D.H.95 Flamingo (Perseus) (Rolls-Royce plc)

Bristol work; he was told to leave the premises, and not even permitted to empty his desk of personal possessions. On the next day brief official notices were issued announcing that Fedden had left, and that arrangements were being made to take over his work. The Minutes of the Directors' meetings show (06.10.42) that "It was to be understood that the Chief Engineer had decided to absent himself, in accordance with the instructions conveyed to him by the Chairman in his letter of 30.09.42.

That evening Fedden called Owner, Stanley Mansell and many other senior staff to a big design and research meeting at the Rotol guest house at Battledown Manor. They worked through a 16-page agenda, covering not only the whole of 1943 but also looking far into the future and laying down plans for how Bristol's Engine Department would meet future needs. Fedden was at the top of his form: "I want this done ... that must be done with all possible speed ... we must pay particular attention to this, and leave no stone unturned ..." Nobody liked to comment that it all seemed slightly unreal, as the central figure would not be coming back any more. The future – for the Engine Department as much as for Fedden – seemed a void.

The following photographs (including the one on the previous page) show a selection of aircraft powered by sleeve-valve engines:

Fairey Albacore (Taurus) (Rolls-Royce plc)

Gloster F.9/37 (Taurus) (Philip Jarrett)

Short S.26M Golden Fleece (Hercules) (Rolls-Royce plc)

Short Stirling V civil conversion (Hercules) (Rolls-Royce plc)

Handley Page Halifax B.III (Hercules) (Rolls-Royce plc)

Short Solent (Hercules) (Rolls-Royce plc)

Handley Page Hermes 4 (Hercules) (Rolls-Royce plc)

Nord 1401 Noroit (SNECMA-built Hercules) (Rolls-Royce plc)

Blackburn B.48 (Centaurus) (Rolls-Royce plc)

Vickers-Armstrongs Warwick GR.II (Centaurus) (Rolls-Royce plc)

CHAPTER TEN

A fresh start

The traumatic shock of the departure from Bristol of Sir Roy Fedden was almost beyond belief. Few things to compare with it have ever happened in industry. Several of the senior staff of the Engine Department described it as "almost unbearable". There had never been a Bristol Engine Department without him. He was so titanic a character, ruling his now enormous engine empire with such overwhelming personal influence, that for weeks after his departure many of these staff went about as if in a dream. This applied even to the clique that had worked for his removal. That such a clique existed is beyond dispute, and such political feuds tend to happen in all kinds of human societies; but the length, depth and intensity of this particular feud was exceptional. Sir Stanley White breathed a sigh of relief when Fedden had gone, because from his point of view the situation had undoubtedly been very difficult. With Norman Rowbotham as the new chief engineer there would be no difficulty at all. The Board soon appointed him a director of the company, together with two other working directors, one from the engine side and one from the aircraft side. The Directors' Minute Book soon recorded that "The Chairman congratulated Mr Rowbotham on the excellent work being accomplished by all concerned", something which would have been utterly inconceivable during the reign of RF. It all seemed to be plain sailing; but Fedden's absence could not merely be glossed over like this.

Political feuding if anything increased. To make up for the sudden absence of long-term technical direction men were shuffled about in all directions, but to no good effect. Bunny Butler had had a heart attack some months previously and Fedden had taken great care to see that he never had to exert himself physically or bear any great stress; but Rowbotham, totally out of his depth, leaned on Butler more and more heavily, sending him on frequent conferences with the Ministry until early one morning he fell dead on the platform at Paddington Station. One by one, most of the senior staff departed, until the fine team was dispersed. Even in the short term the departure of "the Centaurus's father" was a disaster, and the fierce pace of development slumped – in the midst of the Second World War. In the long term the company's engine policy simply fell to pieces. Despite the great interest shown in the Orion, Rowbotham thought it would be "sounder policy to work on lines like those of Pratt & Whitney and go for a Double Hercules". He got the design office to start drawing this 28-cylinder four-row engine, and also an 83.5-litre engine of similar design but with 28 Centaurus cylinders. Ultimately nothing came of these, and the Orion I and II were cancelled. Little attempt was made to exploit the other piston engines to rival the Americans, and the inevitable result was that the world's airlines, including BOAC, were soon flying on American engines almost exclusively. Not until after 1955 did the name of Bristol again become important in aircraft propulsion, as a result of the efforts of Owner (who before long had to take over from Rowbotham) and Stanley Hooker to develop competitive gas turbines. By this time the Bristol Aeroplane Company had been reorganised into Bristol Aircraft Ltd and Bristol Aero-Engines Ltd. Not only was this what Fedden had recommended in his "unfortunate letter" of August 1939 but these were the very names he suggested.

It is no simple matter to try to explain why the architect of the Bristol Engine Department should have been sent away from his post, where he was doing as much to win the war as any other single man except Churchill. Root causes must be sought at the roots, and one cause is clearly the surprising inability of Fedden and the Board to communicate. In a biography of Fedden, especially one written after many long discussions with the man himself, it would be simple to explain it all by saying that the Board were narrow-minded, inbred, and merely expected all their employees to touch their cloth caps and remember their place in society. The Board may have been autocratic, but they were also great men, and Fedden's own view was one-sided. It was largely his great and all-consuming enthusiasm for progress that continually blinded him to more mundane and immediate problems. Coupled with his jaundiced view of the Board and the poor communication between the two sides, the situation could never be put right.

Sir Reginald Verdon Smith, son of Sir William, draws attention to the departure of Sir Henry White-Smith in 1926. "He was a strong personality in the Company, and had exercised a vitally important control over Fedden's indomitable enthusiasm. Fedden would ruin any business he ran unless he was effectively controlled, and the remarkable feature of the great years up to 1939 was that, by and large, he got a mixture of backing and restraint which he would have been unlikely to receive anywhere else." There is no doubt that Fedden was correctly assessed by the Board as incapable of taking an all-round objective view of the matters that most concerned him. In the austere early days, before the Jupiter had begun to win markets, he had no choice but to do so if the little team was to survive. Unfortunately, the very success of the Jupiter removed this spur of self-preservation, and the tragic departure of Sir Henry left him free to run the Engine Department his way. Fedden revelled in this period, but according to Sir Reginald, "He involved the firm in many serious difficulties, both in failing to meet over-optimistic delivery promises and in over-running cost estimates, largely due to endless design changes. It was this situation which led to the introduction of Rowbotham and Ninnes to bring discipline and order into engine production, whilst leaving Fedden in full charge of design and development." There was thus a bit more to it than the supposed toadying of Rowbotham to the Board.

Fedden imagined his worst enemies to be such people as Rowbotham (trying to erode his position at Bristol) and Freeman (anti-Fedden and pro-Hives). In fact his worst enemy was unquestionably himself. Instead of regarding Rowbotham as a creeping worm trying to undermine him, he ought to have paused to consider why the Board should ever have felt it necessary to remove production from his control; but his vision was clouded by feelings of jealousy and intrigue. Instead of regarding Freeman as a spiteful little man trying to harm the war effort in order to hurt Fedden, he should have asked why it was that almost everyone else judged Britain's wartime director of aviation development to be one of the greatest of men. Freeman probably did tend to favour Rolls-Royce, and he certainly subscribed to the widespread and wholly incorrect belief that the fastest aircraft needed liquid-cooled engines; but this should merely have spurred the Bristol team to instal their engines better. Twenty years earlier Fedden would have met such a situation by greater effort at communicating the facts and greater effort to prove the facts, but by the Second World War he had long since totally failed to appreciate that anyone could hold sincere, and possibly correct, views that differed from his own.

His world revolved not around business and money but around engineering. Though he was not a formally qualified engineer at all, he was yet a brilliant intuitive engineer, a gifted designer, and as great a leader of a team as there has ever been. On matters of a technical nature he was invariably right, and where he could not clearly see the answer he immediately sought the opinion of others. If necessary he did not hesitate to seek advice outside Bristol, though not from any of the other British companies building aero engines. His close personal friendship with the leading American firms, Pratt & Whitney and Wright, was quite extraordinary for the time (though today it would seem normal), and on many occasions his staff were able to discuss immediate problems over the transatlantic telephone. But on broader matters, such as the allocation of shareholders' money to the company's competing resources, he was unable even to discuss the matter objectively. As far as he was concerned, he could see with crystal clarity that certain decisions (at any time) needed to be taken to improve his engines. If taken, such decisions would improve the Engine Department's future marketing, and thus benefit the company and the nation. Anyone who put forward a contrary view could not expect reasoned consideration but would be viewed by Fedden as a wrecker sapping at the vitals, as someone jealous of his Department, or a man with a personal grudge.

He was his own worst enemy, again, in that his consummate wish not to offend often caused offence. He had an unhappy knack of framing his utterances in a way carefully designed to be polite – much more polite than was common in industry – yet which had the effect of being intensely irritating. His spoken style was overtly extravagant, while his outpourings of written matter – though edited, retyped and then polished and polished again – seldom had the effect he intended. Though brash clumsiness was something he abhorred, he had such a monumental lack of tact that he achieved even worse results with his painstaking care. Tragically, this was especially the case on the many occasions when real diplomacy would have been the only way to achieve his most worthy objectives.

He was in many ways an enigma. When the writer knew him, from 1950, he was unfailingly the personification of old-world courtesy, even at his most exasperating. He often seemed to have a deep-seated sense of humour, an asset one suspected to be there but which he took pains to conceal. Some of his colleagues agree with this belief, yet others dismiss it, and point out how, late in life, he asked Lady Fedden if she could teach him to have a sense of humour – a request made quite formally as a serious project. Others who knew him well return time and again to the phrase "a man of destiny", suggesting that he was a man obsessed with the importance of his mission and little concerned with creature-comforts for himself or others. Some flatly state that he was, in the strict medical sense, a paranoiac: a sufferer from delusions of his own grandeur and external persecution. Yet others who worked with him for many years disagree. Frank Nixon, for example, says "Delusions of grandeur? Man of destiny? Never in a thousand years! He was far too humble, and it was partly his sense of inferiority that caused his troubles with the Board. In the most private discussion with a confidant he would sometimes indulge in self-pity, a thing he would never dream of doing in public; this now occurs to me as possibly one reason why he so often used attack as a substitute".

The truth is possibly that even his closest colleagues often failed to understand the true man. Nixon has probably got him accurately, yet humility is the last attribute that anyone would normally associate with Roy Fedden. His presence was powerful, and his colleagues knew only too well that a few minutes with him could leave them "sucked dry, wilting like a limp rag". Major Bulman likewise knew how difficult would be each fresh conference with Fedden, once acidly asking "Do you really think me a traitor, because I disagree with you?" (Later Bulman was appointed Director of Construction and Research Facilities, and Freeman roared with delight – "They've made you DCRF: Director for Coping with Roy Fedden!") The Board constantly thought him capable of literally anything to accomplish his own ends, and during the final break did not automatically discount the prevalent rumour that in his negotiations with the Minister he was seeking to get the whole firm nationalised with him in sole charge. If it was humility, Fedden always hid the fact.

Adversity is a better test of a man than is success. There are many successful men who, suddenly brought low, never make it back again. Had he been a lesser man, Fedden could easily have failed to find anything he considered right for him to do, and faded into obscurity nurturing feelings of bitterness. What actually happened is more interesting. Though he quite failed to learn the obvious and important lesson from 1942, his future was to be as great as his past.

Traumatic as was the shock at Bristol, it was no light matter for Fedden. He told the writer "I wallowed in my own self-pity. Looking back over the affair I can now say it came as a blessing in disguise to me. I had had far too much success in life and this jolt did me a power of good. Secondly, had it not been for this unhappy event I should never have had such an interesting and much better time travelling all over the world. I certainly lived a much happier life in a more modest job, being absolutely independent and able to say exactly what I thought."

In the middle of the Second World War Fedden did not have to be at a loose end for long. Though the Bristol Board tried discreetly to let it be known that he, rather than they, had made the break inevitable, it is a fact that job offers came from all points of the compass. Fedden truthfully, as he thought, professed to have no interest in politics; but he chose the main political job offered: Special Technical Advisor to the Minister. The STAM was a post created for him, and he filled it with predictable devotion.

He had worked with Ministers and officials since his Brazil Straker days. During the Second World War he had had an extra ministerial contact that only a few knew about. This stemmed from a letter written on 21st June 1941 by the PPS to the Minister of Aircraft Production to the Secretary of the Royal Aeronautical Society. "Dear Pritchard", it began, "Colonel Moore-Brabazon ... would like to explore the possibility of making more use of the Society in the way of advice on technical problems of interest in the development of aeronautics ..." The Minister wanted expert, unbiased advice on deeply technical matters, often involving the highest degree of security. Sir Henry Tizard, then the Scientific Advisor to the Air Staff, had sought Fedden's opinion on whether the idea was sound. Fedden went to Tizard's rooms at Imperial College and said "I believe it is, but it will be difficult and entail a great deal of tact." But the RAeS Advisory Committee to the Minister was formed in July 1941, with Fedden as Chairman.

Fedden considered the work of this committee one of the high spots in his life. Every member of it was a leader of the British aviation industry, yet each served in his own time, as an individual, "having no regard to the interests of his firm." Subjects for review were raised by both the Minister and the

Committee. Hundreds of specialists, engineers, staff officers and back-room boffins were interviewed. Reports, sent by Fedden direct to the Minister and not via the Society's Council, covered: the high-speed twin-engine day bomber; British engine policy; airscrew blades; contra-rotating airscrew; 110-octane fuel; wheel sizes and tyre pressures; desirable operating height for night bombers; ratio of production to development effort; dive bomber and ground strafing; standard constant-speed propellers; US production policy; high-speed day bomber (again); future powerplants; technical v production policy relative to the war; Operational Requirements liaison between Air Staff, MAP and industry; large bomber; low-level attack aircraft; jet propulsion; F.6/42 specification; gas turbine heavy bomber; post-war civil aircraft; helicopters; next five years of piston engines; landing large aeroplanes; contra-rotating propellers (again); future armament; magnesium; pressurised aircraft; powder metallurgy; beryllium; post-war aircraft policy; and the Aeronautical Research Council. The committee also quickly prepared numerous letters, ranging from such broad topics as the relative merit of a few superior aircraft compared with numerous slightly inferior

The Advisory Committee to the Minister at the Royal Aeronautical Society in 1943: Arthur Gouge (Short), Sir Ralph Sorley (Controller of R&D), Capt J Laurence Pritchard (Seecretary of the Society and of the Committee), visitor Dr Theodore P Wright (Administrator, Civil Aeronautics, USA), Sir Stafford Cripps (Minister of Aircraft Production), RF (Chairman), Sydney Camm (Hawker), Rex Pierson (Vickers), Dr Leslie Aitchison (James Booth and University of Birmingham) and C C Walker (de Havilland). Missing member Roy Chadwick (Avro). (Author)

ones, to specialised subjects such as defeating the flying bomb menace in the summer of 1944.

Meetings, held every two weeks, lasted four or five hours. Their minutes form a fairly complete record of aviation technology in Britain in the Second World War, apart from the hearing of evidence from Harold Roxbee Cox (later Lord Kings Norton) on jet propulsion, which was then judged so secret it was never recorded in writing. The committee was certainly unique in Britain. While some Ministers suffer from too many advisors, this committee undoubtedly exerted a significant and wholly beneficial influence on British aviation at a crucial period. Some of its recommendations were not acted upon, and others would have come to pass in any case, but on the whole the Advisory Committee to the Minister was outstandingly effective.

In early 1942 Brab was replaced as Minister by Col Llewellyn, who was glad to continue to avail himself of this expert advice. Two of the important meetings held in that year were the hearings of eminent Americans; Dr Edward Warner on 14th August and Dr Theodore P Wright and members of the US Technical Mission on 19th October. As a result of these meetings the Committee recommended that a major UK Mission should be sent on an extended fact-finding visit to the USA. The Minister accepted the proposal and, knowing how things were going with him at Bristol, asked Fedden to lead the mission. It was Col Llewellyn who, when the final break came, invited Fedden to be his STAM, though he was replaced by a new Minister before Fedden took up the post. This important new job, coupled with urgent planning for the US Mission, prevented Fedden from brooding over the heartbreaking time he had suffered at Bristol. Instead he had to move for the first time in his life to London, acquiring a house in Trevor Square and then, when this building was bombed, moving to a flat in Wellington Court, opposite Harrods. Each day he would drive to Berkeley Street, park his grey 2-litre Talbot at a small hotel and go to his office in Cook's Building next door. Thomas Cook, the world-famous travel agents, were unable to continue regular business in 1942, and their office became a secure establishment inhabited by various secret MAP departments, most of them dealing with radar. Fedden built up a little empire, quickly importing Ian Duncan and Mr and Mrs Rex Goldby, the latter couple to take charge during the mission's absence (Mrs Goldby had been Nixon's secretary, who opened the preceding chapter).

Fedden was outstandingly well qualified to lead a mission to America, knowing the country, the people, the technical subjects and even the inner politics in a rare combination of skills. The one thing Sir Roy – as he was universally called at the Ministry – lacked or ignored was Civil Service protocol and finesse. Without caring too much about it, he soon put not a few noses out of joint and made a few enemies, despite being most carefully steered by that urbane and vastly capable man Lord Hankey, Secretary to the War Cabinet. The one man whom he simply had to get on with, apart from the Minister, was Sir Archibald Rowlands, Permanent Secretary; and, even though Fedden told him "I'm not a career Civil Servant; I've just been asked to help the Minister, and I'll tell him exactly what I think, no matter who I offend", the two never crossed swords. But – predictably perhaps – Fedden thought some of the more junior staff were "cold and jealous".

As for the new Minister, Sir Stafford Cripps, Fedden considered him absolutely splendid. He called in his advisor on the first morning and said "You have the reputation of being a stormy petrel. That does not bother me in the least. I like people who are prepared to shoulder responsibility." From the start Fedden found himself on the receiving end of a stream of memoranda from the Minister, most of them requiring action. He soon gained the impression that the new Minister was far from being "one of the boys" and that many politicians disliked him intensely. Cripps was not of their ilk: he was an academic, a classically educated left-winger, and a strict vegetarian who appeared to sustain his spare frame on grated carrots. Yet with Fedden there was perfect harmony and trust, and mutual admiration.

Fedden's mission to the United States had the broadest terms of reference: to find out everything of interest in new aviation technology and make recommendations. Verbally Fedden was also asked to keep an eye open for outstanding aircraft which might be produced in Britain. It was an assignment of limitless proportions, and Fedden was realist enough not to try to do absolutely everything nor gather an unwieldy team. The people he chose were: Duncan (general assistant); J Lloyd, W Tye and D M A Leggett (airframes); M B Berks (works organisation), S P Woodley (aircraft production) and W W W Downing (factory planning); B G Markham and N S Muir (engines); C G A Woodford (electrics); and A H Tiltman (manuals, photo lofting and self-sealing tanks). It was a good team; almost all became famed in their spheres.

The mission left by sea on 20th December 1942. George Dowty happened to be aboard the same ship, and was not a bit surprised at what he saw: "Immediately breakfast was finished the whole of his team were taken down to a cabin where they were kept hard at work until lunchtime. As soon as lunch was over they were taken down again and continued work until an hour before dinner. They were not allowed alcohol, but as a diversion they were permitted to go to the gymnasium for a stint at medicine ball! After dinner was over they were sent to bed." It never occurred to Fedden he was in any way unreasonable; he simply was determined that his team should remain constantly on the top line, and spend every available minute planning their mission. Fedden doubtless knew he would have to relax his tight rein when they arrived.

This was very true. Since 1775 Britain had never been so popular in the United States, and American hospitality was lavish. But the war underlined the need for hard work, and under the general guidance of Robert A Lovett, US Assistant Secretary for War, the team covered 40,000 miles, much of it in two Lockheed C-56 Lodestars of the Army Air Force. Seconded to help the mission were an Army Air Force colonel, a Navy Lieutenant, and three of the most renowned men in US aviation, Dr T P Wright, Grover Loening and Dr Edward Warner. Two specialists from the new Pentagon Aircraft Production Board were added, and for short periods the mission was also joined by such famed people as General J B Wolfe, Professor Jerome C Hunsaker and Dr Clark B Millikan.

Early in the mission Fedden listed the following factors which had deeply impressed everyone: the size and scope of engineering departments; flexibility of manufacture in spite of the colossal scale of production; rapidity of introduction of modifications based on combat experience; control of jig and tool offices and planning departments; breakdown of production operations; and intimacy of liaison between design and production. After a week or so the mission had become so impressed at the organisation of the whole production process – and, in particular, the fact that

Mission to America at the Curtiss-Wright plant at St Louis: Lt Nicholas S Ludington, USN; anon; Walter Tye; anon; A H Tiltman; Col William B Bunker, USAAF; J Lloyd; C G A Woodford; anon; anon; B G Markham; RF; W W Dunning; M B Berks; S P Woodley; I G Duncan; N S Muir; D M A Leggett; anon; Grover Loening. Those unidentified are American hosts. (Author)

in thousands of major departments throughout the nation, most of which had been virgin prairie a year earlier, control was vested in university students! – that it broke off its planned visits in favour of discussions at Wright Field. As a result Drs Wright and Warner arranged for members to visit MIT, Caltech, Cornell, Harvard, Columbia and other universities to study the methods that were turning tens of thousands of students (who might have previously been reading drama or archaeology) into key men in countless government or industrial posts. After seeing how the management of major technical projects and departments could be entrusted to these brilliant but untechnical men, the mission thought this "the high spot of the whole tour".

But perhaps Fedden's own high point was when Pratt & Whitney showed him their latest engine projects, of which numerous research prototypes were busily running on test beds: two of the four new engines had sleeve valves! Some of the team went on to Canada, but eventually all but four had returned to Cook's Building by 3rd March 1943. With a mountain of documents to draw upon, the mammoth task of writing the report began. Almost all the things they had seen and been told were of enormous strategic importance, and the final report was carefully prepared with extreme security. The final editing was done by McKinnon, a Ministry civil servant, who had to deal not only with 500 text pages but also with countless tables, graphs and diagrams. The final report was arranged in seven sections, and 120 copies were produced by offset printing by the MAP. For 50 individual "top people" specially bound volumes were produced by a security-cleared bookbinders in Colindale. Each was signed for by its recipient.

Fedden's *Mission to America* report is a classic document. It was the first of several reports to have a "logo" or key symbol designed by Fedden himself, a small concession to frivolity that contrasted with his austere passion for keeping on the job. The vast document was so clearly set forth that it was possible to turn up any section instantly. All recommendations were on pink paper. Recommendations were very numerous, and covered not only broad-brush strategic issues but countless detailed suggestions. Altogether this was the first time a team from the British aircraft industry had ever looked carefully at what anyone else was doing. The industry at which it looked was gigantic, yet still growing rapidly and filled with drive and enthusiasm. The enthusiasm filtered through to almost every page of Fedden's report; but to the recipients it was far from welcome. Though Fedden's team had done a remarkably fine job, which any impartial reader (from Cripps down) recognised as such, the leaders of the British industry were incapable of being impartial.

Their background was one of insularity. The United States, in particular, was thought to be a land where people merely *talked* big; in any case, after four adverse years of war, the British were not disposed to believe they could learn much from the Americans. It was an odd situation. For many years before the war Fedden had been almost the only member of the British industry who was constantly in touch with US developments. He suffered from no emotional hang-up on the US as did his colleagues, and when – for example – the Americans developed a new breed of commercial airliner that was a cantilever monoplane, with such refinements as flaps, v-p propellers and retractable landing gear, he saw no reason not to hail it as an advance. The instinctive British reaction was a smouldering resistance, a dogged defence of old ideas, a wish to prove the new American idea unsound, or inferior or "unsuitable for British requirements", and a general feeling that "that pain in the neck Fedden is on again about how marvellous America is". So when he produced his monumental report, almost all the industrial recipients regarded it with the determination that they were going to pick it to pieces and, if possible, get its value discounted. This was not Fedden paranoia; this is an undoubted statement of fact.

Resistance to the Fedden Report almost amounted to a major campaign. There were hundreds of recommendations contained in its pink pages, almost all of which British industry could with advantage have adopted with all possible speed, yet more than half the most influential men in the British industry did their utmost to ensure that none was even given credibility. Several companies even produced printed reports of their own to show that the Fedden Report was wrong. The Dowty Group, for example, published a major rebuttal of the mission's findings in the fields of landing gears and hydraulics, proving that the US ought to copy Britain. The main conclusion of the Dowty rebuttal was that "nose wheel installations on multi-engined ships (sic) are not economic at present".

Above all other parts of the report, the British hackles rose at the figures for numbers of technical staff employed by the American firms. For years Fedden had preached that Britain lacked qualified engineers, and in this report he had the effrontery – it was thought – to set down inflated numbers in black and white to try to support his arguments. The totals averaged between eight and 15 times as many as the number of technical staff in the major British firms. In October 1944 Wellwood Beall, vice-president of Boeing, visited Britain and was buttonholed by most of the famous names of British aviation, who asked "Have you seen this ridiculous report of Fedden's? We have named it 'Fedden's Folly'. He says you have 3,200 qualified technical staff! We've made it a laughing stock." Beall replied "You are quite right, the figure is not accurate. Like all the other figures in the report it was correct in January or February 1943, but today our technical staff numbers 3,880". The laughter suddenly ceased.

Fedden's mission singled out three types of aircraft for particular attention: the P-51 Mustang, A-26 (later B-26) Invader and B-29

Superfortress. The Mustang, while lacking nothing in other respects, could fly more than twice as far as British fighters and regularly went to Berlin. The Invader, designed by Ed Heinemann, was obviously going to be a first-class machine, easily superior to anything in the tactical multi-role bomber class in Britain. There was nothing in Britain remotely like the B-29. Both bombers might have been improved by being fitted with the powerful Centaurus engine, and the report did make a firm recommendation that examination should be given to the manufacture in Britain of a Centaurus B-29, if necessary without pressurisation and with simple direct-control gun turrets. Had this been done the RAF would not in 1950 have had to equip itself with second-hand B-29s lent by the United States.

In the autumn of 1943 Cripps asked members of the Fedden Mission to visit British firms, to see what action had been taken on the report and offer any further help or advice. Some companies were co-operative and eager to learn, but the majority were far too proud, and some openly expressed the view that the mission had been a waste of time. But it was clear that this myopic view was merely a foolish posture which did not extend below the upper strata of management. At the level of the engineers who did the main design and development work the report was regarded as of immense value, of great interest, and something constantly referred to. Cripps himself called it "Undoubtedly the greatest single volume that has ever been written about a single industry."

By the summer of 1943 Fedden's presence as a competent engineer and troubleshooter – a pathetically *rara avis* in British government circles – seemed to offer a possible solution to a problem that had long worried the Admiralty. For many years the Royal Navy Torpedo Factory at Greenock had obviously been inadequate and unable to deliver the goods. So completely had the Admiralty been out of touch with what an R & D establishment ought to be like that, for years, Greenock's faults went unrecognised. After four years of war Their Lordships began to realise that all was not well, and, as the Royal Navy appeared not to know what to do, it was decided to call in Fedden. He went to the place, accompanied by C S Wright, Director of Scientific Research, and Capt Richards, Superintendent of Torpedo Experiment and Design. He then wrote a report, in which appeared such blunt phrases as "cramped, old-fashioned and inadequate … men with a wealth of experience, but whose confidence has been sapped by a long history of repression and lack of leadership … even a lack of awareness of modern techniques or the pace at which work should proceed." A head-on collision was inevitable, for this establishment was unbelievably archaic, and Fedden was insensitive to the need for delicate and tactful treatment. He drew a new organisational chart, made recommendations regarding the existing site or, if possible, a new one, and also commented how unlikely the RN Scientific Service was to attract good engineers with the salary scales then in force. He started a long overdue process of improvement which initially created little but political activity and resentment, but which over the next 15 years accomplished a great deal.

In September 1943 he was again called to the Admiralty to meet the Engineer-in-Chief of the Fleet, Engineer Vice-Admiral Sir Frederick Turner, as well as Engineer Vice-Admiral Sir George Preece and Capt (E) W G Cowland. He was invited to be Chairman of a committee Sir Frederick was setting up to review the problems of engines for high-speed surface craft such as MTBs and MGBs. Having secured his Minister's approval he accepted, chose his committee within minutes and arranged the first meeting for 9 o'clock next morning. Present were Fedden, Preece, Cowland, C B Dicksee, Harry Ricardo, H Sammons, T Thorneycroft and, as secretary, Peter Ware, who was among those who had left Bristol to work for their old chief in London. It would have been simple for Fedden merely to do as the Admiralty requested and start by considering the number of cylinders, the bore and the stroke of a suitable high-speed diesel. But Fedden appreciated that the kind of engine depended on the kind of boat, and at the first meeting he steam-rollered through an agreement that they would first have to look at future high-speed naval craft.

There followed nine months of intensive work, involving countless discussions with naval officers, hull and propeller designers, engine specialists and many other people, as well as visits to factories, laboratories, naval dockyards and carefully planned trips at sea – after one of which Fedden's occasional dry sense of humour surfaced for a moment, for he recorded "A bomb projector had been mounted forward of the bow Oerlikon, and the rating manning this weapon had to lie flat on the deck at the forepeak. A considerable part of his time was spent partly under water, and it is doubtful whether, under such conditions in action, he would have been able to use the projector accurately." It was only after a thorough review of duties, armament, equipment and operational environment, that Fedden and the MTB Committee got down to engine details in December 1943. Their final recommendation was to fund development of a high-speed diesel rated at 2,500 hp, with promise of development to 3,000 hp, whilst simultaneously doing research into gas turbines. After two years, by which time it was thought that considerable experience would have been gained with single-cylinder diesel units, a decision was to be made between the diesel and the gas turbine. The committee spent a lot of time reviewing possible manufacturers, but what finally happened was that one of its members, Sammons, went back to his firm, D Napier & Son, and pre-empted the situation by developing the radical Deltic diesel along the lines recommended by the committee. This was in production by 1952.

Celerity – the Bristol Aeroplane Company, Marine Department high speed motor craft was powered by four Hercules XVII MB engines in 1947. (Ken Hunter)

Thus did the Royal Navy at last get rid of the petrol engine in combat vessels. But, before it did, it put four of Fedden's Hercules XI aircraft engines into the Fairmile D-type MTB and made this class the fastest Allied naval vessel of any kind. Perhaps remarkably, the Hercules demonstrated excellent reliability in the severe new environment. At full power the noise in the engine compartment exceeded 155 decibels, but it is very doubtful that some 6,500 horsepower had ever before been crammed into so small a space, at sea or anywhere else.

A second fast MTB with aircraft piston engines was designed by the Bristol Aeroplane Company, Marine Department and a single boat – *Celerity* was built by Kris Cruisers (1934) Ltd at Isleworth, and tested in 1947 with four 1675 horsepower Hercules XVII MB engines. The basic design was also capable of taking four Perseus engines of 1150 horsepower, or four Centaurus!

Fedden's MTB Committee had a major long-term effect, but at the same time he was working on a second project which put it in the shade. It concerned the subject that was perhaps dearer to Fedden's heart than any other: the training of young engineers. The outcome of his work was Cranfield, a name that today ranks with that of any post-graduate centre of technology in the world.

Fedden saw Cripps about once a week, but occasionally they took long car rides together because the Minister never liked to visit industry without having Fedden come as well and brief him during the journey. If Sir Stafford addressed the assembled workers he would always begin with the ringing word "Comrades!", which not only made Fedden wince but also, in his view, was a tactical error because, he considered, "The chaps on the shop floor know he isn't really a comrade." It was after one of these trips that Fedden set to work on his favourite missionary task, which was, in a purely British context, "To bridge the gap between the academic approach of the universities and the hard practical needs of industry for all-round engineers with a balanced outlook and a proper appreciation of the importance of weight, cost and timing, as well as a sense of vision, dedicated enthusiasm and high moral fibre."

Cripps knew a hobby-horse when he met one, but Fedden was someone rather special whose hobby-horses were likely to be sound in wind and limb. He said nothing to Fedden but talked the matter over with Professor P M S (later Lord) Blackett. Fedden was not so much concerned with engineers *per se* as with aeronautical engineers, and the Minister then wrote to Sir B Melvill Jones, then Chairman of the Aeronautical Research Council, with a request that the subject be formally referred to the ARC. Jones became enthusiastic, and with Professor W J Duncan prepared a brief report which Cripps then discussed with the Cabinet. The report recommended the setting up of a post-graduate seat of learning for aeronautics.

In October 1943 Cripps called Fedden in and handed him the report. Fedden had no idea his crusade had led to such action, and he was thrilled. The Minister, well aware he was expressing Fedden's own thoughts, yet inspired his assistant with his impassioned plea for a supply of engineers of the very highest quality. After the war, said Cripps, "We shall face a long period of intense competition when nothing but the best will suffice. Excellence will never be in over-supply … We tend to make engineers and scientists the scapegoats for the ills of the modern world … I deplore the exaggerated respect for social position and snobbery on the part of both pure scientists and humanists, and our great schools and universities bear a heavy responsibility for cultivating this separatism. I want you to create something unique … I give you an entirely free hand, at home and abroad, to interpret my ideals …" Fedden wrung his Minister's hand. It was for him a moment of sheer bliss.

Yet the way ahead was to be uphill and rocky. "Rab" Butler, Minister of Education, was not hostile but never quite grasped the proposal, considering it just a bigger polytechnic. Lord Cherwell, on the other hand, was enthusiastic; he wanted a sort of British MIT, starting off with a target of 1,000 students covering the whole spread of technology. Academics from existing universities were, to a man, implacably hostile both to Fedden and to the concept, considering it "thoroughly undesirable". The one group whose support Fedden might have expected, the leaders of the aircraft industry, were the most vitriolic of all. For three years they lobbied Cripps constantly, telling him the proposed post-graduate school would be "a white elephant", an "unwanted monstrosity" and a "useless burden". Cripps was told it would do him great harm, and he was asked by at least 24 academics and 18 industrial leaders – sometimes in formal deputations – to quash the whole idea. Fedden knew what was going on, and it was a profound relief when Cripps told him "I hope you aren't leading me up the garden path. They say you are, but I believe in you."

In late October 1943 Fedden was appointed chairman of an inter-departmental committee charged with "preparing and submitting to the Minister of Aircraft Production detailed proposals for a School of Aeronautical Science" within the general framework of the ARC recommendations. It was a strong committee, with outstanding men drawn from the Treasury, Admiralty, Air Ministry, MAP, Dominions Office, ARC, University Grants Committee, Ministry of Education and Department of Scientific and Industrial Research. N W Graham of MAP was secretary, and Rex Goldby technical secretary. The chief nigger in the woodpile was that the Chairman, Fedden, was not an academic but an engineer (of all things!). The academics said some hard words at the first meeting, treating Fedden, in his view, as "a common huckster". They were not prepared to agree to the way he proposed to work. "This", reported Fedden, "helped me considerably, as most of them did not attend another meeting. With the help of two secretaries I was able to work at a speed which would have been out of the question with the original committee – which had confidently predicted the swift collapse of the project." But Fedden still had to face the wrath of the Civil Service. They decided that not even Fedden could ride rough-shod over their official procedures, and in the end there were three editions of the classic report A *College of Aeronautics:* one written by Fedden, and two – considerably modified in phrasing – written by the officials of the Establishment.

Fortunately the officials never interfered with the recommendations themselves. These were numerous and detailed. The College of Aeronautics was proposed "to provide a high-grade engineering, technical and scientific training in aeronautics to fit students for leadership in the aircraft industry, civil aviation, the Services, education and research." Its site was to be "close to its own airfield and within reasonable distance of London and the principal aeronautical research establishment. The most suitable permanent site is Aldermaston, Berkshire." If necessary it was considered the college could be established by adapting an existing RAF station, and in this case the choice fell upon Abingdon, though Dunsfold was also considered in detail. In the event the splendid plans for permanent buildings, which were exhibited at the Royal Academy in 1946, were not built, and the final choice (reflecting the opening of the Royal Aircraft Establishment at Bedford) was Cranfield.

Cranfield in the 1950s. (Rolls-Royce plc)

Early in 1945 Cripps told Fedden that Air Chief Marshal Sir Edgar Ludlow-Hewitt had been appointed Chairman of the Board of Governors. Much to the surprise of many diehard opponents, the college was opened in October 1946.

After a vast amount of work by Sir Edgar and a small but growing team, the foundations of the college's work were laid by the first principal, Ernest Relf, an aerodynamicist from the National Physical Laboratory, and his staff. Even in its early formative years Cranfield made such a name for itself that it was constantly being visited by delegations from such places as Cornell, Princeton, Caltech and Delft, while its students were snapped up by aircraft companies all over the world. Fedden remained a Governor of Cranfield for many years, and took an extremely active part in its later political life. One of his rewards was seeing Sir Frederick Handley Page, who during the War had been a leader of those who poured scorn on the whole idea, appointed Chairman of the Board of Governors!

On Friday, 22nd September 1944 Fedden was called to a meeting at Great George Street, Westminster, with representatives of the Air Ministry, War Office, Admiralty, Ministry of Production, Ministry of Supply and MAP. The requirements of all these departments – in other words, of Britain as a nation – for the Japanese war were discussed at length, and it was suggested that certain items might be procured from the part of Italy in Allied hands. Fedden was asked to go and find out. He soon formed the view that any prior planning was conspicuously absent. Each representative had plenty of ideas – for example no time was lost in drawing up schedules of products that might be made in Italy, while the Admiralty man suggested skilled Italian technicians might be brought to Britain to relieve the critical shortage of trained men – but the whole thing seemed to be unrealistic and played completely off the cuff. However, Fedden agreed to go. From Rotol he borrowed Bert Newport, his old representative at Alfa-Romeo, and on 29th September they flew from Lyneham to Pomigliano, Naples. After hanging about trying to find transport, they were given a lift by Air Commodore Leigh to Allied Forces HQ at Caserta.

Here Fedden reported to G5 department, responsible for supplies and economics in the Italian and Balkan theatres. Socially they were off to a good start, because the British resident Minister, Harold Macmillan, invited them to the party he was just giving for his assistant, Roger Makins, who was returning to the UK. They thus at once met all the right people, including members of the Allied Control Commission and many prominent Italians who had not fled to the north but thrown in their lot with the Allies. By far his most important contact was his American opposite number, General Hugh Minton, Director of the Production Division of the US Army, who was surveying the whole ETO (European Theatre of Operations). As Fedden expected, Minton knew his stuff. He had been briefed in great detail before he left Washington, and his trip, unlike the British one, had been planned with extreme care.

During Fedden's week in Italy he was in constant touch with Minton, and they spent two days visiting factories together. Minton was discouraging. Before he left Washington he had come to the view that the only thing that might actually be manufactured in Italy for the Allied war effort would be various types of fabric, for tenting or tyres. By the time Fedden arrived he had given up even this idea. The part of Italy liberated, which extended to north of Florence, had been fought over with great violence and systematically demolished by the Germans with impressive thoroughness. Everything usable had been destroyed, and Fedden found that this extended from the main fabric of buildings down through such things as electric generators and machine tools even to individual hand-tools. Worse, the people had spent up to a year with no work, little food, and virtually no transport or electric power. They were on the verge of civil chaos, and their morale was non-existent. Fedden recommended that the idea of making things for the Japanese war be replaced by a programme to try to get the country on its feet once more, to "provide an example of just but firm treatment of countries freed from German domination."

He had several unplanned encounters during his week in Italy. In the Excelsior Hotel in Rome he and Newport instantly recognised an opera singer, surrounded by her Pekingeses, and promptly wondered if her Austrian lover was around. He was well known to both the Englishmen from pre-war days, and they instantly guessed he would be operating as a spy. True enough, they found him in a key post in the British legation working on the Allied Control Commission, and a spy he proved to be. The following day they flew to Bari in a Liberator, and, while Fedden was standing up looking out of the astrodome, the dome blew completely out of the fuselage, leaving a ring of jagged Plexiglas; it was thought the cause was a collision with a large bird. Two days after this, Fedden climbed on a high wall in Florence to take a photograph. He was dressed in an old flannel suit, for he refused to wear the "ersatz" uniform of an RAF air commodore which had been issued to him for this mission. He was shot at from close range by a jumpy negro soldier with an automatic weapon, who somehow managed to miss.

Fedden's Italian report was issued on 20th November, and he then embarked on another major study project, an investigation of the feeder-airline market (roughly equivalent to today's third-level market) and its engine needs. So totally was he wedded to the sleeve-valve piston engine that he devoted little time to the gas turbine, which in 1944 was still quite a new concept almost solely considered in a military context. He spent a much greater time defining the specification of an extremely attractive 1,000 horsepower sleeve-valve engine, which in the back of his mind he was considering as a possible product he might even try to make himself after the war. But Peter Ware, who continued at STAM as his technical secretary, accomplished the remarkable task of making him change his mind. Ware at last convinced Fedden the gas turbine had arrived, and could be made competitive, and at the eleventh hour – and with considerable misgivings – Fedden terminated the sleeve-valve work and began a new report recommending a turboprop in the 1,000 horsepower class. For the first time he became personally involved in the design of centrifugal and axial compressors, in component efficiencies, in blade design and in weight and cost estimates for this completely different kind of power plant.

There is no doubt that Fedden was right, up to this point in time, to concentrate on piston engines and let others do turbines. The post-1945 record shows that the turbine has only slowly penetrated down towards feeder-line and general-aviation aircraft, and it is possible that a really modern 1,000 horsepower sleeve-valve engine in 1946 might have found a large worldwide market. Fedden was the master of such engines, whereas in the new field of gas turbines he had to learn from others and would find it hard to find a niche in which he could become pre-eminent. Even in the high-power field the piston engine was far from dead. After the Second World War the world's airlines and air forces bought approximately 40,000 large new piston engines of 2,000 horsepower or above; but, because of Britain's fixation on gas turbines (which did not have to be at the expense of piston engines), barely 1,000 of these engines were made in Britain. In the lower power classes the piston engine's importance was even greater, and as the War drew towards its final stages Fedden increasingly made plans to try to form his own company to meet the power needs of the time of booming prosperity everyone hoped to see.

But what a wealth of possibilities had to be considered! It was a time of seemingly unlimited change and opportunity. In Europe there had scarcely been a single private car made since 1939, nor a light aeroplane. The helicopter had been turned into a practical vehicle which many thought might soon be parked in everyone's back yard. Certainly there was no doubt that a big market would exist for piston and turbine engines in the 1,000 horsepower class.

Within eight months of leaving Bristol, Fedden was back in that city again having an intense discussion about the future in Alex Moulton's flat. Gordon Wilkins, the journalist and motoring writer, joined them, and the talk centred on what kind of car would be most saleable after the war. Fedden had the stature and money to launch such a venture in a successful way. The meeting in Moulton's flat might be the start of something big. But Fedden was anxious that it should be well managed. His agonising experience in 1942 had taught him nothing about how to run a business, yet had left him with a great yearning to form a new, young team where relationships could be good and happy. His dream was of a company where everyone was imbued with his intense motivation, his wish to make fast progress, and his complete dedication. He believed he could create such a company – Roy Fedden Ltd – in which this dream should be realised. Though it would obviously need to make money, this was not the main object of the exercise, which was really just the love of the thing. Fedden believed his company could be a place where superb engineering would flourish, and where saleable products could emerge as a natural product of the central process of leading the field in design and development.

While Fedden remained tied up as STAM, the prime-mover of the proposed enterprise was Ian Duncan. The company was formed in 1943 and Duncan was appointed chief engineer; he and his secretary Miss Oram were the first employees. During 1943 the basic, and radically unconventional, design of a car was drawn up, the work being centred in Moulton's flat which Duncan shared. As soon as he had got the giant US Mission Report out of the way, Duncan worked full time on the project, mainly on the design of the

At 4 Hamilton Place in 1944, RF's second term as President of the Society. Front row – Maj B W Shilson, Maj R H Mayo, Lord Brabazon of Tara, A Gouge, RF, R K Pierson, Sir Oliver Simmonds, N E Rowe and Griffith Brewer. 2nd row – Capt J L Pritchard, A C Brown, C C Walker, Sir Francis Shelmerdine, Maj F B Halford, S H Evans, G H Dowty, Air Cdre F R Banks, J F Hodgson and Capt A G Lamplugh. 3rd row – A G Elliott, E J N Archbold, R S Stafford, G E Petty and L A Wingfield. (Author)

engine but also furiously scratching about in London setting up contacts and generally laying the base from which Roy Fedden Ltd could operate. The prosperous Dowty Group leased to the infant company Benton House in The Park, Cheltenham, and this was prepared as the future company headquarters. In January 1944 Duncan moved to Benton House full-time, and gradually built up a team of picked people. As yet Fedden could manage only the occasional visit, in shaggy tweeds. On Monday mornings he donned an immaculate dark suit again. He was still the STAM, and Cripps had one more big job for him. In May 1945 Fedden was asked to lead a mission to Germany.

In retrospect the examination of German aeronautical developments might have been accorded more attention at a much earlier date. It certainly was in the United States, where several large and well-equipped missions were being planned in great detail before the end of 1944. In Britain, however, there were merely one or two small missions sent from the industry, and Fedden's group sent by the MAP. Despite prodding by Fedden, no move was made to do anything until May 1945, which meant that the ill-planned little missions sent out in June were cast in the role of second-class citizens trying to find what pickings they could in the wake of the huge and methodical teams of Americans who had already scoured the country and picked the plums.

Fedden was charged with paying special attention to fuel injection (the topic he had been forced to give up through Air Ministry disinterest in 1934), ignition systems, gas turbines and variable-pitch propellers, and to track down "plant, equipment, books, instruments, etc" suitable for the new College of Aeronautics. He chose as members Dr W J Duncan, who had helped prepare the original report on the College; J C King, of the Structural and Mechanical Engineering Department at RAE; Bert Newport; F/Lt A B P Beeton, of the Engine Department at RAE; and Dr W J Stern of the Control Commission for Germany. W/Cdr V Cross was seconded from SHAEF (Supreme Headquarters, Allied Expeditionary Force) as liaison officer. The mission was assigned two RAF Dakotas, under F/Lts Reid and Cheaney, each aircraft also carrying a Jeep. They left Northolt in brilliant sunshine on Tuesday, 12th June 1945.

When they arrived two hours later on a temporary airstrip near Bückeburg they might have been on a different planet. It was bitterly cold, and raining. Germany's vast lands had been destroyed more completely than any territory in previous history. It was soon abundantly clear that the mission had to be totally self-sufficient; and it was equally clear that the planned itinerary was too ambitious. The Dakotas had put down on Summerfield wire mesh laid on farmland because in the month or more they had been occupied no airfields had been made usable. The destruction was indescribable. Getting into a

Jeep and driving down the road was rendered difficult by the fact there were usually no roads, even in the country – just a sea of craters, most of them filled with water. Perhaps most trying of all, there were no telephones, and certainly no post. The Dakota radio operator could talk to air traffic controllers seated in caravans and temporary huts, but the only other way to communicate with a distant place was to try to go there, and this was at least as difficult as it would have been in the Middle Ages.

Gradually the method was worked out of sending one Dakota on ahead to explore the territory, try to organise permits and accommodation, and if possible even arrange appointments with staff to be interrogated. The one bright spot in a desperately bleak landscape was the US Army, which was strongly in evidence, always helpful, and generous in providing food and billets. But the work of the mission was wearisome and time-wasting. Practically every German establishment was at a standstill. Apart from the

German cities lay in ruins but, by the time RF's mission arrived, the roads had been bulldozed clear of rubble by the US Army. RF took this picture in Munich. (Author)

occasional executive, staff had dispersed. It took a long time, usually a matter of days, to find some, obtain permits for them to move from one place to another, and bring them in for interviews. Many engineers had to be brought 50 to 100 miles, and on one occasion members of the mission had to fly 300 miles to a French headquarters on Lake Constance to obtain permission to visit the factories of Daimler-Benz in the Stuttgart area in the French Zone. To make matters harder, the Allied Zones were in the process of being radically changed, which not only meant a great administrative upheaval but also transferred numerous important targets on the mission's itinerary to the Soviet Zone, and the Russians immediately made it clear that none of the Western Allies would be allowed in.

Each day thus became a race against time, a matter of hectic changes of plans, a ceaseless quest not only for their objectives but also for a roof and for food (with the ubiquitous American K Rations becoming almost the staple diet), and a battle to travel as quickly as possible in a land where air attack had not only made communications almost impossible but had changed the appearance of built-up areas into a barren wasteland of rubble where even German guides who lived there found it hard to pick their way. Altogether the faithful Jeeps were loaded and off-loaded more than 150 times, each operation being an extremely inconvenient one involving driving and manhandling the vehicle up two narrow ramps, in at the constricted door and then turning into the Dakota's fuselage. Fedden marvelled at the way the RAF crews became adept at doing this in a matter of a minute or so.

The mission spent the first three days at the LFA laboratory, also called the Hermann Goering Institute, at Volkenrode, near Brunswick. This had been discovered by American troops a few weeks before. It was easily the biggest aeronautical research laboratory in Europe. Fedden had heard before the War such an establishment was being planned, but there followed only conflicting rumours, some prisoners saying it was in East Prussia and others claiming it had been planned but never built. Now it had at last been discovered. Never in the thousands of reconnaissance flights over Germany had its presence been suspected, though photographic interpreters had looked at it in numerous prints. It had no main road, no rail link, and no overhead power line. The whole series of services were brought underground from Brunswick. Yet the place was gigantic. It covered about 1,100 acres in a thickly wooded area. It contained dozens of huge buildings, a great array of wind tunnels far surpassing in size, Mach number and power anything even planned in Britain, and large complexes of laboratories for engines, structures, explosives and weapons (including rocket propulsion and various classes of guided missiles). Yet, so good was the camouflage, even former members of the staff were continually getting lost and having to make huge detours. The biggest wind tunnel, for example, operating up to Mach 1.8, was under thousands of tons of earth in which were growing grass, bushes and small trees.

This mighty establishment was just the first of a succession of surprises. Members of the mission walked miles through ruined machine shops and laboratories to study and discuss huge piston engines, jet engines, rocket engines and new research tools. They discovered a range of optical interferometric methods of picturing aerodynamic flow, and even got a tunnel working with a swept-wing model in it. The use of sweepback to delay compressibility drag-rise had been known before the war, but subsequently forgotten and ignored in Britain, but in Germany it was being accepted as standard in all the latest jet aircraft. While the airflow round the model was being explored a team breezed in from Boeing; next morning Fedden was piqued that the swept-wing model was nowhere to be found (guess who had it). Some years later the author discussed this with Boeing's George Schairer, who said "We couldn't just walk away from it!". A day or two later Fedden had made up two huge truckloads of books for Cranfield from Göttingen. They were about to leave when the loads were commandeered by US troops, on the instructions of a rival US team. Fedden could see there would be trouble, and sought the advice of the Allied Control Commission. They did not want to know, and the rule seemed to be the law of the jungle. Fedden had no inclination to steal things off the Americans, and it was galling when he was robbed of the things he had managed to find for Britain. As he had no troops and could get no backing he had to let the trucks be driven away.

Though his mission was not briefed to investigate aircraft, as such, Fedden did take the opportunity to visit the previously unknown Messerschmitt research and experimental works in a Jaeger barracks in splendid wooded mountain scenery close to the resorts of Klosters and Oberammergau. Evacuated from Augsburg, the experimental team had spent the last year of the war feverishly developing fighters a generation later than anything even considered on the Allied side, with swept wings and buried axial jet engines. Enthusiastic chief designer Waldemar Voigt showed Fedden the P.1101 prototype, captured two weeks before it would have flown, and explained the new technology of swept wings to the intensely interested mission.

Some of the most promising of the German engines were by the BMW company, and Fedden soon visited their headquarters at Munich and tracked down the chief engineer, his old friend Bruno Bruckmann. The latest and most powerful BMW jet, the 018, had existed only in the form of components and even these had been as far as possible destroyed. But the latest engine to run, the 003C, had been hidden in a haystack across the border in Austria. While driving down a navigable bit of autobahn to look for the haystack Fedden was amazed to find upwards of 50 almost new jet fighters and bombers – Me 262s and Ar 234s – parked on the verges. They had been using the straight stretch of road as their final operating base, before being immobilised for want of fuel. This mute evidence of massive jet production was repeated all over Germany, and helped make Fedden ponder on Allied supremacy in the air – gained, he said, with "obsolete aircraft from which every ounce of development has been wrung". He wondered how the air war would have gone had there been a further few months of fighting.

He discussed the matter with Bruckmann as they sat at the roadside eating a snack lunch of K Rations. Suddenly Bruckmann turned to Fedden and said, "Did you known that on Christmas Day 1943 I was reading a copy of your *Mission to America* Report?" Fedden was thunderstruck. Every copy of the highly secret report had been numbered and signed for, yet one had reached Germany within weeks of publication. Fedden showed his horror, but Bruckmann cut him short: "The horror was on our side. On that Christmas Day Goering himself had the report and an interpreter; the rest of us – most of the industry and Luftwaffe leaders – were told what it said. We knew that, with your name on it, it was exact and beyond dispute. We realised at that meeting that we could not win the War, and that within a year or 18 months your air power would overwhelm us. From that time on, our whole outlook was different – though Hitler would have had us shot if he had known. So your report played no small part in your winning the War".

Ever afterwards this almost stunning news perturbed Fedden greatly. He made sustained efforts to find out whose copy it was that had so swiftly got into the enemy's hands. Obviously there was a clever spy right in the heart of the Allied war effort; or was there? Though the idea never crossed Fedden's mind, a more likely explanation is that the Allies were cleverer than he knew. The Germans, and Sir Roy Fedden, tended to think logically, but the history of Allied (especially British) espionage in the Second World War is one of often illogical but supremely successful deviousness. Suppose a copy had been "secretly" spirited away to Germany by a double-agent? Its possession would give the enemy a vast fund of detailed knowledge on US hardware and production methods. But they could hardly put it to practical use. So the forthcoming B-29 had wing skins up to nearly half an inch thick? There was nothing the Germans could do about it. But the detailed analysis of US production would shake German morale to the very core – as it did. How could they – unlike the British planemakers – fail to believe every word of it, when it had Fedden's magic name on it?

In 1979, after this book was originally written, Ballantine of New York published *Piercing the Reich* by Joseph E Persico. It describes on p.70 how in 1943 Allen Dulles of the CIA leaked to a German agent a large report describing the build-up of US aircraft production, and of how this authoritative report convinced all who read it that Germany must lose the

War. There seems little doubt that this report was in fact that written by Fedden.

Fedden's report on his visit to Germany is as much a classic as his American report, though the subject matter and environment could hardly be more different. It was Fedden's German report that first threw into sharp relief the contrast between Germany's massive forward strides into completely new realms of aircraft and missiles, which had no counterpart whatever on the Allied side, and their gross misdirection at the highest level which had diluted the effectiveness of the new technology and greatly delayed its application to the war effort. Fedden had to regard Germany in a schizophrenic way. To him the Germans had always been the supreme engineers, as well as very likeable people individually. Many of the men he tracked down and interrogated had been his personal friends for over 20 years. Yet under the Nazis German behaviour had often been vile. Whenever he asked about slave labour the immediate answer was that it did not exist, and that it was part of the propaganda of the Allies. Fedden soon made a point of establishing as many facts as he could before the interrogation, so that he could tell the man he was lying. The response would then be that the whole matter was entirely out of their hands – and that in any case they could not be expected to make such a fuss over the way some of their workers were treated as to endanger their own positions, if not their lives.

One place where nobody tried to make excuses was Nordhausen, and this was because the management – under SS General Kammler – knew better than to stay there. Nordhausen was officially the biggest production plant in Germany – it was called Mittelwerke, Middle Works – but one could equally accurately have called it a concentration camp. Once a vast sulphur mine, tunnelled into the Hartz Mountains, it had been enormously extended since 1942 and Fedden saw no reason to disbelieve the statistics of 22 miles of tunnel, 25,000 machine tools and 50,000 slave workers. Nordhausen was, he wrote, "the epitome of megalomaniac production and robot efficiency. Everything was ruthlessly executed with utter disregard for humanitarian conditions ..." When it was overrun it was building 1,000 Jumo 213 piston engines per month, 1,000 V-2 rockets, 600 BMW 003 turbojets and several hundred Hs 117 guided missiles. Until recently it had been making vast numbers of V-1 flying bombs (it had made virtually all of them). The somewhat chastened mission never knew what fresh horror they would encounter as they explored the place. Fedden himself saw the "processing plant" for the 250 or so slave workers who died each day. He never forgot the contrast between the bright sunshine and beautiful scenery outside and the hell that he found in this enormous and devilish factory.

While the mission had been touring it had done its best, in the absence of any instructions from the Government, to send back hardware to London.

One such item was Bruckmann's latest turbojet, which was eventually lifted from its Austrian haystack and trucked to the faithful Dakota. The Jeep and several other items were put on board, while the captain pondered on the 600 yards of rough grass field, telling Fedden, "I think we'll be able to get through between those two big trees". Fedden managed to signal to Rex Goldby "COLLECT ONE ENGINE NORTHOLT TOMORROW", and young assistant Newman met the BMW jet, managed to dismantle it without metric tools, and eventually took the parts up to the STAM offices in the lift.

One item Fedden was desperately keen to bring to Britain was a wonderful jet engine test plant in which engines could be run not only under sea-level conditions but also under simulated conditions up to an altitude of 54,000 ft and an airspeed of 560 mph. This "Herbitus" plant was at BMW Munich, and similar installations were in operation or being built at Rechlin, Berlin, Stuttgart and Dessau. Like almost everything else really valuable, the whole installation had been earmarked by the Americans before Fedden's mission was even arranged, but before it was shipped to the USA Fedden managed to test two German turbojets in it and also arranged for two British turbojets to undertake their first altitude tests, a Rolls-Royce Derwent V and, to the delight of designer Frank Halford, a de Havilland Goblin. Fedden was hamstrung by the fact that he could find nobody in London to show any interest in his mission in Germany. He repeatedly requested permission to ship back items for the College of Aeronautics and received no reply. He had recommended that skilled fitters and packers be sent over to arrange for the dismantling and shipment of major items of equipment. He had also collected a team of German jet and rocket specialists, but delays in London seemed interminable.

Most of the mission returned on 26th and 28th June, though Fedden and a few others stayed until 4th July. He then set up in his STAM offices a remarkable collection of jet engines, rockets, air-cooled blades, and numerous items of advanced technology that had never before been seen in Britain. Fedden was perhaps not the right man to arrange such an exhibition, because so many of those who came to see it had great chips on their shoulders or arrived in such a sceptical frame of mind they were unable to show impartial interest. Even making allowance for this, Fedden was probably right to feel alarm at the views expressed. Almost everyone regarded the exhibits as quaint. It was as if they came from a Jules Verne fantasia, and bore no relevance to the real world of 1945. One of the greatest British fighter designers – Camm – pointed to a drawing of the Messerschmitt P.1110 (later than the 1101), one of many German swept-wing fighters, and said, "Did you ever see anything more ridiculous?" He was to take nine years to produce a swept-wing fighter for the RAF. In general, the official attitude was "Why waste time looking at these German things? Haven't we won the

War?" The two men who most markedly differed from this prevalent view were Sir Stafford Cripps and, especially, Winston Churchill, who regarded the exhibition very seriously indeed, and with a sombre face said, "It would be foolish indeed if we were to fail to make the greatest possible use of this amazing harvest. We may be sure our Allies will …"

But the British mentality in the summer of 1945 was one of blind superiority. On 17th July Fedden went back to Germany to witness the jet testing on the Herbitus plant. He took Peter Ware with him, and as they were driving along the repaired autobahn Fedden pointed to a signpost to Fallersleben, mentioning that in 1938 General Milch had taken him there to show him the production line of the new People's Car, the Volkswagen. Ware was quite excited, and asked if they could pay the works a visit. They found it badly bombed, and with a B-17 Fortress still in the main erecting hall, whence it had entered via the roof. Fedden commandeered a Volkswagen, brought it back to England in a Dakota, and called a conference of British motor-industry leaders to study it. One and all were scathing. Ford in particular saw not one good feature, and ridiculed the use of an air-cooled engine mounted in the rear. The only man who did not actually laugh was Billy Rootes, and his attitude was one of pity. "It's actually got some ingenious features. Indeed I'm grateful to you, Roy, for bringing it over. But of course it's all a waste of time. Even if the Germans try to go on making it, it'll never sell."

CHAPTER ELEVEN

Projects and politics

The STAM office was disbanded as soon as the War was over. As ever, Fedden had laid his plans well in advance. The idea of forming his own company had been in his mind many years earlier, because he knew deep down that, however successful he was at Bristol, his position there was never going to be a happy one. As STAM he had watched his company come into existence. By the summer of 1945 he was ready to take charge of Roy Fedden Ltd full-time. He was then 60, an age when many men retire.

He had said it was to be a modest little organisation, doing fine engineering for the love of it, and trying to avoid slavish searching for profit. But the very existence of Roy Fedden Ltd was a contradiction of some of its deepest ideals, and was inherently bound to meet trouble. Fedden had embarked on the venture with a sore deep inside him, put there by the White family. In his own words, "It smarted, and to soothe it I was determined to show everyone how good a fellow I was". When this was allied with his natural enthusiasm it inevitably led to the little company trying to do far too much, and to a management situation that would never have been tolerated by Gavin Grieg. Fedden's own company secretary would never have dared to check the stores at dead of night; worse, there was nobody able to curb the leader's decisions (though his team were chosen as men of forceful character, well able to argue).

The company started reasonably enough, with a single project, though even this contained strategic errors. Fedden was anxious to produce what was in effect a British Volkswagen, though he might have been offended to hear it called that. He wanted a better people's car, and his knowledge of the innate conservatism of the British car industry merely spurred him all the harder along the path of radical innovation. Perhaps the biggest single mistake was to take it for granted that the engine would have sleeve-valves. Fedden's long battle to perfect the sleeve-valve had yielded what was without doubt a superior engine in the large and highly rated class for high-speed aircraft. Sleeve-valves to him were the route to a smooth and sweet-running engine, which was true enough, but they gradually had become the answer to everything else as well. Sleeves were probably not the best answer to a conservatively rated family car, where the dominant requirements were low cost and all-round economy. Good oil control, an absence of visible exhaust smoke and a very long background of development were also important. Fedden tried to extrapolate, from the problems of combustion, chamber shape and cooling in large aero engines of high specific power, across to car cylinders where the problems are entirely different. But he had a locked-in approach where the engine was concerned, and his wish to demonstrate that the sleeve-valve was good for cars was a Holy Grail crusade.

Indeed, throughout the design of his own products he adopted not so much the logical approach of the engineer or businessman as the intuitive approach of the female. His family car had little relevance to any of his previous experience since the First World War, yet, much as he had hankered after an unconventional light-weight car with an air-cooled engine in 1919 (and made it a great technical success), so did he fill his post-Second World War car with novel features. Duncan, a sound chief engineer, happily supported him – and not only because there would have been an explosion if he had disagreed. Duncan planned the engine in 1943 as a 67 cu in (1,100 cc) four-stroke with three-cylinders spaced at 120° around a vertical crankshaft. It was to be fitted into the rear of the car as a quickly removable "power egg" package. Instead of a gearbox the drive was to be taken through an automatic torque converter to the rear wheels, and the body was to be a monocoque pressing in non-corroding aluminium, with the front and rear ends made separately and each detachable by undoing four bolts.

Body styling was typical of the way futuristic, streamlined cars were planned over 50 years ago. It was not tunnel-tested, but it would undoubtedly have demonstrated low drag. The original shape was due mainly to Gordon Wilkins, who made Plasticine styling models in 1943. By the time the team

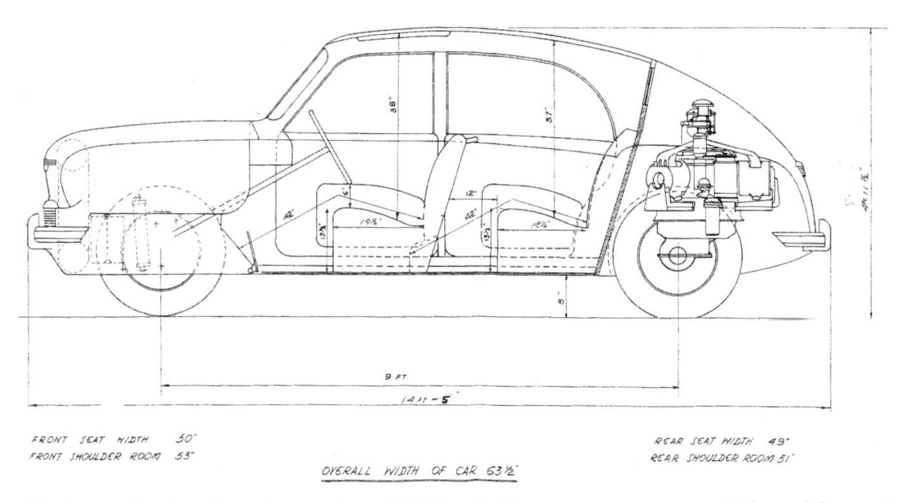

The first side elevation of the car dated 28 May 1945. (Science Museum)

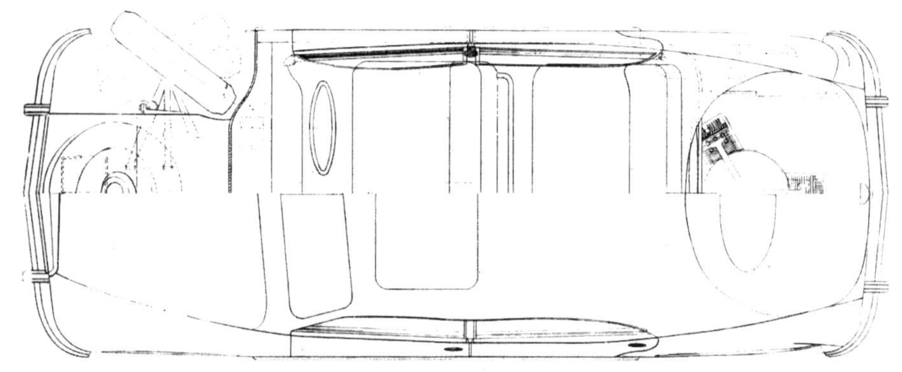

Plan view of the car. (Author)

gathered at Benton House the work had progressed to detailed tooling models in wood and plaster. Gradually the little band grew. It absorbed A Senkowski, the former chief engineer of PZL, the main Polish aircraft company, whom Fedden had welcomed at Bristol as a refugee in 1939. Derek Waters came from Gloster Aircraft; ulcer-tormented Bill Renwick, from Daimler; Bishop, the stressman; Hulberton, a great designer with a rare feeling for shapes; and Dick Warbourn, whose false arm (a memento of Dunkerque) was mysteriously stolen one day from a carrier basket on his bicycle. Imperceptibly, as it grew, the operation became tighter and more serious. True to form, Fedden produced an Executive Organisation Manual ("First Complete Edition, December 1946") which ran to 580 meticulous pages, and was to be kept up-to-date by periodic issue of amendments. Financial support was provided not only by Fedden but also by Dowty, Hugo Cunliffe-Owen, Leo d'Erlanger and by the Government Finance Corporation for Industry.

The first Christmas card of Roy Fedden Ltd. It was probably drawn by Gordon Wilkins (artist/author/broadcaster), who is in the rear seat of the device being driven by Duncan. (Science Museum)

The little team beavered away at Benton House for a year, and by mid-1946 had completed the basic engineering design. Dowty let the company turn most of the house into drawing offices, and a model shop was established in the stable yard. But it was inevitable that the work should soon outgrow Benton House, and in 1946 the whole operation moved to larger premises owned by Black and White Motorways. This large Cheltenham bus garage provided not only extended drawing-office facilities but also small-run manufacturing plant and an engine test-bed. Detail design of the engine, the rubber suspension and the body went ahead rapidly, and an order was placed with Motor Panels at Coventry for three prototype sets of body pressings. But Fedden was having second thoughts about the car itself. It had started in Moulton's flat in the middle of the War as an advanced technical exercise. By 1946 Fedden was thinking he would not sell many technical exercises, and the national cry was for exports. So he decided the four-seat 1,100 cc car must be turned into a six-seater with a bigger (1,600 cc) engine. That this was done, quickly, without any traumatic hiccup in the programme, is remarkable in view of the strong personalities involved.

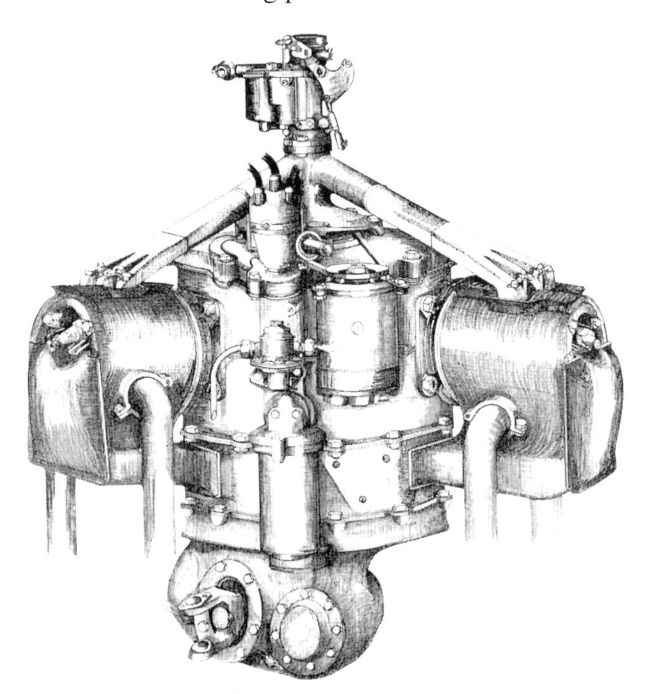

Sketch of the 1600 cc engine. (Author)

But the revised car was even further from being a truly logical concept. Taken separately, the body, engine and transmission were interesting and well-executed, but the overall product did not fit the market need. Moulton, who appreciated Fedden's towering stature and the unshakeable validity of his basic philosophies, yet realised that the car was based on faulty reasoning. He left amicably to complete his degree studies at Cambridge – interrupted in 1939, when he joined Fedden – and enter the family business, Spencer Moulton. Later he showed his own truer grasp of market needs by such major successes as the Moulton bicycle and the Hydrolastic car suspension which has been made by the million. A very different departure was that of Duncan, the king-pin of the whole car programme, who had a thundering row with Fedden centred around Duncan's wish to hang on to his radical ideas in the face of Fedden's justifiable instruction to play safe and produce an export winner.

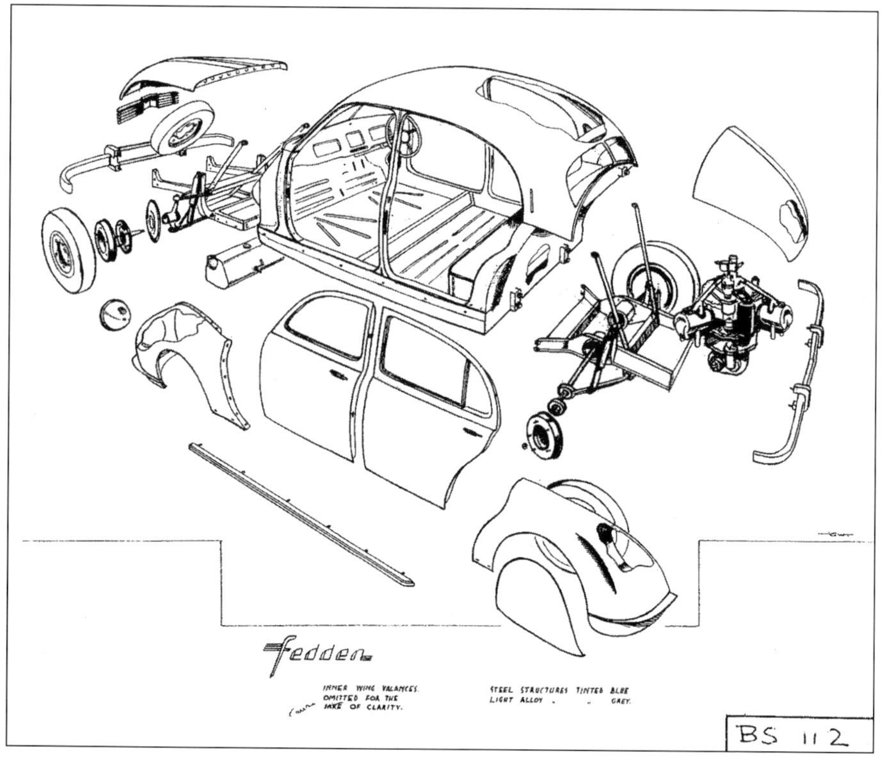

The first Fedden car (above) and those projected (opposite). (Rolls-Royce plc)

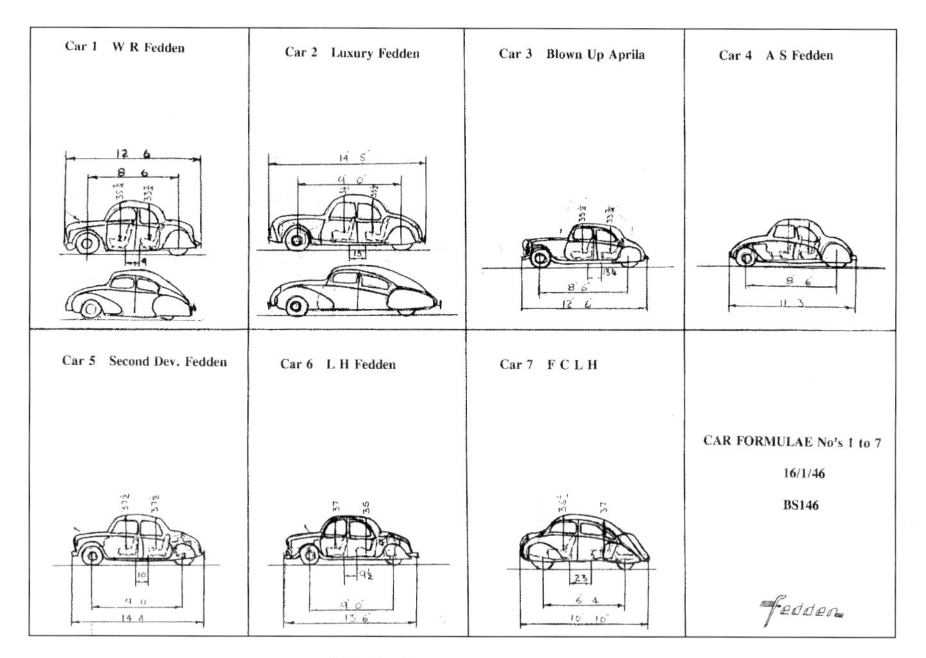

CAR FORMULAE No's 1 to 7
BS146 16.1.46

CAR NO	DESCRIPTION	WHEEL BASE	TRACK	O/ALL LENGTH	O/ALL WIDTH	O/ALL HEIGHT	WEIGHT Cwt	SEATS	C.C.	GROSS BHP	ENGINE TYPE	ENGINE POSITION
1	W. R. FEDDEN	8 6	4 2½	12 6	5 4	4 9	18	5	1600	65	RAD3SL	REAR
A	LANCIA APRILA	9 0¼	4 2	13 7½	4 10	4 9½	17¾	4	1352	47	V4 OHC	FRONT
2	LUX. FEDDEN	9 0	4 2½	14 5	5 4	5 2½	23	6	2600	104	V6SL	FRONT
B	2 ½ LTR JAGUAR	10 0		15 6	5 6	5 1	32	5	2663	102	ST6OHV	FRONT
3	BLOWN UP APRILA	8 6	4 2¼	12 6	5 4	4 9	18¾	5	1800	72	V4SL	FRONT
C	LANCIA APRILA	9 0¼		13 7½	4 10	4 9½	17¾	4	1352	47	V40HC	FRONT
4	A. S. FEDDEN	8 6	4 0	11 3	4 10	4 6½		3			ST4POP	FRONT
D	(NON IDENTIFIED)											
5	2ND DEV. FEDDEN	9 0	4 2½	14 4	5 4½	5 0½	18¾	6	1600	65	RAD 3SL	REAR
E	1 ½ LTR JAGUAR	9 4½	4 7	14 5	5 5⅛	5 0	28	5	1775	65	ST4OHV	FRONT
6	L. H. FEDDEN	9 0	4 2½	13 6	5 4½	5 0½	18½	5-6	1600	65	RAD3SL	REAR
F	1 ½ LTR JAGUAR											
7	F.C.L.H.	6 4	3 5	10 10	5 1	5 0	11¾	4-5	946	-	H04SL	REAR
G	FIAT 500	6 6¾	3 6½	10 8½	4 3½	4 7	10	3	570	-	ST4SV	FRONT

(i) Cars A to G are the principal competitors of Fedden cars 1 to 7.

(ii) Fedden Engine Types
Car 1 = Radial 3 Cylinder Sleeve Valve
Car 2 = V6 Cylinder Sleeve Valve
Car 3 = V4 Cylinder Sleeve Valve
Car 4 = Straight 4 Cylinder Poppet Valve
Car 5 = Radial 3 Cylinder Sleeve Valve
Car 6 = Radial 3 Cylinder Sleeve Valve
Car 7 = Horizontally Opposed 4 Cylinder Sleeve Valve

(Rolls-Royce plc)

One of the major problems was the torque converter. Driven by a worm gear on the vertical crankshaft, this was intended to be a brilliant infinitely variable automatic transmission, but it would have been better if such a fundamental advance had been started ten or twenty years earlier. One of the many difficulties was that it seemed impossible to get adequate stall torque, so that the tractive force with the car at rest was poor. The answer appeared to lie in filling the converter not with ordinary mineral oil but with a special fluid of higher specific gravity. After some discussion with oil companies a brown liquid – a di-phenyl-something – was offered, with the warning that it was thought to be unstable. Peter Ware took it to their consultant, Professor Peck, who held the chair of mechanical engineering at Loughborough. They filled the converter on the test bench and then started it up. Peck's falsetto voice could be heard above the din saying "Ah, this really is much better … these readings are very good indeed, in fact I think we can call them magnific…" BANG!!! Suddenly there was a mighty explosion. Acrid fumes poured out of the shattered windows, and the light-alloy casing of the converter was scattered in fragments all over the lab. Miraculously, neither of the men was hurt, but they decided they had not yet found their better fluid.

Eventually the torque converter was made to give adequate performance, and from the start Hulberton's ratchet solenoid reverser had worked well; but the whole transmission added an unnecessary element of unproven radicalism that had seemed an advantage at first but which RF came to regret. Worse, the engine installation was such that there was no room beneath it for an ordinary gearbox. Even as it was, the engine was mounted higher up than Fedden liked, and he worried about the high centre of gravity and the car's behaviour on corners. But at least the growing team was moving fast. In late November 1946, after three days and two nights of non-stop work, the first complete engine was run. Close by, the first car was taking shape.

While all this was going on, Fedden decided he could no longer repress the schemes that had been forming in his mind for engines for light aircraft. In the months since VJ-day such engines had once more become extremely important products, and in the summer of 1946 Senkowski, who succeeded Duncan as chief engineer, was bidden to lead a new team on horizontally opposed flat-four and flat-six designs with – of course – sleeve valves. Fedden remembered that in 1942 Geordie Lee (originator of the bronze junkhead) and Don Copley at Bristol had designed a new kind of air-cooled cylinder with a longitudinally finned barrel. The result was better cooling, with lower pressure-drop and no tendency for the barrel to bend and thus cause sleeve seizure. Work went ahead on the new engines with extraordinary speed, and the only obvious criticism that could be levelled at them was that, as Barrington had demonstrated, only certain configurations of sleeve-valve engines are possible without counterweights, and the Fedden horizontally opposed designs did not have a fully balanced crankshaft. Experience showed, however, that the concepts were sound. The unusual straight cooling fins worked marvellously, and single-cylinder running soon demonstrated bmep beyond anything previously available in lightplane engines, and better than typical general-aviation engines today.

Unlike the car, Fedden's light aircraft engines were potentially great winners. They were an order of magnitude superior to the in-line engines of much older concept then made in Britain, and were technically superior to the flat-four and flat-six engines produced in the United States. Henry Berliner, founder of Engineering and Research Corporation and the moving spirit behind the Ercoupe lightplane, was in 1946 one of the biggest forces in the entire light aircraft field in the United States. He had no doubt of the promise of Fedden's engines, and negotiated for a flat-six for the Ercoupe and a flat-four for a twin-engined pusher he was designing. Fedden also secured the enthusiastic support from young Peter (later Sir Peter) Masefield, Director-General of Long-Term Planning at the Ministry of Civil Aviation, who had come to yearn for a really good new British family of light aircraft engines.

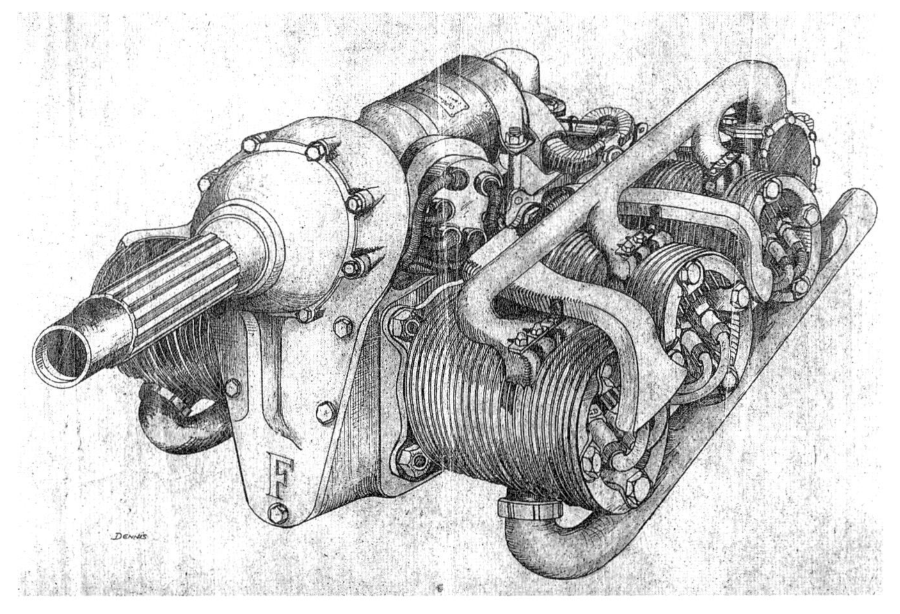

First sketch of the flat-six aircraft engine. (Author)

Before the end of 1946 the first flat-six had been made – in a matter of weeks – and run on the bed. It was a fine engine and ran beautifully at up to 3,750 rpm. A key factor in the design of the car engine had been the use of aeronautical experience and aero-engine design features. This made it relatively easy to use the automotive components in order quickly to achieve high reliability and produce the engine at a competitive price. At first it had a bore of 3.4 in (86.4 mm) and stroke of 3.6 in (91.4 mm), giving a capacity of 195 cu in (3.2 litres). The engine was designed in two forms, one with direct drive to be rated at 100 hp, and a geared version to weigh 275 lb and be rated at 140 hp at 3,750 rpm. Compression ratio was to be either 7, for 80-octane fuel, or 7.5 for 90-octane. Unfortunately, as often happens, the customer kept demanding greater power. By August 1946 it was reluctantly accepted that the car-engine cylinders would have to be abandoned, and capacity was increased successively to 4.05 litres, 4.62 litres and finally, in April 1947, to 5.3 litres.

As actually built and tested, the aircraft engine had longitudinally finned cylinders.
(Science Museum)

By the end of 1946 the only serious problem with Fedden's light aircraft engines was proliferation of projects. There were many possible cylinder sizes, and the cylinders could be arranged in various ways. Engines could be supercharged, and they could have a propeller reduction gear. The total number of permutations was astronomic, and before 1947 dawned Fedden was having to terminate about a dozen light-plane projects before breakfast each day. This still left an unreasonable spread of studies, and the light-plane engine department swiftly overtook the car team in number of personnel, the total company payroll now reaching 200. This imposed a heavy burden of salaries and wages, on top of massively escalating research and manufacturing costs. Roy Fedden Ltd was already several times bigger than the Bristol Engine Department had been in the early 1920s, and it had yet to sell anything.

Probably the last straw was that, almost unbelievably, Fedden launched out into the field of gas turbines. His final STAM report, advocating a 1,000 horse-power turboprop, was sound enough, but others had got in first. Rolls-Royce had quickly produced an engine called the Dart, using compressors scaled up from the two-stage supercharger of the Griffon piston engine. Armstrong Siddeley had run a more ambitious axial engine called the Mamba. Napier was at last getting into the turbine field with a 1,500 hp axial called the Naiad. Yet Fedden not only decided to compete as well but even, through sheer force of character, managed to get a Ministry of Supply development contract. He called his 1,305 shp engine the Cotswold. It had an 11-stage axial compressor and two-stage turbine, weighed 760 lb and had the calculated specific fuel consumption of 0.665. This meant a completely new design and development team and an enormous expansion in facilities.

Components of the flat-six aero engine. (Author)

Fedden cast envious eyes upon a site at Newent, doubtless because of the fine fishing, but eventually he closed an exceptionally favourable deal with the Ministry of Supply for an almost unused government factory at Stoke Orchard, about five miles outside Cheltenham. It had

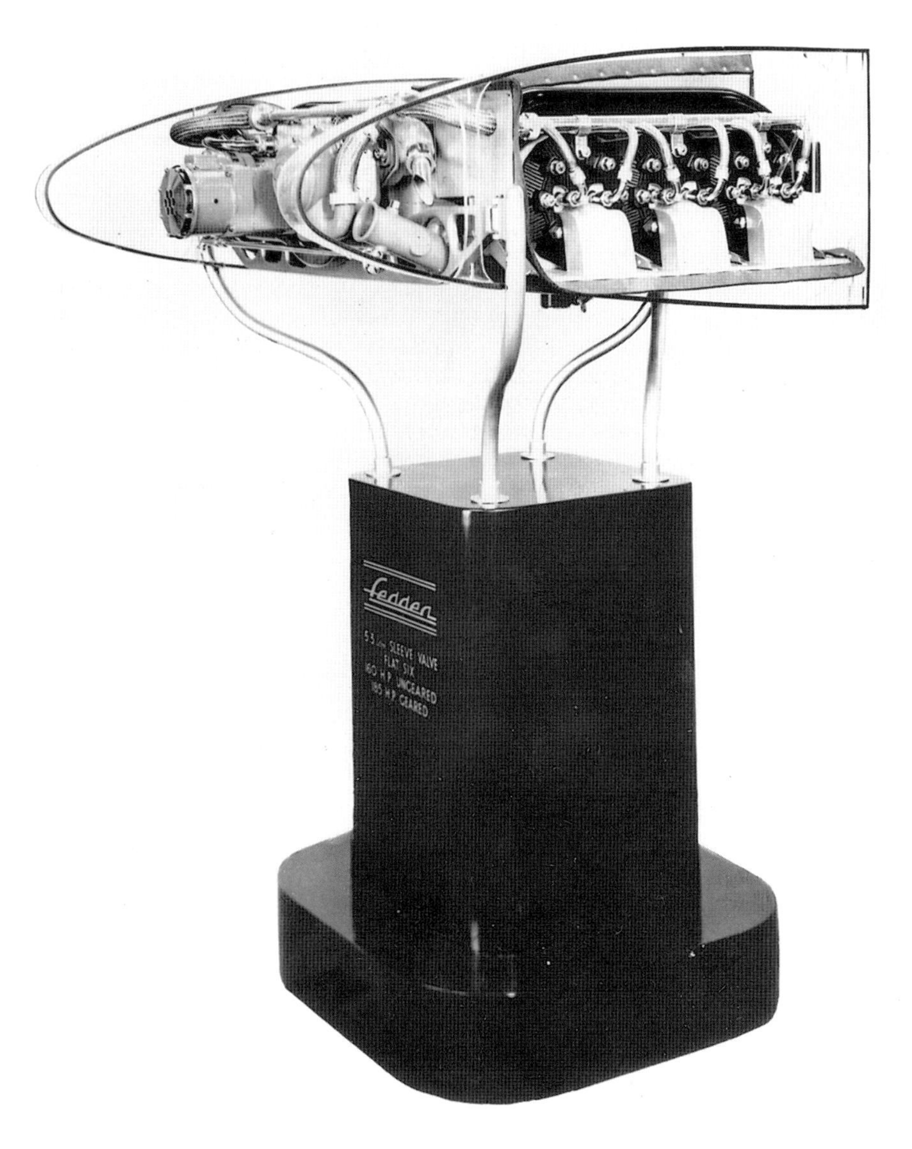

Display model showing the engine buried in a wing. (Science Museum)

been intended as a dispersal facility for Gloster Aircraft, and exactly suited Roy Fedden Ltd. The company moved to Stoke Orchard in February 1947. It was now a very impressive operation indeed, with three quite distinct product-lines all superficially of an advanced and potentially successful nature. There was no question but that the company was possessed of a vast fund of engineering talent, and by now Fedden was urgently striving for saleable products and a return on the considerable investment. But fate decreed otherwise.

In January 1947 the first prototype car was secretly driven about at night. The three big sleeve-valve cylinders pulled surprisingly smoothly. The peripheral chain that drove the sleeve cranks was reliable and not unduly noisy. The torque converter seemed to be out of the wood. Various drivers, including Fedden, took it out on to the Stoke Orchard airfield perimeter track and ran at high speed on the runways. But the car obviously had cornering instability. One driver after another sheepishly came back and reported he had "overcooked it" on a turn, or just "lost it" in a sudden inexplicable swerve. Fedden had feared as much from the engine location, but the real culprit was the use of swing axles at the rear. Peter Thornhill's hydro-pneumatic suspension struts gave a wonderfully comfortable ride, but the swing axles made many of the team nervous, especially after Fedden bought a rear-engined Czech Tatra to explore its handling and discovered that it too had severe cornering problems. The high rear engine of the Fedden car caused "toggling" or "tucking under" of the outer wheel on the swing axle, resulting in a major change in slip angle and the cornering power of the tyre.

Extensive tests were made at different camber angles, and the best handling appeared to be with quite marked negative camber, with the axles sloping upwards so that the wheels tilted inwards at the top. On the final run of the programmed series the chassis designer, Waters, opted to go along and see how it felt. Alec Caine, who had been driving very well, lost control completely in a fast turn. The car rolled and somersaulted; a door flew open and Waters was thrown out, breaking his hip. Fedden was in as much mental agony as Waters was in physical. He agreed with Ware that "This has to be the end of the swing-axle concept"; but he wanted to continue with a car much closer to what he felt the world needed. In a mere four weeks the talented and experienced car team raced through almost the complete design of a new six-seat car with a water-cooled in-line engine at the front, with four sleeve-valve cylinders of 1,977 cc capacity, driving the rear axle through a conventional gearbox. But Nemesis was rushing at Roy Fedden Ltd.

The engines for light aircraft, though technically excellent, were becoming diffused into a proliferation of projects. While the flat-six remained furthest advanced in development, there were various other numbers of cylinders from four to twelve, and several possible customers wanted a radial. While a 14-cylinder radial was planned to meet a Directorate of Engine R & D Specification for a neat 450 hp engine, plans went ahead for a series of engines of 4.3 in bore with various configurations to try to plug every hole in the market. Masefield continued to do his best to support Fedden but became concerned at the inability of the firm to find even one basic design which it could get into production. Then Berliner and his Ercoupe ran into such financial trouble that he gave up building aircraft, and did his best to diversify into simulators and armament, so Fedden's best product lost its only immediate buyer.

On 6th February 1947 Fedden encouraged his engine team by writing Senkowski a note which began: "1. Do not be despondent about what has happened. We have learned a lot, and eliminated some quite important points. 2. Act on the following points quickly, grasp the various nettles boldly and produce specific answers." There followed 37 questions, any of which could well have taken many hours of deliberation by a large committee. By February 1947 Fedden had got to the stage where he wanted all 37 answers in hours, and most of the questions were phrased in the form "Can we agree ...?" The consequence of anyone failing to agree can be imagined.

The prototype car. (Science Museum)

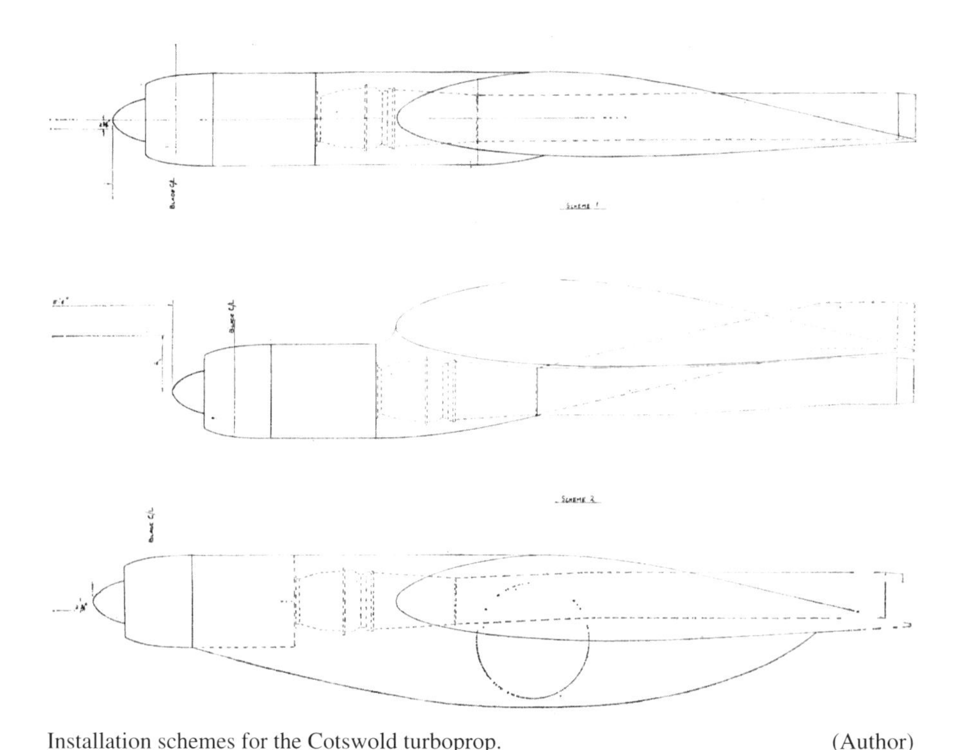

Installation schemes for the Cotswold turboprop. (Author)

As for the gas turbine, even in the earliest hardware stages this was in a financial category distinctly more ambitious than cars and small piston engines, and the Cotswold turboprop was soon running at an annual budget approaching £1 million. But the Government was getting value for money. The team developing the Cotswold was still very small by comparison with established gas turbine staffs, yet they completed the design in six months, and in February 1947 had a prototype axial compressor on test at the National Gas Turbine Establishment, recording pressure ratios and efficiencies officially described as "exceptionally good". One of the leaders of the Cotswold team was Butler's son-in-law Don R Amor; others were Arthur W Pope, J C Morrall and Edward Hawthorne, forming yet another great Roy Fedden team.

Hope springs eternal. On 17th April 1947, on Fedden's bidding, Morrall issued a brochure which began "Bearing in mind that it is the policy of this firm to produce small engines, it was thought that an examination of a 500 hp turbine engine would help when deciding on the next engine for

Cotswold flame tube with two experimental fuel-cone inserts. (Author)

manufacture". The engine proposed was, in the context of its time, thoroughly sound, with a pressure ratio of 5.5 and maximum gas temperature of 1,200K (927°C); the only snag was that the market for such an engine did not really "take off" for another 20 years. Fedden did not get the chance to wait. In May 1947 an economy-minded Government came to the conclusion that, though the Cotswold was an extremely promising turboprop which Rex Pierson was hoping to use in his VC.2 airliner (which became the Viscount), Roy Fedden Ltd was one place where development costs could be cut, and the Ministry of Supply contract was terminated. Troubles come in threes. The terms of the lease of Stoke Orchard were altered to permit research and development but to prohibit manufacture of production articles for sale. Fedden's main financial backers then withdrew their support. The firm's liquidation followed in June 1947.

Mrs Goldby was profoundly affected by the last days at Stoke Orchard: "I observed him from the close position of a private secretary, and saw a man to whom defeat was impossible. Long after most people would have given up, he continued to fight with a tenacity which filled me with awe. Until then I had looked upon him merely as an 'important' man, but in that final month I realised that he was a 'great' man." Fedden spent the next weeks in finding

TELEPHONE: - - CLEEVE HILL 241.
TELEGRAMS: FEDDEN, CHELTENHAM.

ROY FEDDEN LTD.

DIRECTORS:
SIR A. H. ROY FEDDEN, M.B.E., F.R.AE.S., M.I.A.E.,
C. H. YOUNG.

SECRETARY: R. G. R. GOLDBY.

OFFICES AND WORKS
STOKE ORCHARD,
NR. CHELTENHAM,
GLOS.

F/QA/95307.

9th November, 1946.

R. Pierson Esq.,
Vickers Armstrongs Ltd.,
Brooklands House,
Weybridge,
Surrey.

My dear Rex,

Thank you very much indeed for your letter of the 28th October, with the interesting memorandum enclosed.

I was very encouraged by my discussion with you and your people on Friday, and came back full of enthusiasm. In the meantime I have had a good talk with my people here on my visit to you as well as on the memorandum you sent me, and whereas we fully appreciate that you are in a difficult position in so much as you have already laid out the design, and you are also trying to compromise for four different types of propeller turbine, I cannot refrain from saying, knowing nothing about aircraft design, that it is an awful pity to have this huge wetted surface out ahead of the machine, and that even though the mechanical problems are severe, the straightened type of jet pipe should be tackled.

It appears to us that the firm who is willing to face up to the difficulties is going to win a great reward. They are going to have a classic type which will remain modern and up to date for years, whereas any compromise is only going to be a temporary stopgap. Is not this a great chance to make a D.C.1. or a Wellington which is going to carry on for years? Your proposed design seems to us one which is bound to be replaced when someone has got the boldness to face the music, and do the job in the way in which it must obviously be tackled at some not too future date.

I hope you do not think I am being very impertinent in saying this, but naturally I have got a very big prize to win.

Yours sincerely,

Roy

Could RF ever have replaced the Dart as powerplant of Pierson's VC.2? Over 20 years later, a man who spelt his name differently (Sir Denning Pearson, Managing Director of Rolls-Royce) called the Dart "agricultural machinery", but pointed out that his company had delivered over 7,100. RF's "bound to be replaced" was thus wide of the mark.

(Science Museum)

the best possible jobs for his engineering team. He devoted immense efforts to this: he felt sharp personal responsibility. Then he went into retirement.

Despite his remarkable accomplishments as STAM and with his own company, he had really been under-employed ever since he left Bristol, and now for the first time he was in the wilderness. He began to get builders in to extend the Mill, though he lived mainly at Wellington Court. He got out his 14-ton yacht *Pegasa* and did a little ocean racing, a sport he had had no time for since long before the War. *Pegasa* was a far cry from the great *Teal* which he had raced in the mid-1930s. *Teal* was an aristocrat among racing yachts, one of the Swedish 30 square metre class with a cockpit invariably half-full of water. It was a boat for enthusiasts, and Fedden's enthusiasm is shown by the fact that in the 1938 season, amidst the pressures of sleeve-valve engines and a crash rearmament programme, he and John Hopcraft raced *Teal* to gain 25 firsts, 7 seconds, 4 thirds and a fourth place. *Pegasa* in contrast, was a Bermuda-rig Gauntlet, a "good old plugger" (said Fedden), rated A.1 at Lloyds. He kept it at Lymington. Though he was not a man to frequent pubs, he could hardly fail to become acquainted with the yachtsmen on adjacent moorings. One of these was Henry (later Sir Henry) Spurrier, Managing Director of Leyland Motors, who of course knew Fedden by repute.

Obviously they were birds of a feather. Fedden appreciated the way Spurrier ended each high-pressure week by driving as fast as possible from his truck plant in Lancashire down the narrow roads to Lymington. Soon they were confiding in each other. Spurrier, a powerful but impulsive man, had found he could hardly put a foot wrong during the War, and 1945 found Leyland in a strong position. It did not take Spurrier long to decide he could use Fedden, who of course was living off his capital. Spurrier felt isolated in Lancashire, and had long wished he had a London office where he could tap directly into "the City", into Government Departments, and other activities in the capital.

Teal, "an aristocrat among yachts" (Author)

Fedden, now 62, had been content to retire; but he could not resist Spurrier's invitation to join the

Leyland Board and set up a London office. It was the open-endedness of the deal that appealed to Fedden. Long before he reached London he had begun to think of all the things he might do for Leyland.

At that time the giant British Leyland Motor Corporation had yet to be formed, and the man who later was its chief architect was still young Donald Stokes, salesman, who managed to take a keen interest in Fedden's activities without becoming involved. He was not the only one interested. One does not import a man like Fedden without electrifying the political atmosphere, and it was absolutely predictable that within weeks the upper strata of Leyland was becoming divided into pro-Feddens and antis. The company's main business was commercial vehicles. Fedden was quite at home in this field, but he had no intention of merely running a passive liaison office. As Spurrier probably expected, he at once began an R & D cell, brought in a few bright staff, including the unconquerable Peter Ware, and soon the new Leyland Motors office at Hanover House was seething with activity.

Ostensibly its assignment was to feed the Head Office with useful intelligence and undertake market research. Fedden would have liked also to launch forth into a massive programme of new design and manufacture. What actually happened was something in between. At all times Fedden was totally loyal to Spurrier and to the Board in general, and he never failed to deliver any goods requested. Indeed it was soon abundantly evident that the London office was a good idea, and worth its cost (though the latter was always rising sharply). On the side, Fedden gained a thorough appreciation of the company's limitations and ambitions, and compared these with the market opportunities. Very soon he came to Spurrier and said "Look here, do you realise your biggest engine gives only 140 horsepower? I'm certain you're going to need a much more powerful engine before long. You'll need one for commercial vehicles, which are going to get bigger and go faster. And I have a hunch there's going to be a boom in big earthmoving equipment – bulldozers, scrapers, dump trucks and things of that kind. Even if Leyland chooses not to make any of these, it could make the engines. I don't think much of the General Motors two-stroke that people use at present [he had been flown by Bernard Sunley, whom he had met on the Mission to America voyage, to see an open-cast coal site littered with the unreliable GM diesels torn out and left where they lay]. If Leyland chose, I believe it could make a killing with a really good 240 horsepower diesel. I could have it running very quickly".

It was this kind of proposal, allied with Fedden's intense drive and his stormy reputation, that split the Leyland Board. Looked at dispassionately, Fedden's proposal was eminently reasonable. What he said was absolutely true, his predictions were correct, and Leyland could have produced the standard high-power engine for an extremely wide spectrum of arduous duties. Whether Fedden had been hired to do any more than merely make recommendations was another matter. One man who vehemently considered Fedden had no right to poke his nose into any part of Leyland's design and development activity was the chief engineer, Stanley Markland. He was an intensely political animal, and he was quite ruthless in stopping Fedden. In view of his much younger age he did not regard the newcomer as a rival; his attitude was just that there was not room for both in the same company. Fedden would probably have felt the same at Bristol.

At first Markland was unable to arrest the growth of Fedden's little empire. The design of the new engine was authorised, Fedden's team grew in strength and experience, and soon there came the time to begin manufacture and testing. But then the Board came to the conclusion they did not have the money (actually they did). Fedden wanted to build a new Leyland development laboratory beside the enormous London Transport service depot at Boreham Wood. It could have been an excellent investment, but Markland succeeded in polarising the opposition into refusing such expenditure point-blank in December 1949. As he had hoped, Fedden quit. Fedden remained on good terms with Spurrier and most of the Leyland Board, and in 1957 wrote for them a monumental report on the car industry, which helped launch the company into its later role as one of the biggest car makers in Europe. Many at Leyland later realised that Fedden's advice had been sound, and regretted that they had been unable to use him without stirring up a hornet's nest. And they missed out on the big diesel market.

Having left Leyland, Fedden thought he might do some more sailing, and he began a big programme of improving the Usk and his Mill. He got Watkins and Bevan, local builders and undertakers, to add on new rooms in the same charming style, using matching stones raised from the river bed. Mervyn Watkins told Fedden how his father used to clock on at work in Merthyr Tydfil at 6 each morning after having walked the 11 miles over the great Mynydd Llangynidr mountain. Every evening he would walk back. The country round the Mill is outstandingly beautiful. It had been part of the Buckland Estate owned by the three gifted Berry brothers, who had an ironmongery business in Merthyr. Their political services to Prime Minister Lloyd George in the First World War had been such that he created them respectively Lord Buckland, Lord Camrose and Lord Kemsley, better known as the great newspaper barons. Lord Buckland was thrown from his horse and killed, the estate passed to Sir David Llewellyn, and David's brother Monty sold the Mill to Fedden early in the Second World War.

Late in 1940 Fedden had rescued what he could of the furniture and effects from Widegates, and the items worth repairing were mended and used to furnish the expanding Mill. Over the years it ceased to be a quaint fishing bolt-hole, and became a most desirable property. And after the Second World

War Fedden seldom visited the Mill alone. In a quiet ceremony in 1948 his childhood sweetheart Norah became Lady Fedden. Never could a couple have been more devoted to each other. Though Lady Fedden was anything but a weak and pliable character, her strong personality dovetailed perfectly into Roy's, and their union, achieved after so many turbulent years, could not have been happier. She died in August 1977.

Utterly fearless when skiing, Lady Fedden retained a dread of water yet never hesitated to sail in *Pegasa* under conditions when only a rash or extremely experienced sailor would have ventured forth at all. Her husband may not have realised the torments she suffered on stormy seas, but most of their happy days in 1950 were spent – with Tinker, Fedden's fox terrier – visiting such places as Lake Garda, Chartres and Venice. It was the first relaxed time of his life, but on one occasion he drove his Bentley S.2 at an *average* of more than 60 mph from Rome to Calais between dawn and dusk on a summer's day. Even such hurried European travel appealed greatly to him. His next job brought him plenty.

In 1949 the North Atlantic Treaty Organisation had at last brought together the major powers of Western Europe and North America into a military union which, it was hoped, would provide some measure of collective security in what looked like being perilous days ahead. The Soviet Union had long since embarked on its policy of chill confrontation from behind the Iron Curtain, it had nuclear weapons, and in conventional forces it far outnumbered the total available in Western Europe. In June 1950 war broke in Korea, finally shattering the calm of the Western statesmen, and in particular the policy of the British Labour Government which had decided that armaments were one area where little money need be spent. Panic is not too strong a word to use for the military planning of Western Europe in the latter part of 1950, and it did not help matters to recall that most defence hardware cannot be put into production overnight but needs several years of gestation. It was, in fact, a situation akin to the period after 1937.

Fedden, forever aware and active in the political scene, could do little but write to the papers. But in October 1950 he was timidly approached and asked whether he would be prepared to take a full-time job with the NATO planning staff. This was a bolt from the blue. It smacked of cloak-and-dagger activity, because this aura pervaded the atmosphere when Fedden was called to confidential meetings at strange little offices in London. He sought the opinion of influential friends and was "warned off". Negotiations involved spending many hours on long-distance telephone calls, Fedden having to go from the Mill to the nearest public telephone at Llangynidr as his own telephone was years down the queue. Eventually in an interview with the Chief Executive, General Wood of the British Army, he took the job of Aircraft Advisor. The post was an important one, and he fitted it like a glove, because he intimately knew almost all the aircraft and engine firms of Western Europe and was intensely motivated with a desire to help back up the feeble NATO alliance with some industrial muscle and military teeth.

For the first six months the Feddens lived at their London flat at Wellington Court. Sir Roy worked at Belgrave Square as Technical Advisor to Lord Ismay, NATO Director-General. This steeped him in the rigid official procedures, the multiplicity of languages (and he was no great linguist) and the overall immensity of the job. The aircraft industries of the NATO nations of Europe had either been more or less destroyed during the Second World War, or else, as in the case of Britain, been allowed to wither away in an environment where every necessity from skilled men to materials was either in short supply or else non-existent. Out of this unpromising landscape modern combat aircraft had to be fashioned by the thousand. The main questions were: how many thousands? what types? who will make them? how will the work be allocated? where will the skilled personnel and materials come from? how long will it take? what will it cost? what might go wrong? how much assurance can be put upon the planning? do we need everything we can get, at whatever price, at the earliest possible date, or can we stretch out the timing by a few weeks or months in order to save huge sums, or have later aircraft? who will operate the aircraft? what are the missions, the present shortages and the most urgent needs of the NATO air forces? When questions of this kind are posed it needs a supreme czar, of the type that Fedden had campaigned for in 1938, to get fast action. Instead, as in 1938, there was no czar; the fifteen NATO nations were mutually rather suspicious, and inclined to collaborate wholeheartedly provided that each got a better deal than his neighbours (just like today, in fact). Fedden was meant to act in a purely technical capacity, but he would not have been Fedden if he had not at once become deeply involved in the politics, and he was soon expressing forceful opinions on people, on companies and even on whole nations.

During 1950 the newly-created NATO hierarchy sorted itself out, under conditions of considerable strain. A Working Group on Aircraft Production Planning was formed to answer the formidable questions. It had a Military Sub-Committee and a Production Sub-Committee. Fedden was appointed to both, and made Secretary of the former. Chairman of the Military Sub-Committee was Group Captain A G Weston, RAF, a most capable officer who – somewhat to Fedden's surprise – worked everyone hard for eight hours a day and expected homework to be done at night. Meetings, seldom involving fewer than 10 languages because that was the composition of the committee itself, charged through mountains of work in the utmost detail, generating and perusing vast amounts of paper and with constant scrupulous attention to accuracy, secrecy, formality and international protocol. Two interpreters would constantly be in attendance in a glass cubicle, preparing transcripts in languages which were usually English and French. They could not work longer than 30 minutes at a time, being relieved after each stint in a state of mental and physical exhaustion, with perspiration running down their faces.

Fedden had an efficient office staff with whose aid he would prepare agenda, minutes and thick stapled books of notes and background information, and have everything translated and circulated to an average of 50 named individuals. Most documents were labelled either SECRET or COSMIC, the latter being the classification grade higher than SECRET and used only rarely in Government circles. Fedden felt COSMIC was used much too freely for material which did not warrant it, but he was meticulous in adhering to the strict rules of security and in never leaving a single piece of paper outside a safe at night.

After four months of feverish work in London, Lord Ismay called the staff together and announced an immediate move to the new NATO headquarters which had been established in Paris, at the Palais de Chaillot. Within days the Feddens had uprooted and moved into a splendid apartment overlooking the Longchamps racecourse. Everything about it was delightfully chic and French, from Anna the maid to the fact that the flat's owner unwisely tried to get Fedden to sign a paper certifying that he was a close friend and paying no rent. Each evening, after a tiring and often frustrating day at the Palais de Chaillot, Fedden would drive the eight miles home and sit on the verandah with his wife just looking at the lights of Paris. They hardly ever went into the city together, but after knocking off on a Friday at 1 pm – what a contrast with the tough old Bristol regime! – they would be off, with Anna, to Rambouillet or the Loire Valley. Lady Fedden frequently accompanied Roy on his many trips to check on how things were going in factories from Norway to Southern Italy. After each trip his report was invariably that the true state of affairs was nothing like as optimistic as witnesses had testified.

Gradually the vast production plans were thrashed out. Most of the aircraft involved were British, with especially large numbers to be bought of the Swift and Venom (no relation to the pre-war Venom), from factories throughout Europe. By March 1951 the gigantic plan covered more than 8,300 aircraft, costing well over a billion US dollars, and manufacturers, prices and timing had been agreed. It was a stupendous achievement. Once every two weeks Lord Ismay had a meeting with senior staff at which he explained how the work was going and what would be required of each man. Ismay did his best, and almost everyone in the NATO top strata seemed to be a good man and hard worker (if they were not, Fedden let everyone know about it, which was judged dashed bad form by the RN captain who served as Ismay's secretary). Yet, as the vital weeks and months ticked by, Fedden gradually came to feel it was all an unreal cloud-cuckoo land. It was all very well to make huge and complicated plans, but all NATO was actually producing was piles of paper. Unless the 15 governments voted the money, nobody would be trained, raw material would not be ordered, and none of the 8,300 aircraft would take the air – ever.

Fedden's big reports assumed a familiar tone. The Main Costing Report to examine deficiencies in June 1951 began with "The industrial feasibility of these programmes can only be realised by the immediate availability of the necessary funds and the utmost collaboration on an international basis. There is not a day to lose …" And, three months later, Fedden was lamenting the lack of action: "This is equivalent to the loss of three months' production at 1954 levels … This loss cannot now be made good." Ultimately, some factories did get into production and make some aircraft, but the overall programme suffered from constant change, continual failure to agree, technical failure of some of the aircraft (notably the Swift) and the fact that interminable delays kept changing the requirement before anything could be built. Fedden toiled mightily and spoke his mind fearlessly, and though most of his colleagues considered him invaluable there inevitably grew a hard core of opponents whom he had either caused to feel guilty or whom he had outraged by his bluntly expressed views. It led – of course – to a parting of the ways. To continue in a political appointment one has to be a different kind of human animal, one who knows how to soothe and calm people instead of ruffling their feathers, and Fedden had no intention of doing anything but what he saw clearly to be his duty. Much against the wishes of Ismay and Wood, Fedden left NATO of his own choosing in August 1952 and went back to the Mill. He was sad that the bickering nations should not have pulled together, but left behind him solid achievements. Paris had been wonderful, but the Brecon hills were better.

At 67 Fedden had yet again retired. He continued improving the Mill and the Usk fishing. But one day in 1952 Lady Fedden found herself at a dinner sitting next to Sir George Dowty, who asked her whether Sir Roy might be interested in a post as a consultant to the Dowty Group. Dowty had gone into business on his own account in 1930, renting a small room in Cheltenham and possessing a drill-press and a few metalworking tools. By 1952 the Dowty Group had become one of the world's major engineering enterprises, with dozens of companies in many countries all operating in advanced technology but guided at all times by a sound business sense that made them prosper. As soon as he heard of the invitation from Sir George, Fedden got him on the telephone. The two men had always liked and respected each other, and Dowty was one of an extremely small group of individuals for whom Fedden could cheerfully work hard over a long period with no clash of personalities. He took the job like a shot.

Though they never ceased to improve the Mill, the Feddens moved into a suite of rooms at the Queen's Hotel, Cheltenham, from Mondays to Fridays while Sir Roy worked in Arle Court. He had an office and secretary close to Sir George, and on his desk each morning would arrive a pile of letters and memos. Sir George knew his man, and made the consultancy genuinely hard work. It involved considerable travel, and Fedden found himself for the first time in his life selling products which he had had no hand in designing. In his own view, this made what he said totally credible – "whereas, when you are selling your own product, you can become worked up and highly strung, and without actually lying, you can overstate your case". Perhaps the chief reason why Dowty hired him was that he was universally known and respected, and the mention of his name at once opened every door to the highest levels. In any case, his job was not really that of a salesman, other than that he was "selling" a great enterprise that he believed in. His real job was to go anywhere in the world, take a keen look at certain things, and report to Sir George.

He went to most European countries, to most continents – and also to boys' schools in the Cheltenham area to advise Sir George where to send his son. One of his first foreign missions was to West Germany in October 1955. He went straight to the beautiful house near Cologne of Dr W J Stern. Stern was always one of the least-known great men of British aviation. This was largely because of his sensitive position in Technical Intelligence, but his early career had been that of a "legitimate" boffin. Fedden had been impressed with his work at the Air Ministry Laboratory in South Kensington in the First World War, and avidly read his prophetic paper "The Internal Combustion Turbine" published (price two shillings) in 1920, long before even Farnborough had begun any gas turbine research. In 1945 he had been a tower of strength on Fedden's mission to Germany, not least because of his fluent German. Now, in 1955, Stern briefed his old friend on the swift rebuilding of Germany. Three years earlier the German language had been absent from the frantic NATO planning at the Palais de Chaillot. Now the Federal Republic was about to be elected a full member of NATO, and it was not only rebuilding its aircraft industry – previously forbidden – but also making plans to create a powerful new Luftwaffe. Fedden found the Germans dismayed by Britain's apparent lack of interest in selling aircraft to this huge new market. "If you want us to buy Hunters" said the procurement director in Bonn "it is Sir Sydney Camm we want to see". But everything had to be channelled through Whitehall, which showed no apparent interest; so, to Fedden's deep chagrin, almost the entire first phase of Luftwaffe procurement – over 1,500 aircraft – was based on imports from the USA, France and Italy.

Fedden attended a conference in Augsburg which was a memorable occasion; it was the first official get-together of German aviation men since 1945. He renewed dozens of old friendships, including Professor Willi Messerschmitt, Dr Ernst Heinkel and Dr Claudius Dornier. He drove the prototypes of the "bubble cars" which Messerschmitt and Heinkel were about to launch on the world, and did his utmost to find out about engineering and aviation in the Soviet Union. The main purpose of his trip was to evaluate Professor Thoma's hydrostatic transmission, and he concluded an agreement with the Professor which started a new line of Dowty business, at first assisted by the Professor's son Oswald Thoma. Fedden's reports on Germany also spurred Dowty to set up Dowty GmbH at Darmstadt.

He undertook many other missions for Dowty, but the thing he was most grateful for was being introduced to New Zealand. In the autumn of 1958 he went there for the first time, to evaluate the Hamilton water-jet propulsion system for small boats. On the way his eagle eye spotted his old yacht *Teal* in Sydney harbour; her Australian owner had been glad to buy her for four times what Fedden had paid in 1931. When he got to New Zealand he at once fell in love with the place. So at home did he feel that he visited New Zealand twice later, at his own expense, and considered that, had he known the country earlier, he would probably have made his home there. How much of this was due to the scenery and how much due to Bill Hamilton and his wife Peg one can only guess. Hamilton, a former winning co-driver at Le Mans, had built up a versatile and profitable engineering business. He also had a 25,000-acre sheep station, which was bounded and crossed by wonderful rivers and lakes, but these were unnavigable because of dangerous rapids and shallows. Hamilton reasoned that with an efficient water intake, hydraulic pump and propulsive jet, it should be possible to drive a boat over the entire estate. The rest is part of history. Fedden drove one of his jet boats for hundreds of miles, through some of the most wonderful scenery in the world, and with increasing experience came to appreciate the considerable advantages of not using a propeller. These advantages included higher acceleration, higher speed over shallow water, absence of any cavitation even in turbulent water, and outstandingly improved manoeuvrability. Dowty took up manufacturing rights for the Hamilton system and produced it for many years, though the company could never decide whether or not to make the boats as well.

One product that Fedden did not take up was the Wankel engine. On this trip Sir Roy and Lady Fedden were driven by Drew, Sir George's chauffeur, so that they could enjoy the scenery on the long journey to Graz. Fedden liked Felix Wankel, but though he was attracted to his rotating-combustion engine, he considered it needed a great deal of development to perfect the sealing and lubrication, and he was also strongly influenced by the fact that the Dowty Group had never made an engine of any sort. In contrast Alex Moulton at that time favoured the Wankel, though in his last letter to his old master, dated one week before Fedden's death, he admitted that the increasing need to reduce fuel consumption would keep the traditional reciprocating engine in its dominant position.

Dowty had offered Fedden £5,000 per year; Fedden had replied "No, I'm not worth that much to you; I'll take £4,000". It is hard to assess the value of the job he did for Dowty, but Sir George probably got a bargain. Though Moulton, for one, would say that Fedden's talents were not fully utilised from 1943 onwards, it is a fact that well into his seventies he was working harder for Dowty than many men ever work at all. The volume of reports, correspondence and other papers that his consultancy generated is truly formidable. Often a single piece of paper passed to Sir George might be the result of a great burden of work, especially when it was the distilled essence of many hours of delving in response to a crisp request beginning "What is your opinion on …?" Writing speeches is no sinecure either, and Fedden did this often, for both Sir George and Lady Dowty, particular when the subject involved education. Sometimes the two old friends had hard words, but on the whole the consultancy worked excellently. It was terminated by mutual consent in 1960, when Fedden was 75. Sir George gave a dinner in his honour at Greenway's Hotel, Cheltenham, on 5th July.

Officially this fifth retirement was the end of Fedden's life-time of work, but he was still extremely fit, had a brain that worked faster and more continuously than most people liked, and his incessant pre-occupation with setting the world to rights caused him to keep his secretary, Olive Stahl, constantly writing to the papers, writing to influential friends and even, in 1957, writing a book (*Britain's Air Survival,* Cassell – not one of their best sellers). In this book he harped on his familiar theme of trying to plan ahead in British aviation. He cited the Finletter Committee, set up in the United States by President Truman in 1947, as the sort of long-term planning that was needed, and made detailed recommendations for the management of British aeronautical research and government procurement of military and civil aircraft. On the whole his views have stood up well, and he expressed them just at a time when the Government management of British aviation was about to fall to pieces, so that for a decade the whole national effort in this field lay in tatters. But Fedden was cast in the role of the prophet without honour in his own country. He was beginning to be of an age when those who disliked his advice tried to dismiss him as being a cantankerous old man, without spending too long actually examining his arguments.

There had always been opponents of Fedden, as there must always be of anyone who speaks his mind. And after his 70th birthday he had more time to take well-judged swipes at situations he found disquieting. For example, at the Institution of Production Engineers conference in January 1956 his Lord Sempill lecture declaimed "About 25 per cent of the people employed in all spheres of aeronautical endeavour in this country have, over the past ten years, worked harder and have devoted themselves more wholeheartedly and selflessly to aviation than ever before, but … the remainder have let the side down. Many of them thoughtlessly, through lack of leadership; others have rushed vainly about, both physically and mentally, while the balance have gone the way of the Welfare State and been pretty carefree and idle". The Welfare State mentality was, naturally, anathema to him. It appeared to him the self-evident route to complete decay of individual moral fibre and, eventually, to soaring inflation and collapse of the national economy (this was long before it actually happened). On the other hand, he always believed he could lay himself alongside "the under-dog" and appreciate and sympathise with the latter's point of view. But the form the underdog took undoubtedly coloured his outlook; skin colour mattered not at all, but long hair and a slovenly appearance certainly did. Nothing distressed him more than to be invited to lecture at famous public schools and there find fortunate sons who appeared to take no pride in their appearance and to have no inclination to work hard. The sons might have considered him prejudiced.

Education remained to the end a matter of prime importance to him. This vast subject has many faces. Fedden's deepest concern was to see boys "of the right sort" trained as engineers, but he also felt the public needed training about engineering. Speaking at Clifton he said "The remarkable accomplishments of this first industrial revolution, which gave us the steam engine, revolutionised transport by land and sea, provided textile machinery, machine tools, and a host of other things, all of which increased our standard of living, emotionally left the traditional hierarchy of British education cold, although they were glad enough to make use of the amenities so provided. Grudgingly it was brought home to them that engineering was a great calling that had to be reckoned with; but the esteem of other professions, such as for example, medicine or the law, was never conceded to it. There are many people even today who cannot see their way to do this, and unfortunately most of them move in very influential circles …"

On another occasion he exclaimed "Old-fashioned housemasters hate my guts … They think I am peddling some kind of inferior product, and that I want to see the cream of our youth with spanners in their hands, doing something a trained monkey could do. Their background makes it hard for them to understand even what an engineer is – and the fact that the members of the Engineering Union are always popularly described as engineers, which they emphatically are not, makes it harder … Your classical man is respectable. He soars ahead in pay, in influence and in honours. He takes it for granted that he should tell the inferior technical man what to do. We have compulsory Latin for entrance to the public schools, but nobody would dream of a compulsory examination in technology!". He explained that pure science had gradually become acceptable in Senior Common Rooms, but the despised applied science was definitely *persona non grata.* The head of science in one of the noblest British seats of learning had lately said to him, in tones showing unspeakable distaste, "Only over my dead body will there ever be such a thing as a 'Department of Production Engineering' in this university!". He obviously was entirely ignorant of what the subject was, and doubtless equated it with filing and riveting.

For 14 years, from 1946 to 1960, Fedden was Chairman of the City and Guilds of London Institute Advisory Committee on Aeronautics. This was an unpaid post, but he spent a great deal of time at the renowned London seat of technical education discussing not only formal training for the Ordinary and Higher National Certificates but also the whole field of making an engineer. Fedden was a great believer in basics. He considered the absolute essentials for any engineer were: a solid grounding in mathematics and physics; the ability to express oneself clearly and briefly, to write neatly, spell correctly and be able to write a quick précis; and to be able to draw a clear 3-D freehand sketch, with correct perspective. Complicated "machine drawing", difficult higher mathematics, and deep specialised knowledge were things which might come later, depending on one's job; so too were any highly developed practical hand skills at the bench, which were unlikely ever to be needed. A metalworking shop could well be an extra-curricular subject voluntarily explored in the boy's own time. On the other hand, the curriculum ought to include "at least one foreign language; religious, moral and philosophical studies; the humanities, but not conforming to Greek and Latin antiquity; and a broad treatment of the history of engineering, and modern industry organisation and problems, with

RF was always passionate about education, especially for "the Flag Officers of industry". Here, at age 81, he is with E G Sterland, Principal of what had become the school of the Rolls-Royce Bristol Engine Division at the foot of Filton Hill, Bristol. (Author)

especial concentration on management and trade unions". Fedden's term for the sort of engineer he wanted to see in vastly greater numbers was "the Flag Officer type". He constantly fretted over Britain's pathetic output of such people, and contrasted it with the relatively enormous numbers trained in the Soviet Union and the United States. One can imagine his feelings when the chaotic governmental aviation scene in the 1960s led to the "Brain Drain" which took away many of Britain's tiny supply of good and experienced aero engineers.

In the post-graduate field Cranfield was from the start the tangible model of Fedden's ideals. He had never comprehended the ways of the British academic. Not having been to a university himself, he was astonished that his brother Vincent should have taken his bath at Cambridge in a large tin container brought into his room by his bedder, and filled and emptied by the said servant using a bucket. Not having suffered a career amongst professors, he was likewise astonished that they should themselves construct balances for their wind-tunnels, making their own gears and filing the teeth by hand. Against such a background the revolution of Cranfield can be seen in perspective. Like MIT and Göttingen, this new centre of advanced technology was to have the most complete and most advanced equipment that could be found. Such excellent tools were, thought Fedden, generally regarded by the academics as un-British and rather degrading. The national tradition was to be so superior that better results could be obtained with bits of string and sealing wax.

Once established, Cranfield carved out its own enormous niche in the world of advanced technology without too many academics looking down their noses at its fine equipment. Until about 1960 its work was directed entirely towards the broad field of aerospace, its central role being to turn out previously qualified aeronautical engineers with the additional letters DCAe after their names. These letters soon came to be appreciated all over the world, especially in the United States where a man with the College of Aeronautics Diploma could choose his employer and almost choose his salary. But Cranfield increasingly wanted the power to award not just a diploma but a degree, such as an MSc or DEng having immediate and universal recognition. Then came the incredible *White Paper on Defence* of April 1957 in which was expressed the belief that the RAF would be "unlikely to require" any new designs of fighters or bombers but would instead arm itself with guided missiles. This nonsensical edict threw the aircraft industry into turmoil, drastically cut the entry to Cranfield, and made the College ponder on diversification.

Such a move was expressly contrary to the ideals of Cripps, as vociferously expressed by his "disciple" Fedden, who remained a Governor. To Fedden the vital ingredient needed for Cranfield to fulfil its purpose was its devotion to aerospace. If it became diversified, thought Fedden, "you could have the most marvellous structures department in the world, attracting structural engineers from all industries; but if the leadership is not centred in doing the impossible – as aviation has had to do throughout its history – the vital spark will be lost, and there will be nothing to stop Cranfield degenerating into just another institute of technology." Argument continued. Then in 1961 the Robbins Committee on Higher Education was appointed, with wide powers to reshape the whole field of higher education in Britain. Fedden noted with gloom that "The average age of the Committee is about 60, its constitution is almost entirely academic, and there are no representatives from the modern precision engineering industry, or from any organisations familiar with the types of people needed in the coming generations to govern the country, to build up and manage industry progressively, and deal with the tremendous competition from all over the world." Fedden was not alone in being apprehensive: so was everyone else who knew anything about British industry.

In November 1963 the Robbins Committee's findings were at last published. Fedden commented: "I feel like Job: the thing I greatly feared hath come upon me!" The committee recommended that Cranfield be brought within the ambit of the University Grants Committee; it did not like the idea of "a relatively small college of this kind" having power to award its own degrees, and suggested "it should be urged to form an appropriate association with a university." Fedden carefully read the entire report. He then commented that he understood exactly how, given the available data, the "back-room civil servants" who had written the report had arrived at their conclusions. He regarded them as extremely serious and well-intentioned but, because of the complete ignorance on the part of the Committee and the civil servants of the nation's needs in advanced technology, correct conclusions were impossible. Robbins appeared to think size was everything, and to want to turn out vast numbers of average-quality engineers. What the nation needed with increasing urgency were the "Flag Officer" breed – no matter in what small numbers – who had knowledge, vision, and character for leadership. Robbins he regarded as an unmitigated disaster.

Cranfield's Senate at once issued a paper reviewing the Robbins recommendations, meekly falling into line with them, and saying nothing about aerospace but plenty about diversification and size. Fedden called this paper "weak and indeterminate ... I have heard all I want to, for some time, about diversification ... I am not mesmerised by size. If we realise our goal of quality and only turn out 75 students a year we should make our awards on our own and not be beholden to anyone ..." There followed a long period of extraordinary strain and uncertainty, which often at times assumed a personal nature as those involved split into cliques, lobbied behind the scenes, and at times almost appeared to lose sight of what the nation most urgently needed through the intensity of the internecine conflict. Whereas in Fedden's immediate post-Robbins documents one found "tooth and nail" quite often, the recurring phrase in 1964 and 1965 seemed to be "a thread of misrepresentation". Fedden's own answer was for Cranfield to settle at a size not greatly in excess of 1,000 students and to be called The Royal College of Aerospace (degree-awarding, of course), with "logical and analogous" satellites such as The School of International Transport and Communications. By 1966, after long deliberations by an Academic Advisory Committee appointed by the University Grants Committee, Fedden proposed a small committee formed from members of the Cranfield Society and the Royal Aeronautical Society to look at the problem. Wires got crossed, perfectly plain statements were interpreted in unexpected ways, and old friendships became strained. But it all came right – more or less – in the end. Cranfield received a Royal Charter, changed its name to the Cranfield Institute of Technology, yet for a while contrived to seek the elusive ideals true to the spirit of quality laid down by Cripps and Fedden. Only after Fedden's death did what is now called CIT take a wrong turning.

Cranfield afflicted by Robbins could have tried to shut itself in an ivory tower, and it might conceivably have withered away there; but while Fedden lived this would have been impossible. The same is true of that august body the Royal Aeronautical Society. Fedden was the RAeS President in 1938, 1939 and 1952 – the only member since 1925 to hold this office three times – and a Member of Council from 1936 to 1952. The role of the Society is, broadly, "the general advancement of Aeronautical Art, Science and Engineering". It is universally regarded as the premier professional body in the world of aeronautical engineers. It is a fine society, comprising some 18,000 members all over the world, almost all of them professionally engaged in aviation "art, science and engineering". It has immense prestige and influence. At least, it has influence in certain directions. But what does such a society do when the Government of the day is widely considered to be taking decisions of a great and long-term nature that appear to be highly detrimental to aviation art, science and engineering?

This was the situation in Britain from 1956 onwards, when the Government appeared to have no policy whatever in aviation other than to cause as much cancellation, disruption, re-organisation and upheaval as possible. Fedden, who never for a moment doubted that Britain would always need a strong and confident aircraft industry, felt he was serving the national interest by writing to the papers, by speech-making, and by the occasional broadcast. But what about the great and proud Society? In 1961, when there were only three military aircraft left to cancel, he addressed a letter to each member of Council suggesting that perhaps the Society ought to make its corporate voice heard. After some discussion and further exchanges of letters, Fedden submitted a letter requesting that it be published in the Society's *Journal*. Council said they would do better: they offered him the floor at an open meeting, which took place on 4th December 1962. At that meeting he put forward an extremely long series of questions and proposals, some concerned with the Society and some with British aviation. His 48th point was "Is it right and proper for a learned Society, such as the Royal Aeronautical Society, to enter the national policy making arena? If the answer is 'Yes' then you must face up to the greater and more critical one. Does the Society at long last intend to emerge from its own particular ivory tower and publicly advocate certain national policies within its technical sphere? In so doing, will it, particularly the younger generation, face up to, with determination and pertinacity, all that this implies?".

Council debated the notion that the Society could, or should, make public statements of any kind regarding Government policies. It decided the answer was that it most certainly should not. But some members felt otherwise and, as a result, a further meeting was held at 4 Hamilton Place – the lovely house near Hyde Park Corner which Fedden and Devereux had bought for the Society in 1939 – on 29th July 1963. It so happened that this was shortly before the last three British military aircraft programmes were all cancelled by a new Government, and replaced by American purchases. But even without this traumatic upheaval, which was not then predictable, the atmosphere at that meeting was tense, urgent and at times acrimonious. Nothing like it had ever before occurred in the previous 97 years of the Society's existence.

It is perhaps unfortunate that so much lobbying and clique-forming had gone on beforehand, because what Fedden had proposed, and what so many members had eagerly applauded, was merely the idea that the Society they all loved and honoured should perhaps have something on record for posterity to prove that it was upholding its original objective. But no suggestion of this nature could be put forward by anyone, least of all by Fedden, without many of the most influential members jumping to the defence of the *status quo*. Many, by accident or design, took the view that the Fedden clique was proposing that the Society should become a "noisy pressure group" trying to coerce the Government in a completely ineffectual way and perhaps trying to frighten it by threatening to publish critical articles in its staid *Journal*. Some took the view that the proposed politically aware Society would have much less influence than before, because all its most influential members – the ones holding the highest positions within Government departments and the armed forces – would have to resign. Some considered that Fedden's proposals would cost a lot of money which could not be found. Some took them as a personal affront. Some made comparisons with other countries, or other professional bodies. And the biggest group of all made clear their deep distress at what was being done to the British aviation industry, and called for a vote to be taken to determine the feeling of the meeting. But the Chairman – that year's President – resolutely rejected the holding of a vote, claiming that it was "not appropriate" and that "if a vote had been proposed, the representation here might have been quite different" (though never before had the 310 seats in the new lecture theatre been filled for a mere meeting to discuss policy).

Fedden did well. Though nearly 80, he noted everything said at the meeting, and finally rose to his height of six feet and said how "profoundly interested and encouraged I am by the attendance tonight. I think it shows an enormous interest in what is being attempted, and I must congratulate you, Mr Chairman, on the terrific onslaught of your pressure group. But, in spite of this, I want to say that our small, weak team who are trying to put a new proposal in front of the Council, are not going to be downhearted ...". One cannot know how the meeting would have voted, had a count been taken. Many members undoubtedly merely sensed the bitter clash of personalities, and whilst sympathising with Fedden's objective, may have doubted that the Society could function in the proposed way. Certainly the Chairman of the meeting resented the proposal, and in closing the unique occasion he said "Back-seat driving, and by this I mean the sort of thing which involves barbed shafts which pierce and fester, do in fact create a sub-stratum of unfortunate feeling in the Society, which is quite inappropriate for a Society of this kind where we really are all trying to do the same thing, and I would make a strong plea that this sort of back-seat driving should cease". It was a pity that Fedden's reasonable suggestion that, because of the disastrous state of British aviation, the Society might at least think about the matter in a corporate way, should have instead evoked such bitter feeling.

In spite of its refusal to take a vote, the Council was impressed – and clearly surprised – by the large measure of support for RF's views among the membership. A few days later Professor A R Collar, the 1963 President, and Dr A M Ballantyne, the Society's Secretary, visited the Mill, together with some of Sir Roy's more tactful supporters. They proposed, and subsequently implemented the idea that the Society should set up a committee to make recommendations to the Government on general aviation policy. Sir Roy was delighted, but did not serve on the committee himself, wisely expressing a wish for it to be formed from younger members who might have an easier passage. Several of his nominees, including Harold Caplan, Val Cleaver and Walter Tye, were accepted as members. But events overtook the committee's work, in that the Labour administration elected in 1964 themselves set up a committee under Lord Plowden with basically similar objectives.

Unfortunately the Plowden Committee operated in a less collaborative manner, seeing itself as a kind of judge and jury. That the results of this unfortunate committee were not more disastrous than they actually were was partly due to the RAeS Committee, which was re-convened to prepare and submit evidence to Plowden. Thus the Society proved that it was prepared to stand up for the future of British aviation; what RF abhorred was "supine inaction", and he always had sympathy for anyone who at least tried.

Many of the members who had opposed his proposal were probably motivated by the feeling that Fedden was tiresome and lacking in humour. Certainly his office at Bristol, at Berkeley Street or at Stoke Orchard, was never the hearty thigh-slapping sort of place one associates with the engineering industry. Yet, as suggested earlier, he perhaps had a sense of humour that was deep and refined. His niece Elizabeth Thomas, who saw a great deal of him and acted as hostess during his two pre-war terms as RAeS President, is of the opinion that "He actually had a juvenile sense of humour. For example, he loved to see the reaction caused by sounding the horn on his Bentley, which perfectly mimicked a very loud cuckoo."

Virtually never did it show itself at work or in conversation, but there was the occasional glimpse. In 1956, as the newly elected first President of the Cranfield Society, he advised his audience that the chairman had instructed him "Whatever you say, make it short and sizzling." He had looked up

RF standing by one of his weirs built across the River Usk. (Author)

"sizzling" in the Oxford dictionary, to discover it meant "To make a spluttering sound, as in frying." Yet four years later, at a two-day symposium of the same society, he regretted his inability to add "a light, witty, humorous touch" as he had been asked to do; "nothing, to my mind, is more ludicrous to attempt if it is not your line of country, as in my case." When he was 88 his secretary told him how President Nixon asked Mrs Golda Meir how Israel came to have such brilliant generals. The Israeli premier replied "I'll swap two of mine for two of yours" whereat Mr Nixon said "It's a deal. Which ones of mine do you want?" And Mrs Meir said "General Electric and General Motors". Instantly Fedden replied "I always admired Alfred P Sloan of General Motors: he worked his way from the bottom right to the top". He appeared not to notice the joke and she did not dare take the matter further in case he had simply thought it un-funny.

Yet in his 80s this remarkable man helped to shift tons of concrete and build walls and weirs to protect the banks of the Usk and improve the fishing. By this time he was unable to fish the whole of his great length of the Usk, and he sold the rights upstream of his suspension bridge in the early 1960s. The buyer was a Mr Harding, who in a booming voice said "I know who you are; my father supplied all the pencils and paper for your drawing offices at Bristol." Part of the money was used to improve the Usk upstream of the bridge. Fedden's knowledge of aerodynamics made him question the tradition of putting bushes into the banks to protect them. He considered that the rough edges thus created caused violent eddies, and his left bank was in a particularly poor state, the back swirl from the bushes eroding the good farmland at a rate of about a foot a year in places. He decided to put into practice his theory that laminar flow is good.

British Railways had lately closed the line to Brecon, and Fedden was able to buy 4,000 concrete sleeper pads, each weighing 170 lb, at a price of sixpence (2½p) each. About half were used to build a large weir, with two rows of pads held by 12 inch bolts and 14 inch spikes to a very straight 60 foot birch tree, the whole then being covered in many tons of concrete to give a smooth profile. Upstream is the deep pool "Belinda", named after Lady Fedden's grand-daughter by her first marriage. Further weirs, banks and pools were added later, with a reserve of 350 pads for future eventualities. In true Fedden fashion, everything was beautifully recorded in detailed reports and photograph albums.

Fedden loved his home at the Mill. By the 1960s it had long since been a comfortable dwelling that perfectly reflected the life of its owner. Everywhere there were photographs, trophies (the ones gained since December 1940), model aircraft and engines, model yachts, countless books, files, reports and old drawings – and, constantly, in the background, the peaceful roaring of the Usk over the rapids of the mediaeval mill-race. On the mantelpiece, next to a Samurai sword given him by the Government of Japan in 1929 which survived the destruction of Widegates, was his favourite text, by a great American aircraft engineer, "Dutch" Kindelberger: "It may not always be the best policy to do what is best technically, but those responsible for policy can never form a right judgement without knowledge of what is right technically." Next to this was a clock presented to him by the English Steel Corporation incorporating a slice of the millionth sleeve valve for one of his engines.

In his twilight years, which can be considered to have begun at about the age of 85, he was visited by countless people, one of whom drove up in a Straker Squire car. Only very gradually did his almost indestructible frame become slightly bowed and frail. The writer would rather leave him in his prime. During the Second World War he called on George Dowty late at night, eager to have his friend's opinion. Fedden talked volubly for more than three hours, outlining the whole of the problem and all possible ways of dealing with it. He then got up, shook Dowty's hand and said "How very good of you to see me; I value your opinion so highly, and I'm most grateful for your co-operation. It's so thoughtful of you". After he had gone, Dowty chuckled. He hadn't been able to get in a single word.

Buckland Old Mill (taken in 1990). (Rolls-Royce plc)

APPENDIX I

Bristol piston engines – BHP increase and weight per BHP decrease.

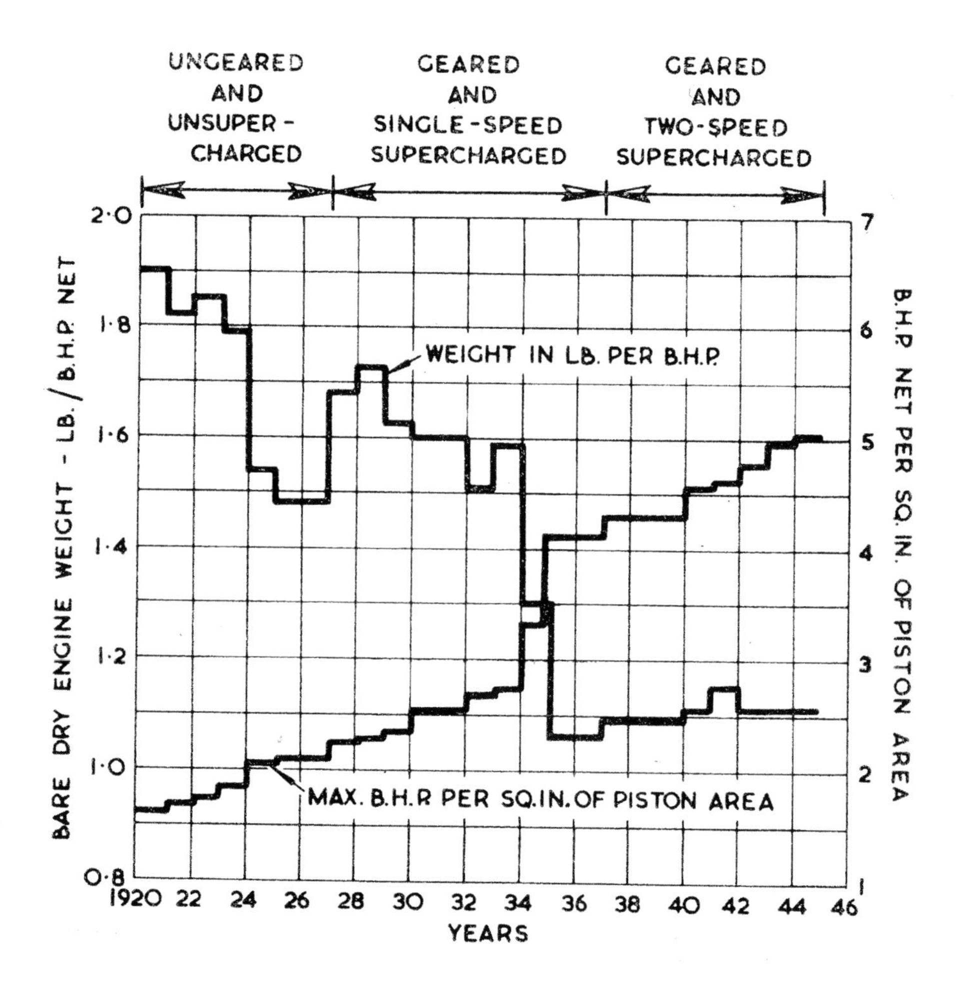

What RF and his team accomplished for Bristol engines, of which over 134,000 were made. (Author)

APPENDIX II

THE MANUFACTURE OF PISTON AERO ENGINES IN BRISTOL
(AND FOREIGN LICENCE-BUILT)

UNITED KINGDOM								
COMPANY	**ENGINE**	**APPROX DATES**	**NUMBER BUILT**	**REMARKS**				
BRAZIL STRAKER	CURTISS OX-5	1914-16	300	ONE SOURCE QUOTES 400 FOR ADMIRALTY				
	HAWK 1	1916-17	200	SUB-CONTRACT FROM ROLLS-ROYCE				
	HAWK 2	1917-19	13 +	SUB-CONTRACT FROM ROLLS-ROYCE				
	FALCON	1917-20	1175 ?	SUB-CONTRACT FROM ROLLS-ROYCE				
	EAGLE	1917-18	-	MAJOR SUB ASSEMBLIES FOR ROLLS-ROYCE				
	RENAULT WS	1918	610	SUB-CONTRACT WORK FOR ADMIRALTY				
	MERCURY	1918-20	3	FIRST INDIGENOUS FEDDEN / BUTLER ENGINE				
COSMOS	JUPITER	1920	5	SECOND FEDDEN / BUTLER DESIGN				
	LUCIFER	1920	2 +	1/3RD OF A JUPITER				
BRISTOL AEROPLANE COMPANY - ENGINE DEPARTMENT BRISTOL AEROPLANE COMPANY - ENGINE DIVISION BRISTOL AERO ENGINES BRISTOL SIDDELEY ENGINES, BRISTOL	JUPITER	1920-35	1910	ENGINES PRODUCED IN THE UK BY 'SHADOW FACTORIES'				
	LUCIFER	1920-30	114					
	CHERUB	1920-29	82		'CAR' SHADOW FACTORIES	BRISTOL SHADOW @ ACCRINGTON	HAWTHORN UNDERGROUND AT BATH	OVERALL TOTALS ENGINE
	ORION	1926-30	5					
	MERCURY#	1927-40	3168		18149			21317
	TITAN	1928-30	2 +					
	NEPTUNE	1929-31	2					
	PEGASUS#	1931-44	8273		12195			20468
	PHOENIX	1932-34	1					
	DRACO	1932-35	1					
	PERSEUS	1932-42	2892					
	HYDRA	1934-35	2					
	AQUILA	1934-38	6					
	HERCULES#	1936-65	10878		39990	14379		65247
	TAURUS	1937-42	3724					
	CENTAURUS#	1938-59	4750			32	548+	5330+
				# ENGINES WERE PRODUCED AT THE SHADOW FACTORIES DURING THE FOLLOWING YEARS:-				
	RIGS AND STARTERS							
	HERC DIESEL	1924-29	1					
	PERSEUS 2	1923-32	1					
	RAE GAS	1922	6	MERCURY 1938 - 1944				
	BRISTOL GAS	1922-35	395 +	PEGASUS 1939 - 1945				
	6C ILSV	1930-32	1	HERCULES 1940 - 1945				
	RESEARCH UNITS (SINGLE CYLINDER RESEARCH UNITS)	1918-45	55	CENTAURUS 1942 - 1945				
UNITED KINGDOM		TOTALS	38877+		70334	14411	548+	
		OVERALL UK TOTAL				124,170+		
OVERSEAS - LICENCE PRODUCTION								
	JUPITER		8008					
	MERCURY	)	2820					
	PEGASUS	)						
	HERCULES		1375					
OVERSEAS		TOTAL	12203					
GRAND TOTAL UK AND OVERSEAS 136,373								

THIS TABLE HAS BEEN COMPILED BY JOHN HEAVEN OF THE ROLLS-ROYCE HERITAGE TRUST - BRISTOL FROM THE BEST AVAILABLE INFORMATION

Piston aero engines built in Bristol 1914-1965 and the shadow factories and licencees.

APPENDIX III

The Evolution of Rolls-Royce

This book published by the Rolls-Royce Heritage Trust details the life of Sir Roy Fedden, the early part of which, as Chief Engineer of the Engine Department of the Bristol Aeroplane Company, was in direct competition with Rolls-Royce.

The chart below starting with Brazil Straker, as far as Bristol is concerned, shows how the main aero engine producers in Britain merged together over the course of fifty years, such that by 1966 there were only two major companies in the business – Rolls-Royce and Bristol Siddeley, which itself had resulted from a merger in the late Fifties of Bristol Engines and Armstrong Siddeley Motors and that Company's subsequent acquisition of de Havilland Engines and Blackburn.

The process was completed in 1966 when Rolls-Royce took over Bristol Siddeley and thus was created a single aero engine company in Great Britain – now known as Rolls-Royce plc.

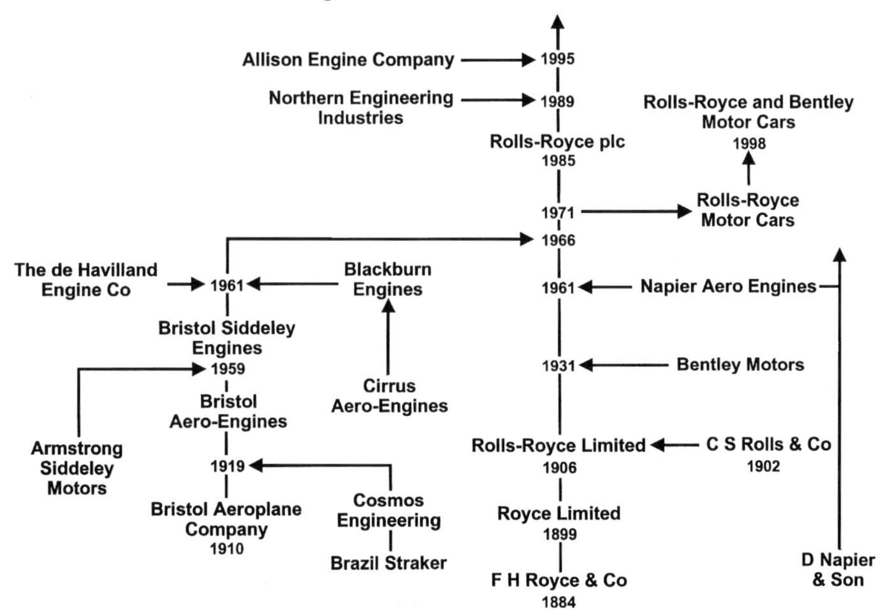

APPENDIX IV

Butler

The success of Bristol Engines resulted from Fedden himself and the teams that he built.

Several people – Whitehead, the Mansells, Stammers, Swinchatt, Damsell, Jefferies, Owner, etc – all made massive contributions to the overall success, but special mention must surely be made of Butler who turned Fedden's concepts into detailed mechanical designs.

The following is a very brief précis of the life of "Bunny" Butler:-

LEONARD FREDERICK GEORGE BUTLER (1888-1943)

Leonard Butler was born on the 29th day of March 1888. After completing his education at Sexey's school, Somerset, he was apprenticed to the Bristol engineering firm of Brazil Straker and Company from August 1904 until November 1909 and, during 1907, worked side-by-side with Roy Fedden on the drawing board designing the first Straker Squire car. Butler left Brazil Straker in November 1909 and worked for Rolls-Royce in the Drawing Office on the 40/50 car design, before leaving in October 1910 to work first for David Brown and Son, followed by Crossley Brothers, and then returning to Brazil Straker in December 1911 at Fishponds, Bristol.

Upon his return, he was engaged on design work of the 15hp engine for the Straker car, the engine for Straker commercial vehicles, and in 1914 on the engine for the Straker TT racing cars. In 1914, he was appointed Chief Draughtsman, under the direction of Roy Fedden. As Brazil Straker turned their efforts to aero engines during the war, Butler became involved with the Rolls-Royce Hawk, Falcon and Eagle, the 80hp Renault and the partial re-design of the Curtiss OX engine.

Next came the indigenous design of the 350hp 14-cylinder Mercury engine and, in 1918, after Brazil Straker had been taken over by the Cosmos Engineering Company, Fedden and Butler, in response to a request from the Air Ministry, designed a nine-cylinder radial air-cooled engine. The drawing for this engine was completed by Butler working all through the night, so as to be ready for the Air Ministry on the next day. This drawing, dated "April 16th 1918", for a long time was hung in Butler's office. The engine was subsequently named "Jupiter".

In 1920, following the collapse of Cosmos and subsequent take-over by the Bristol Aeroplane Company, Butler along with Fedden and about 30 other staff moved to the airfield site at Filton, where he retained his position as Chief Designer to the Chief Engineer – Roy Fedden. During the next twenty years, Butler was involved with every major engine project, including all of those which were actually built and run, ie Jupiter, Lucifer, Cherub, Titan, Neptune, Pegasus, Mercury, Draco, Phoenix, Perseus, Aquila, Taurus, Hercules and Centaurus. Butler remained Chief Designer until 1941 before a serious illness, partially resulting from the tremendous stress that he had worked under, resulted in his absence for over a year, which included the traumatic time of Sir Roy Fedden's departure, before he returned in late 1942 as Technical Advisor.

Although it was believed that he had made a complete recovery, on September 3rd 1943 "Bunny" Butler, as he was always affectionately known, collapsed and died at Paddington Station whilst on Company business.

Amongst the tributes paid upon his death, he was described as "…a gentleman who loved his job and one who preferred further effort for his country, to the limelight of past achievements".

Sir Roy Fedden himself said, "Throughout our long association, extending over 30 years, Mr Butler was a most loyal collaborator and became one of my closest friends. I learnt to have the highest regard for his criticism of engine design. His fine ability on detailed mechanical design had a strong influence on the success of the engines resulting from our association".

The Butler name is perpetuated to this day, albeit largely unknowingly. For several decades, all of the Engine Division drawings, from washers to complete general arrangement drawings, were number FB_____, the FB standing for Fedden/Butler. Although this numbering system is no longer used for new drawings, hundreds of small 'standard' items – nuts, bolts, washers etc – are still in use and still retain the original FB part number.

APPENDIX V

Flying Bristol Piston Engines

The 1998 situation

Over 134,000 Bristol piston engines were built in total, however, the number today which remain flying or may be returned to a flying condition, is very small. This is almost entirely because of the thoughtless destruction of the last of each of the famous types of aircraft they powered.

Jupiter

There are no Jupiters currently airworthy – the last flying example was in the Shuttleworth-operated Bristol Bulldog which was lost in a crash at Farnborough in September 1964. There is an ambitious plan to build a replica Gloster Gamecock and power it with a Jupiter engine, plus at least one other project utilising a Jupiter.

Lucifer

A Lucifer engine has been ground run and, if satisfactory, may fly in a replica Bristol M1D aeroplane – manufactured in the UK.

Cherub

Several Cherubs fly in a number of light aircraft types, all being maintained by their owners.

Mercury

The Mercury is used in the only flying Bristol Blenheim aircraft restored and kept in the UK and there are other Blenheim projects in Canada, Belgium and the USA. Also, the Mercury is the powerplant of several Westland Lysander aircraft which fly in the UK, Canada and Belgium and a Mercury flies regularly in the Shuttleworth Trust's Gloster Gladiator.

Pegasus

The Pegasus flies in two Fairey Swordfish aircraft operated by the Royal Navy Historic Flight (RNHF) from Yeovilton and further examples fly in

Canada and the USA. Two Supermarine Walrus amphibious aircraft are being restored to flying condition in the UK and Australia and there is, in the country of its origin, a plan to build and fly a replica of an indigenous Lithuanian ANBO aircraft.

Perseus and Taurus

There are no Perseus or Taurus engines in a flightworthy condition. However, if suitable engines could be found, a team in the USA restoring an Australian-built Beaufort would complete the project as a Taurus-engined version.

Hercules

Despite the fact that over 65,000 Hercules engines were built from the Thirties to the Sixties, the only examples currently flying are late model 758s in a sole Nord Noratlas in France. Hercules were flying in two Bristol Freighter aircraft, but both have recently been lost. There is, however, now another Freighter flying in Canada. Several Bristol Beaufighters are being restored – two in the UK and one in Australia – and another is being investigated in Canada, but early Hercules are very difficult to locate.

This Nord 2501 Noratlas of the French Armée de l'Air is powered by two SNECMA-built Hercules 758 engines each of 2040hp. Until 1989, it trained radar navigators for Mirage IVA supersonic bombers.

Centaurus

The most powerful Bristol piston engine, the Centaurus, is currently flying in several Fury and Sea Fury aircraft, including several ‘pylon racers’ in the USA, as well as other examples in the UK, Canada and Australia. There are also two Hawker Tempest II projects in the UK and another under investigation in the USA.

APPENDIX VI

Bristol Bulldog

The engine which started and ensured survival of the Bristol aero engine industry in the 1920s – the Jupiter – was still flying at the start of WWII in Bristol Bulldog aircraft in Finland, but these aircraft were withdrawn soon afterwards. (One of these aircraft has been restored and is displayed in the Finnish Air Force Museum).

In the late 1950s, the one-time Bristol-owned Bulldog demonstrator aircraft, G-ABBB, was refurbished at Filton and a Jupiter engine was rebuilt at Patchway using components from several engines.

The combination took to the air again in the early Sixties and was later presented to the Shuttleworth Trust and was operated by them carrying the markings K-2227.

In 1966, the aircraft was destroyed in a crash at Farnborough. The photograph shows the aircraft taxiing out at Farnborough on the Saturday before the aircraft was lost on the Sunday.

However, this Bulldog is shortly (1998) going to re-emerge as a static exhibit – the airframe having been re-built/re-manufactured by Skysport Engineering and the engine having been restored by the Bristol Branch of the Rolls-Royce Heritage Trust. The aircraft will then be exhibited in the RAF Museum at Hendon.

APPENDIX VII

Museum Engines

Examples of Fedden's Bristol piston engines have been restored and are displayed in Museums all around the world.
Many engines are displayed at various locations in the UK, but the two major collections are to be found in Bristol.

The Bristol Industrial Museum at Princes Wharf, City Centre has on loan from the Rolls-Royce Heritage Trust a fine collection from the earliest Jupiter, with most of the air-cooled radial engines exhibited, plus gas turbines including a Theseus, right up to the present day Pegasus, Olympus and RB199.

The Rolls-Royce Heritage Trust centre on the Patchway site of Rolls-Royce plc has a similar, although less complete, collection of the earlier engines, but has a larger collection of the later gas turbine engines produced from the Forties up to the present day.

The photographs below show engines on display in both collections.

(Rolls-Royce plc)

(Rolls-Royce plc)

(Rolls-Royce plc)

(Rolls-Royce plc)

In the History section of Russia's Monino Aviation Museum is this part-sectioned 480hp direct-drive M-22. This derivative of the Jupiter IV (originally imported from Gnome-Rhone) was made in the Soviet Union for the Tupolev 1-4 fighter.

(Author)

APPENDIX VIII

Buckland Old Mill – The Cosmos Lucifer Chandelier

Buckland Old Mill has withstood the ravages of time and was visited in 1990 by members of the Bristol Branch of the Trust. The ultimate picture in the text of this book is a view of the Mill taken at that time.

Also hung in one of the downstairs rooms was the chandelier shown below, which consists of the crankcase and the three cylinders of a Cosmos-built Lucifer, converted at some time to its new duties. This is the only surviving Cosmos artefact of which we are aware. The chandelier is still at the Mill, although no longer hung, but the present owner of the Mill has plans to re-install it.

(Rolls-Royce plc)

APPENDIX IX

Extract from the Clifton College Register – 1962

5057 Fedden, Sir Alfred Hubert Roy
North Town, Brown House

Born 6.6.85; 4 years Engineering Apprenticeship, 1904-1908; Designer and Chief Engineer Straker Squire Vehicles 1908-14; in charge complete manufacture Aero Engines for RAF, 1915-19; joined Bristol Aeroplane Company, founded Engine Division, 1920; responsible Design and Development all Bristol Aero Engines, 1920-42; Special Technical Adviser to Sir Stafford Cripps, MAP, 1942-45; Research Gas Turbine Engines, MOS, 1945-47; Aircraft Technical Adviser to NATO, London and Paris, 1951-52; Aircraft Consultant, Dowty Group, Cheltenham, 1953-60. Member and Chairman of many Technical Education Committees.

President Royal Aeronautical Society 1938, 1939, 1944; KBE, 1942; MBE 1919; DSc 1935; Honorary Fellow Royal Aeronautical Society, 1956; Hon FIAS (USA) 1935; Hon FSE, 1954; Hon FIWE (USA) 1941; MIMechE, 1910; Liveryman, Guild of Air Pilots, 1958; Fellow British Interplanetary Society, 1960; Bronze Medal, International Air Conference, Brussels, 1929; Silver Medal, RAeS, 1933; Manly Gold Medal, Chicago World Fair, 1933; Simms Gold Medal, 1934; Guggenheim Gold Medal (USA), 1938; Lilienthal Ring, Berlin, 1938; Wilbur Wright Lecture, RAeS, London 1948; Simms' Gold Medal, Centenary of Society of Engineers, 1954.

Publications

Rex Pierson Memorial Lecture, Weybridge; Britain's Aircraft Needs; Britain's Air Survival; Frank Barnwell Memorial Lecture, Bristol, 1960.

Address

Buckland Old Mill, Bwlch, Breconshire, South Wales; Royal Thames Yacht Club; Bristol Yacht Club.

INDEX

The Historical Series is published as a joint initiative by the Rolls-Royce Heritage Trust and The Sir Henry Royce Memorial Foundation.

Also published in the series:

No.1 Rolls-Royce – the formative years 1906-1939
Alec Harvey-Bailey RRHT 2nd edition 1983 (out of print)

No.2 The Merlin in perspective – the combat years
Alec Harvey-Bailey, RRHT 4th edition 1995

No.3 Rolls-Royce – the pursuit of excellence
Alec Harvey-Bailey and Mike Evans, HRMF 1984

No.4 In the beginning – the Manchester origins of Rolls-Royce
Mike Evans, RRHT 1984

No.5 Rolls-Royce – the Derby Bentleys
Alec Harvey-Bailey, HRMF 1985

No.6 The early days of Rolls-Royce – and the Montagu family
Lord Montagu of Beaulieu, RRHT 1986

No.7 Rolls-Royce – Hives, the quiet tiger
Alec Harvey-Bailey, HRMF 1985

No.8 Rolls-Royce – Twenty to Wraith
Alec Harvey-Bailey,HRMF 1986

No.9 Rolls-Royce and the Mustang
David Birch, RRHT 1987

No.10 From Gipsy to Gem with diversions, 1926-1986
Peter Stokes, RRHT 1987

No.11 Armstrong Siddeley – the Parkside story, 1896-1939
Ray Cook, RRHT 1989

No.12 Henry Royce – mechanic
Donald Bastow, RRHT 1989

No.14 Rolls-Royce – the sons of Martha
Alec Harvey-Bailey, HRMF 1989

No.15 Olympus – the first forty years
Alan Baxter, RRHT 1990

No.16 Rolls-Royce piston aero engines – a designer remembers
A A Rubbra, RRHT 1990

No.17 Charlie Rolls – pioneer aviator
Gordon Bruce, RRHT 1990

No.18 The Rolls-Royce Dart – pioneering turboprop
Roy Heathcote, RRHT 1992

No.19 The Merlin 100 series – the ultimate military development
Alec Harvey-Bailey and Dave Piggott, RRHT 1993

No.20 Rolls-Royce – Hives' turbulent barons
Alec Harvey-Bailey, HRMF 1992

No.21 The Rolls-Royce Crecy
Nahum, Foster-Pegg, Birch, RRHT 1994

No.22 Vikings at Waterloo – the wartime work on the Whittle jet engine by the Rover Company
David S Brooks, RRHT 1997

No.23 Rolls-Royce – the first cars from Crewe
Ken Lea, RRHT 1997

No.24 The Rolls-Royce Tyne
L Haworth, RRHT 1998

No.25 A View of Ansty
David E Williams, RRHT 1998

Special Sectioned Drawings of piston aero engines
L Jones, 1995

Technical Series

No.1 Rolls-Royce and the Rateau Patents
H Pearson, RRHT 1989

No.2 The vital spark! The development of aero engine sparking plugs
K Gough, RRHT 1991

No.3 The performance of a supercharged aero engine
S Hooker, H Reed and A Yarker, RRHT 1997

Books are available from:
Rolls-Royce Heritage Trust, Rolls-Royce plc, Moor Lane, PO Box 31, Derby DE24 8BJ

RR
ROLLS-ROYCE
HERITAGE TRUST